PETROLEUM GEOLOGY
A CONCISE STUDY

PETROLEUM GEOLOGY
A CONCISE STUDY

RICHARD E. CHAPMAN

Department of Geology and Mineralogy,
University of Queensland,
St. Lucia, Australia

ELSEVIER SCIENTIFIC PUBLISHING COMPANY
Amsterdam - London - New York 1973

ELSEVIER SCIENTIFIC PUBLISHING COMPANY
335 Jan van Galenstraat
P.O. Box 1270, Amsterdam, The Netherlands

AMERICAN ELSEVIER PUBLISHING COMPANY, INC.
52 Vanderbilt Avenue
New York, New York 10017

Library of Congress Card Number: 72-97426

ISBN 0-444-41117-8

With 88 illustrations and 7 tables.

Printed in The Netherlands

PREFACE

When I was given the task of lecturing on petroleum geology to undergraduate and graduate students (after 16 years of practising rather than preaching), I found that the subject could not covered in the time allotted in a way that satisfied any of us. Precisely the same difficulties arose when I started this book. One tended to dwell on unsatisfactory generalities, and it seemed that one was being buried under a mountain of empirical data with little coordinating theory. It became clear that a different approach was needed; and that this approach should be more restricted, so that the student would be provided with a deeper treatment of a central theme that would give him a sound basis for understanding petroleum geology from his own reading and his own experience. It also seemed important that a student who decided not to follow a career in petroleum geology should not regard his time spent in its study wasted.

This small book is the result. It has been written for students who have completed at least one year of undergraduate study of geology. No upper limit has been placed because many practising geologists, finding it difficult to keep up with the literature, will be unfamiliar with some aspects of the subject treated in this book. Much of the contents has been developed with students of geology in their third and fourth years at the Queensland University.

The theme

Roughly half the world's petroleum reserves are in sand reservoirs, roughly half in carbonate reservoirs. Sedimentary basins tend to accumulate either a dominant sequence of sands and clays (shales) or a dominant sequence of carbonates. The emphasis of this book is on the geology of petroleum in sand reservoirs rather than carbonates. There are several reasons for this: (a) my own practical experience has been almost exclusively with sedimentary basins with sands and clays; (b) the diagenesis (particularly compaction) of sands and clays is far better understood than that of the carbonates; (c) the geology of very many petroleum occurrences in sand reservoirs has been described in a vast literature, but the literature on carbonate occurrences is relatively restricted.

While taking petroleum in sand sequences as our central concern, I have chosen petroleum in regressive sequences for particular attention. Again, there are several reasons for this; but, apart from this being my main experience, the most important is that one can understand the processes leading to petroleum accumulations in regressive clastic sequences better than those leading to other accumulations. This understanding suggests, by analogy, the directions in which understanding of the other associations may lie.

Furthermore, the emphasis is on *young* petroleum occurrences in regressive clastic sequences, for in these we see more clearly the essential elements without the complications that obscure many older accumulations.

It has not therefore been my purpose to write a comprehensive text book on petroleum geology, but rather to take this central theme, which is relevant to a great many of the world's petroleum occurrences, and to seek to show that several apparently unrelated or loosely related geological phenomena are in reality closely related — and related in such a way that their study not only makes sense of important parts of petroleum geology, but also contributes something to our understanding of wider aspects of geology.

The book is divided into two parts: the first (Chapters 1 to 7) on the central theme, the second on some practical aspects of that theme.

Chapter 1 discusses the concept of a sedimentary basin, for this is the "habitat" of petroleum and no progress can be made in petroleum (or other) geology without a clear understanding of what a sedimentary basin is.

Chapter 2 contains a synopsis of petroleum geology. The purpose of this chapter is to outline the subject as a background to the more restricted approach that follows.

Chapter 3 considers the compaction of sediments — mainly clays — and its consequences. This is an important chapter. It discusses the fluids in the rocks, their influence on the mechanical properties of the rocks, and their migration paths.

Chapter 4 discusses the contemporaneous growth of structures with sediment accumulation. This is a rather neglected aspect of geology that is common in structures that contain petroleum. It leads on to:

Chapter 5, on diapirism, the probable cause of many growth structures. Clay diapirism is particularly significant in petroleum occurrences, and an important conclusion is reached at this stage that the loading of clays under a regressive permeable sequence leads to clay diapirism and growth structures.

Chapter 6 takes the rather speculative topic of the origin and migration of petroleum. Again, this topic is broadly understandable in the light of compaction phenomena. This leads us to gather up the threads in:

Chapter 7, to consider the nature of the deformation of sedimentary basins and to outline a synthesis of petroleum geology.

The second part begins with:

Chapter 8 on drilling boreholes, describing briefly the operations that lead to the subsurface geological data.

Chapter 9 discusses the logging of boreholes, with emphasis on the determination of interstitial fluid pressures.

Chapter 10 discusses correlation and the compilation of geological data, with emphasis on the detection of growth structures. An important aspect of this is enlarged in:

Chapter 11, on the difficult problem of distinguishing faults from stratigraphic hiatus in boreholes.

Chapter 12, the final chapter, discusses three aspects of professional work — prognoses, political and economic influences, and report writing. This is intended to prepare the student in some measure for professional work as a petroleum geologist.

Most chapters have a summary at the beginning, and a Selected Bibliography at the end. In the latter, all references cited in the text are given, and these are augmented by works that may be regarded as necessary reading in the topic of the chapter.

Not all the works listed in the selected bibliography express views or interpretations consistent with those in this book. It must be left to the reader to examine each topic critically, and make his own judgement on the evidence available to him.

There has been no intention of duplicating material that is readily available in other books. Sedimentology and stratigraphic analysis, for example, are formal subjects in any university course in geology, and are not treated here. Likewise, there are specific books on subsurface geological methods and borehole logging for those who seek a fuller treatment. These topics are only discussed to the extent considered necessary for an understanding of the theme of this book.

A glossary is included. The main purpose of this was to avoid the need for digressions in the text to explain terms that many readers will know

At a time when plate tectonics is the current fashionable thought in geology, it may surprise the reader that no mention is made of it. The omission is not entirely due to ignorance. While not disputing the evidence of sea-floor spreading and continental drift, I regard the subject as peripheral to the study of sedimentary basins in which petroleum has been found. All earth processes probably play some part in the formation of significant geological features. The evidence presented in this book suggests that gravity is the most important force affecting the geology of petroleum accumulations.

Finally, perhaps I may be permitted some words of advice to the reader. First, many students have difficulty appreciating the immense spans of geological time, in which the human life − or even the history of Man − forms such an insignificant part. It may help to think of the rocks as viscous fluids, for this is just a matter of scale. Secondly, the reader of this book is recommended first to seek to understand the broad framework, then to understand the components of the framework. The next step is, of course, to improve on the treatment presented here.

Acknowledgements

I owe more to others than I find it comfortable to admit. Pierre Freymond, a friend for many years and a colleague for several, read and criticized much of the manuscript in draft. His criticisms have materially improved the book, and I am glad to acknowledge not only his help in this matter but also the benefits I derived from our earlier association.

From 1952 until 1963 I worked as a geologist (and for part of the time as a petroleum engineer) in companies of the Royal Dutch/Shell Group. This was principally in Netherlands New Guinea (now West Irian), Brunei, and Nigeria. My practical experience was acquired during these years, and I am grateful to the many people of several nationalities who contributed to this. They are too numerous to mention by name. Furthermore, I gladly acknowledge the material that the Group provided for inclusion in this book, and its permission to publish the methods described in Chapter 11, which I developed when in its employment.

In this university, I have greatly valued the help of the following in the Department of Geology and Mineralogy: Dorothy Hill (general), A. Ewart and D.C. Green (geochemistry), G. Playford (general), E.J. Heidecker (structural geology), S.H. Hall and J.P. Webb (geophysics); I am indebted to the following in the Department of Mathematics: H.M. Finucan (statistics), J.M. Fitz-Gerald, and V.G.M. Hart; and to R.L. Whitmore in the Department of Mining and Metallurgy.

A. Davis of the Queensland Geological Survey helped me with matters relating to coal. J.F. Kennedy of Mines Administration Pty Ltd. Brisbane (who, as Senior Toolpusher in Brunei when I was a petroleum engineer, taught me much) was kind enough to read and criticize the chapter on drilling. H. Crocker of Schlumberger Seaco Inc., Sydney, read and criticized the chapter on logging boreholes; and I gladly acknowledge their permission to use material of theirs in this chapter. J.M. Hunt of Woods Hole Oceanographic Institution, U.S.A., kindly found time to read and criticize the chapter on the origin and migration of petroleum.

It will be apparent from the references that I owe a debt to the authors of many published works. If I single out five men, it is because their work has had an immense influence on my geological thinking. They are: R.W. van Bemmelen, S.W. Carey, M. King Hubbert, W.W. Rubey, and Lewis G. Weeks. It has been my very good fortune to cultivate some of the seeds they have sown.

Grateful acknowledgement is given to the following authors and organizations for permission to use their material:

W.C. Leslie, Beaver Exploration Australia N.L., Australian Petroleum Exploration Association, for Fig.2-7.

Mines Administration Pty Ltd for Fig.9-1 and 10-1.

H.P. Schaub and A. Jackson, American Association of Petroleum Geologists, for Fig.7-5 and 7-6.

J. Weeda, American Association of Petroleum Geologists, for Fig.7-7 and 7-9.

J.H.L. Wennekers, American Association of Petroleum Geologists, for Fig.7-10.

R.P. Koesoemadinata, American Association of Petroleum Geologists, for Fig.7-11.

D.L. Barss, A.B. Copland, and W.D. Ritchie, American Association of Petroleum Geologists, for Fig.1-3.

W.A. Visser and J.J. Hermes, Koninklijk Nederlands Geologisch Mijnbouwkundig Genootschap, for Fig.7-8.

Marathon Petroleum Australia Ltd, and their draughtsman, K.J. Corrie, for the drawing of the following figures for this book Fig.1-2, 1-3, 5-5, 7-5, 7-6, 7-7, 7-9, 7-10, 7-12.

I am grateful to the American Association of Petroleum Geologists for permission to draw freely upon my own work published in their *Bulletin,* v.56, pp.790—795, and pp.2185—2191. Fig.3-7, 3-8, 6-1, 6-4, 6-5, 6-6 and 6-7 were first published in the *Bulletin.*

Likewise I am grateful to the Australian Petroleum Exploration Association for permission to draw freely on my paper "Petroleum and geology: a synthesis" in which the main conclusions of this work were first outlined. This was published in *The APEA Journal,* v.12, part 1, in 1972.

I also record here my gratitude to the anonymous reviewers of papers submitted for publication, for their criticisms led not only to better papers but also to better treatment of those topics in this book.

It is also a pleasure to acknowledge the stimulation received from my undergraduate and graduate students, for whom much of this material was originally prepared.

Much as I owe to so many people, any errors of omission, fact, or interpretation are mine alone.

Finally I thank with all my heart my wife, June, and my sons, Edward, John, Nigel and Paul, who have had so much to put up with during the last two years.

Note on terminology

Throughout this book, the rock types have been considered broadly in terms of sand or sandstone, limestone, or clay. The term "clay" is used to embrace all fine-grained, compactible rocks. In certain contexts in petroleum geology, it is customary to use the word "shale" for fine-grained rocks (that may include silt), irrespective of whether the rock has cleavage or fissility. Thus no significance is to be attached to the use of "shale" rather than "clay", particularly in the contexts of drilling and borehole logging.

Department of Geology and Mineralogy,
The University of Queensland.
Brisbane, September 1972

CONTENTS

Chapter 1. **SEDIMENTARY BASINS**

Summary

(1) Sedimentary basins are areas in which sediments accumulated to a significantly greater thickness than sediments of the same age in neighbouring areas. The sediments accumulate by virtue of subsidence.

(2) The nature of the sediments that accumulate is related to the environments of the physiographic basin from which the sediments are derived, and in which they are deposited.

(3) The geographical concept of a physiographic basin is distinct from the geological concept of a sedimentary basin. Sedimentation is also distinct from sediment accumulation, for not all sediment deposited is accumulated for a significant period of time in the geological record.

(4) Sedimentary basins typically begin with a transgressive phase and end with a regressive phase, but they may have a long and complicated history. Transgressive sequences in sedimentary basins record the reduction of land area and the migration of facies towards the land. Regressive sequences record the extension of the land and the migration of facies seaward.

(5) Most significant carbonate sequences are transgressive. Arenaceous sequences may be transgressive or regressive, but almost all important regressive sequences are arenaceous.

Introduction

The geology of petroleum is largely the geology of sedimentary basins, for it is in these that the major accumulations of petroleum occur. It is therefore essential to have a clear idea of what a sedimentary basin is.

A simple definition of a sedimentary basin is "an area in which sediments accumulated during a particular time span to a significantly greater thickness than in the surrounding areas". This is not entirely satisfactory because of the vagueness about thickness — yet this vagueness exists. The essential part of any definition concerns the *accumulation* of sediment relative to neighbouring areas, and its relative rather than absolute thickness.

The surface of the world can be divided into three broad categories: areas of erosion, areas of sediment accumulation, and neutral areas in which neither erosion nor accumulation is dominant. Active sedimentary basins are areas of accumulation. They may be large or small, deep (thick) or shallow (thin); they may persist for a significant span of geological time, and they may persist in one area or migrate to some extent. The age of the basin is the age of the sediments accumulated in it. They are of infinite variety, and so individually unique.

The concept of a sedimentary basin is distinct from that of a physiographic basin. A physiographic basin is a depression in the surface of the land or the sea floor that may or may not fill with sediment. Part of the area of a physiographic basin is an area of erosion, providing the materials that will form sediment in other areas of the physiographic basin. In those areas in which the sediment accumulates, the surface of the sediment does not *necessarily* form a depression everywhere, and the upper surface of sediment accumulating in a sedimentary basin may be physiographically indistinguishable from the neighbouring areas that are not accumulating sediment.

For example, there is a large physiographic basin occupying the mid-continent region of the United States of America, drained largely by the Mississippi and Missouri rivers into the Gulf of Mexico. The physiographic basin occupies a significant area of North America, and includes the Gulf of Mexico. Within this area, sediment is derived from the peripheral areas, and transported towards the sea. Some of this sediment accumulates on and in the flood plains of the rivers, some accumulates along the Gulf Coast, and some is carried out into the Gulf, where it accumulates. One of the important sedimentary basins of the world lies under the general area of the coast; and here sediments have accumulated to a far greater thickness than the contemporary sediments in the deeper areas of the Gulf of Mexico. The site of this sedimentary basin does not in itself form a depression, and the area of obvious depression in the Gulf of Mexico is not the main area of sediment accumulation.

The nature of the sediments in the physiographic basin is determined by the physiography and climate of the basin, and by the nature of the materials eroded. The nature of the sediments accumulated depends on these factors, the processes of transportation within the basin, and the position of the sedimentary basin in the physiographic basin. If the sedimentary basin is in the coastal area, paralic sediments will accumulate; if in the coastal plain, fluviatile sediments will accumulate; offshore, marine sediments will accumulate.

Sedimentation is one thing; sediment accumulation is another. The mouth of a river may well be the site of heavy sedimentation; but if the energy of the environment in which the sediment is deposited — the energy of the waves and the currents — is sufficient, the sediment will be transported elsewhere, and the *accumulation* of sediment near the river mouth may be nil or very little. The redistribution of sediment depends on its physical properties — the density, size, shape of the particles — and the energy available to move it. Sediment will therefore be moved mainly along the sea floor under the influence of waves and currents until it arrives in a position from which it cannot be moved further. There it will tend to accumulate.

But if the accumulation raises the depositional surface to a higher energy level, where the water is shallower and the waves and currents stronger, it will only accumulate to the level at which the energy is sufficient to move the sediment elsewhere. This is the concept of baselevel in the marine environment that was developed by Barrell (1917) in one of the more important papers on sedimentary geology.

Baselevel is the level at which sediment neither accumulates nor is eroded: it is also the conceptual level at which this equilibrium would be achieved.* It not only fluctuates with changing tides, seasons, and weather, but also is different for different materials. The energy of the environment is one side of the equation, as it were, while the physical properties of the sediment are the other. It is this general process that leads to the accumulation of sand, for example, in one area, clay in another. It is a process that has been operating since the material became incorporated in the stream load. Hence one must not think of a rock unit or lithological unit as a *representative* sample of the sediment brought to the area any more than one may consider the sediment brought to the sea as a representative sample of the rocks eroded by the streams and rivers. The sediment that accumulates in a place is that fraction of the total sediment in that place that cannot be transported further.

On the continental shelves, fluctuations of baselevel will accompany fluctuations of current intensity and wave and swell *lengths* (for the energy of waves decreases exponentially with depth as a function of wave length rather than of wave amplitude). It seems reasonable to suppose that few areas on the continental shelves are permanently below the lowest baselevel induced by exceptional circumstances once in a 100 or 1,000 years. If the shape of the continental shelf and the level of the sea relative to it were to remain constant, and the mean level of storm intensity, current strength, and the variation about the mean, were to remain constant, there would be a tendency for sediment to accumulate evenly and thinly over the shelf, with the bulk of the total sediment eventually passing off the shelf to deeper water. The increasing depth of water away from the land, and hence decreasing mean or

---

* Baselevel is used in the singular, and must be thought of with reference to a particular, perfectly sorted sediment. This is a device to simplify the more complex reality. The real situation is that there is a baselevel for each grade of sediment. Thus, a poorly sorted sediment in a given position has a range of baselevels; and sediment accumulates or passes on according to whether the baselevel for each grain lies above or below the depositional surface. It is for this reason that Fig. 1-1 is drawn with a constant lithology implied.

Baselevel may be viewed another way. In each position on the sea floor there is a grade that just (but only just) cannot be moved by the energy available, and the baselevel for that grade coincides with the sea floor in that position. Finer grades cannot accumulate there.

maximum energy at the depositional surface, would result in a general sorting of clastic material from coarse to fine seawards, dense to less dense, spherical to angular, from the coast towards the margin of the continental shelf. The geological record does not show more than a general tendency for this to happen, and it does show significant accumulations of sediments in some areas, not in others. There is another influence, namely, *subsidence* of the depositional surfaces relative to baselevel.

Accumulation of sediment

The essence of Barrell's concept of sediment accumulation is embodied in his diagram, reproduced here as Fig.1-1 (Barrell, 1917). It depicts the consequences of a generally rising baselevel that includes two minor orders of fluctuation. The diagram is valid for a rising baselevel or a subsiding sedimentary column: it is the relative change that is important. Sediment accumulates during periods of rising baselevel. The process is both additive and sub-

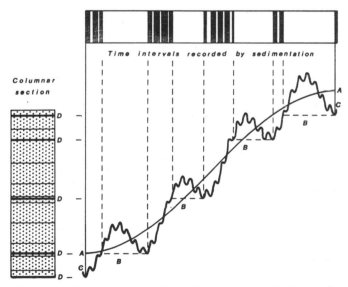

Fig.1-1. Sedimentary record resulting from oscillations of baselevel. $A-A$ = primary curve of rising baselevel; B = oscillations giving disconformities D; $C-C$ = minor oscillations (schematic). (Redrawn from Barrell, 1917.)

tractive, and only the sediment that is left permanently below the fluctuations in baselevel is accumulated permanently. *Diastems* result from the small oscillations: disconformities from the larger. The actual sediment in a sequence may represent only a small proportion of the total time elapsed for the accumulation of the sequence, for the sequence on the left side of the diagram accumulated during the black intervals along the time scale at the top.

Subsidence of a depositional surface (that is, a surface over which sediment was being transported) provides a potential to accumulate sediment because there is a tendency for part of the sediment to be removed permanently beyond the reach of fluctuations in the baselevel. The more rapid the subsidence, the larger the proportion of sediment accumulated permanently (up to the limit, of course, of total accumulation of the sediment supplied).

Hence sediment accumulation may be viewed as the difference between the supply of sediment and the capacity of the environment to remove it. Sedimentary basins are areas that, over a span of time, have had a supply of sediment and a capacity to retain part or all of it.

It is clearly erroneous to consider sediment accumulation generally as resulting from sediment falling directly from suspension. Sediment accumulates in this way only when the depositional surface lies below baselevel — and then it usually consists only of sediment of a very fine grain. In general, sediment is redistributed on the sea floor of the continental shelf, and this generalization also applies to clays and other fine-grained sediments — partly because few areas of the continental shelves are below baselevel, and partly because the baselevel for clays lies lower than that for coarser fractions.

The work of Barrell forms the basis for an understanding of sedimentary basins. The concept of fluctuations in baselevel, leading to discontinuous sediment accumulation, reconciles the long-standing observation that the maximum net rate of sediment accumulation over major intervals of geological time (eras, periods) is very much slower than that suggested by the sediments themselves.

The maximum net rate of accumulation, obtained by dividing the period of time in years by the maximum known thickness of

TABLE 1-I

Phanerozoic rates of sediment accumulation
(Based on data from Holmes, 1960)

Phanerozoic	1 m per 4,400 years
	1 ft. per 1,300 years
Palaeozoic	1 m per 5,700 years
	1 ft. per 1,700 years
Mesozoic	1 m per 4,100 years
	1 ft. per 1,200 years
Cenozoic	1 m per 2,100 years
	1 ft. per 600 years

Note: The apparent increase in the accumulation rate with the passage of time must be interpreted with caution, because there has been less opportunity for younger rocks to be destroyed and more opportunity for them to be measured.

sediment accumulated during that time, is given for the Phanerozoic in Table 1-I.

By contrast with the rates in this Table, Holocene (Recent) sediments of the Orinoco delta at Pedernales accumulated at a rate of 1 m per 100 years (Kidwell and Hunt, 1958) and, as Barrell pointed out, the preservation of tree trunks in the geological record in many parts of the world, in rocks of various ages, indicates that they were buried before the wood rotted, implying a rapid rate of sediment accumulation to be measured in tens of years per metre rather than thousands.

Barrell's concept also requires us to exercise extreme caution in the interpretation of Holocene accumulations and present sediments. Only a small proportion of the sediment at present in transport along the sea floor will normally be accumulated near where it is at present, and not all of that accumulated will be accumulated for a significant time span geologically. Moreover, if the post-Pleistocene time has been one of general transgressive tendency, with rising sea level and rising baselevel, then it has also been a period of active, but not necessarily permanent, sediment accumulation.

In general, it is erroneous to consider rock units in the stratigraphic column as analogous to sand banks, shoals, etc., on the sea floor today, although there are clear exceptions to be found, such as surfaces with ripple marks and animal tracks, and organic reefs.

It is generally much more accurate to regard rock units as the incomplete record of the passage of sediment of different compositions.

For example, the migration of a large sand bank may be recorded in the sedimentary sequence by a thin, laterally discontinuous sand unit that consists only of that portion that came to be below baselevel. The dune shape will not be apparent, and there may even be no trace of current bedding. Likewise, on a smaller scale, the preservation of ripple marks requires that a surface that was close above baselevel on one tide be buried under a protective layer of sediment by the next tide, and for baselevel to be elevated permanently above the surface of the ripple marks. Only in areas of extremely rapid subsidence are ripple-marked surfaces likely to be common; and it is hard to escape the feeling that they are a common feature preserved by uncommon events — that the ordinary ripple-marked surface in shallow water and between the tide lines is unlikely to be preserved.

While the concept of a physiographic basin is quite distinct from that of a sedimentary basin, a sedimentary basin is necessarily situated within a physiographic basin, because it is the latter that is the dominant influence on sediment supply and transport. The combined concept is dynamic, for changes in the physiographic basin affect the type and character of the sediment accumulated in the sedimentary basin.

Sediment supply is often apparently in very close balance with subsidence, because we find considerable thicknesses of sediment of a particular environment. The balance is more apparent than real; and true balance is probably rare. It is commonly said that the rate of subsidence is equal to the rate of sediment accumulation, and this leads to the idea of balance. More correctly (and more usefully) one should think of the rate of accumulation being equal to the rate of subsidence. The accumulation of considerable thicknesses of rocks of the same facies merely reflects the constancy of the physiographic environments over the area of the sedimentary basin, the surplus sediment being removed.

The primary control on sediment accumulation is subsidence (assuming sediment supply) because sediment accumulation without subsidence is vulnerable to subsequent dispersal. The primary controls on the lithology of the sediment accumulated are the sediment sources and the energy of the environments of the physiographic basin. The matter of lateral continuity of a particular lithology, or rock unit, involves considerations of the three dimensions of space and that of time. A lithological unit may be discontinuous over an area because the sediment: (a) was not distributed over the whole area; (b) was distributed but did not accumulate over the whole area; (c) was distributed and accumulated, but accumulation was only temporary over parts of the area due to changing energy patterns.

One conclusion is clear: the margin of a discontinuous lithological unit in the sedimentary record is not necessarily the margin of that environment in the physiographic basin. The sequence of lithologies and their areal distribution in a sedimentary basin constitute a variable and very incomplete record in space of the variations of the environments in the physiographic basin over that area with time.

Transgressions and regressions (Fig. 1-2)

When subsidence in a physiographic basin exceeds the supply of sediment, that is, the area has a capacity to accumulate a larger volume of sediment than is supplied, the sea tends to deepen over the depositional surface, and facies tend to migrate towards the land. This is a *transgressive* phase of basin development, leading to the accumulation of a transgressive sequence of sediments. Where this process raises baselevel above the depositional surface, pelagic sediments may accumulate, and may accumulate to a considerable thickness. Sedimentary basins tend to be enlarged during transgressive phases, but the enlargement is only permanent if the subsidence relative to baselevel is permanent.

If the sea over part of a physiographic basin becomes shallower, and the facies migrate seaward, the development is *regressive*. Let us clarify the terms and concepts involved in transgressions and regressions. There are advantages in taking regressions first.

"Regression" is defined as a lowering of sea level relative to the land. This results in the migration of the shore-line and the facies

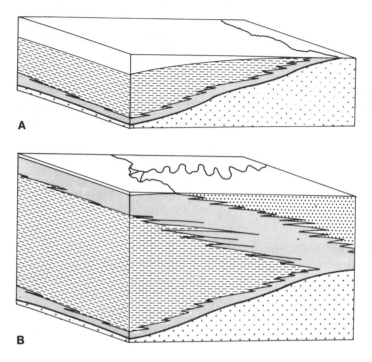

Fig. 1-2. Block diagram showing accumulation of transgressive sequence (A) followed by a regressive sequence (B). Neritic facies, dashes; neritic-paralic, fine dots; paralic-terrestrial, coarse dots.

of the sediments in a seaward direction, with an extension of the land area. This is the basic concept. A second concept is derived from the first, in the following manner. If the mass of sediment supplied to an area requires more energy for its dispersal than is available, baselevel rises and the surplus sediment accumulates: the accumulating sediment tends to extend, the land area, and the facies also tend to migrate seaward, or *prograde*. There is thus a subtle difference between the two aspects of regression, but a difference that is of considerable importance geologically. Both can result stratigraphically in a sequence that shows sediments of shallower water facies overlying those of deeper water facies (or terrestrial over marine), *provided sediment accumulates*. The important difference between the two types of regression is that the relative lowering of sea level *results in a lowering of baselevel*, while regressions of the second type *result from a rising baselevel* — more sediment being supplied than can be removed.

Regressions of the first type are important for the erosion and redistribution of previously accumulated sediment: regressions of the second type are important for the accumulation of regressive sequences of sediments. Let us call regressions of the first type *erosional regressions,* those of the second type *depositional regressions.*

Deltas are examples of depositional regressions, for they result from the volume of sediment supplied by the river exceeding the volume that can be removed by the sea, with a consequent extension of the land area. Many of the present deltas have strong seasonal influences, with periods of high river level and massive transport of sediment. Over a longer time interval, deltas change their shape. The building of the delta may be episodic, but the dominant trend is one of depositional regression.

"Transgression" has two aspects analogous to those of regressions. The basic concept is that of a rising sea level relative to the land, with a consequent migration of facies landward and reduction of land area. The derived concept is this: when the energy of the environment is greater than that required to remove the sediment supplied, the surplus energy may erode and redistribute sediment previously accumulated (e.g., coastal erosion). This also tends to reduce the land area and to lead to the migration of the facies landward. Both types of transgression may result in the accumulation of sediment in a stratigraphic sequence in which deeper water facies overlie shallower (or marine overlie terrestrial). The rising baselevel of a rising sea level relative to the land results in a *depositional* transgression, while the falling baselevel due to surplus energy results in an *erosional* transgression. (Note in passing that a break in the stratigraphic sequence is not necessarily regressive.)

Petroleum geology is concerned with the accumulation of sediment as well as the accumulation of petroleum. We are therefore concerned largely with depositional regressive and transgressive sequences in sedimentary basins. Depositional regressions tend to accumulate porous and permeable rocks (potential petroleum reservoir rocks) on top of fine-grained porous but relatively impermeable rocks (potential petroleum source rocks): depositional transgressions tend to accumulate potential source rocks on top of potential reservoir rocks.

Dominant trends must be distinguished from episodic reversals, for there are usually transgressive episodes in a dominantly regressive (depositional) phase of basin development, and vice versa. Consider for a moment such a transgressive episode. It may result from a change of energy and sedimentation patterns, so that sands accumulate in areas that were accumulating clay, and clays accumulate in areas that were accumulating sand. The latter would be a transgressive episode and may be quite local. Such a change could be associated with a changing geography along a coast-line, perhaps with deltas changing their position, or rivers finding new courses to the sea. Episodic reduction in total sediment supply could result from climatic changes, leading to an erosional transgressive episode: episodic accelerations of subsidence could lead to a depositional transgressive episode. While the accumulation of sediment is more readily understood in the light of depositional transgressions and regressions, erosional transgressions and regressions may lead to the accumulation elsewhere of redistributed sediment.

Lithological associations in sedimentary basins

If one considers the sedimentary rocks broadly as clays/shales, sands/sandstones, and carbonates/evaporites, sedimentary basins tend to accumulate either clay/shale and sand/sandstone, or clay/shale and carbonate/evaporite as a dominant association of lithologies. These associations reflect the fact that physiographic basins tend to generate, transport, and deposit' sediments of a similar character over great spans of time. But they do change, and some important sedimentary basins record such changes in associations (such as the Maracaibo basin in Venezuela, and the East Borneo basin in Indonesia).

In the context of transgressions and regressions, three associations are evident. There is an association between transgressive sequences and carbonates; between regressive sequences and evaporites; and between regressive sequences and sand/sandstone. These associations can easily be expanded into generalizations that are too sweeping.

The upper Devonian organic reefs of the Western Canada basin are well known because many of them are petroleum reservoirs. The results of much highly competent research have been published (see Barss et al., 1970, and Hemphill et al., 1970, for a recent account of two areas). There is no doubt that the reefs grew during a dominantly transgressive — depositionally transgressive — phase of the development of the physiographic basin. In general, the more southerly their position, the younger their age (Fig.1-3); and many are overlain by clays or calcareous clays and marls of a

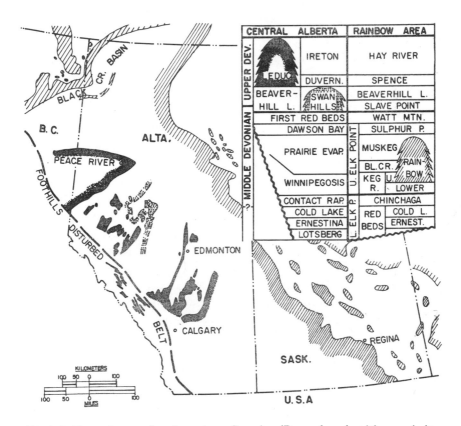

Fig.1-3. Devonian reefs of western Canada. (Reproduced with permission from Barss et al., 1970.)

deeper-water facies than that implied by the reefs themselves. Are organic reefs always transgressive? What is a transgressive reef?

The matter of transgressive and regressive reefs is complicated, and is not to be related solely to changes of sea level relative to the land. The reason for the complication lies in the nature of an organic reef. Lowenstam's widely accepted definition of a reef requires that it contains organisms that were frame-builders, the organisms growing to create a wave-resistant structure; and that the organisms were important for sediment retention and sediment binding (Lowenstam, 1950). There are thus two important parameters, the biological potential to build and the environmental potential to destroy, that determine the form of the reef — whether biohermal or biostromal, whether isolated as patch or pinnacle reefs, or associated with a back-reef facies (perhaps including evaporites).

A reef is a facies of a physiographic basin. So the simplest concept is that a reef that migrates landward is transgressive, while one that migrates seaward is regressive. Another simple concept is that when the true thickness of a reef exceeds the presumed depth tolerance of one or more of the reef-building organisms, such a reef is transgressive by inference even though the facies may not migrate.

Modern colonial corals, for example, are sensitive to light, water temperature and salinity; and their depth tolerance is to about 30–45 m (100–150 ft.). It cannot be assumed that the same tolerances applied to ancient reef organisms; and as yet there are no accurate means of determining them. It does seem reasonable, though, to assume that their tendency to form wave-resistant structures, to migrate, and to be exterminated by muddy sediment or hypersalinity, all indicate a rather restricted range of favourable environmental conditions in which light and salinity played an important part.

Ingels (1963) estimated the water depth around the Silurian Thornton reef to be about 60 m (200 ft.), and Terry and Williams (1969) suggested a similar depth around the Paleocene Intisar "A" bioherm in Libya (this bioherm was known as "Idris" in the literature from discovery in 1967 until 1969, "Intisar" thereafter). But depth of water around a reef is not a reliable indicator of depth of tolerance of the organisms. What is required is the maximum depth at which reef growth can start, for this establishes the maximum thickness of reef that can develop with constant water depth. Whatever the true figure may be, it is unlikely to exceed 100 m (300 ft.) and may well be half that figure.

This concept places many of the Silurian and Devonian organic reefs (many of them petroleum reservoirs), the Cretaceous reef reservoirs of Mexico, some of the Mesozoic and Tertiary reef reservoirs of the Middle East, and (from the little published information) some of the Paleocene reef reservoirs of Libya, into the transgressive category.

The association of evaporites with regressive sequences is an important association for petroleum, for the evaporites provide seals to the petroleum reservoirs in many carbonate provinces – particularly the Middle East, some areas of western Canada, and in the Permian basin of West Texas and New Mexico. In all these areas, evaporites tended to cover large areas eventually. In western Canada, the evaporites formed behind the barrier reef that grew in Middle and Late Devonian times across Alberta into the Northwest Territories (Fig.1-3). This evaporite development appears to be a direct result of the enclosing of the seas by reefs. It is profitless to speculate further on the nature of this association on present knowledge. We merely note that evaporite sequences are commonly intercalated with, and eventually terminate the development of extensive carbonate sequences, and that such sequences are significantly associated with petroleum occurrences.

As regards the association between regressive sequences and sand/sandstones little need be said here, for this is the common situation. Nevertheless, these three associations, indistinct as they may be, are sufficiently distinct to suggest that the rate of sediment supply is a material factor that determines whether or not a sedimentary basin preserves the record of a transgressive or a regressive phase in the development of the physiographic basin. It is suggested that massive sedimentation, such as is observable today in the U.S. Gulf Coast, the Niger delta, the large deltas of the Indian subcontinent, Southeast Asia and China, is the principal cause of regressive periods of the development of the physiographic basins and thus also of the regressive sequences recorded in sedimentary basins. Carbonate and evaporite deposition, by their very nature, tend to be much slower processes taken over large areas, and in general these are incapable of inducing a *depositional* regression.

Classification of sedimentary basins

Sedimentary basins are of great variety, each being individually unique. Their ages vary, their time spans vary, and the type and distribution of the sediments they accumulated vary. A complete classification would require two separate classifications — one of physiographic basins, and one of the geometry of sedimentary basins — for, as we have seen, the nature of the sediments accumulated in a sedimentary basin depends upon the environment of the physiographic basin and the position of the sedimentary basin in relation to these environments. Several classifications have been proposed (some are listed in the Selected Bibliography at the end of this chapter) but few are wholly satisfactory. Classifications of continuous variables are always to some extent arbitrary and artificial. It is sufficient to make but a simple classification here.

Sedimentary basin geometry

The geometry of sedimentary basins in section may be classified as either symmetrical or asymmetrical (Fig.1-4). These may be further subdivided on the basis of the nature of their margins, that is, faulted or unfaulted (but it must be realized that the nature of the margin of a sedimentary basin is not always determinable because subsequent geological events may have obscured it or it may be beyond the reach of investigation). The asymmetrical basin has received much attention in the literature, and was called a "half-graben" by Weeks (1952) when the asymmetry is due to a fault or fault system. The symmetry of sedimentary basins in this context refers to geometrical symmetry, not to the symmetry of the facies accumulated in the basin.

In plan, sedimentary basins may be circular, oval, or rectangular (asymmetrical basins usually having one fairly straight side), and

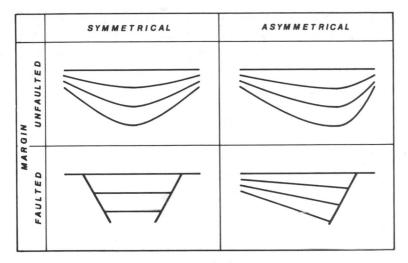

Fig. 1-4. Simple classification of sedimentary basins.

they vary in size from a few kilometres to several hundreds of kilometres in horizontal dimensions. *Geosynclines* may be regarded as particular forms of sedimentary basin of which the length is considerably greater than the width, and in which a great thickness of characteristic sediments and volcanic rocks accumulated (Kay, 1951; Kündig 1959).

Physiographic basins may be open or enclosed, silled or unsilled, continental or marine, or a combination of these. The Gulf of Mexico, the northern part of the Bay of Bengal, and the South China Sea, are examples of open basins. The Black Sea, the Baltic, and the Mediterranean, are examples of enclosed basins; and the area around Lake Eyre in South Australia is an example of a closed continental basin. The environment of physiographic basins is very variable according to its climate and the general geography and geology of the area. Of particular significance in petroleum geology is the alternation of environments in the course of time between euxinic, or areas of anaerobic, reducing conditions, during the accumulation of fine-grained sediment and those environments that led to the accumulation of porous and permeable sediments.

The discrete concepts of physiographic basins and sedimentary basins merge in this respect. Reducing conditions, which are essential for the preservation of organic material, occur in the aqueous environment near the sedimentary surface or within the sediments. Hence sediments may either accumulate in a reducing environment (euxinic), or be buried to a reducing environment by rapid subsidence.

Generalizing, sedimentary basins usually begin with a transgressive phase during which the rate of subsidence exceeds the rate of sediment accumulation, and end with a regressive phase during which the rate of sediment accumulation exceeds the rate of subsidence. Some sedimentary basins record a simple, single *cycle* of sediment accumulation (Fig.1-2), others record a long and complicated history.

The deformation of sedimentary basins is also a central theme of petroleum geology. The nature of this deformation is considered in Chapters 4 and 5, and again more broadly in Chapter 7.

Selected bibliography

Aubouin, J., 1965. *Geosynclines. Developments in Geotectonics,* 1. Elsevier, Amsterdam, 335 pp.

Barrell, J., 1917. Rhythms and the measurement of geologic time. *Bull. Geol. Soc. Am.,* 28:745—904. (There is much in this long paper that is of historical interest only.)

Barss, D.L., Copland, A.B. and Ritchie, W.D., 1970. Geology of Middle Devonian reefs, Rainbow area, Alberta, Canada. In: M.T. Halbouty (Editor), *Geology of Giant Petroleum Fields. Am. Ass. Petrol. Geol., Mem.,* 14: pp. 19—49.

Dallmus, K.F., 1958. Mechanics of basin evolution and its relation to the habitat of oil in the basin. In: L.G. Weeks (Editor), *Habitat of Oil.* American Association of Petroleum Geologists, Tulsa, Okla, pp. 883—931.

Eicher, D.L., 1968. *Geologic Time.* Prentice-Hall Inc., N.J. 149 pp.

Glaessner, M.F. and Teichert, C., 1947. Geosynclines: a fundamental concept in geology. *Am. J. Sci.,* 245:465—482; 571—591.

Gretener, P.E., 1967. Significance of the rare event in geology. *Bull.Am.Ass. Petrol.Geol.,* 51:2197—2206.

Hemphill, C.R. Smith, R.I. and Szabo, F., 1970. Geology of Beaverhill Lake reefs, Swan Hills area, Alberta. In: M.T. Halbouty (Editor), *Geology of Giant Petroleum Fields. Am. Ass. Petrol. Geol., Mem.,* 14:50—90.

Holmes, A., 1960. A revised geological time-scale. *Trans. Edinb. Geol. Soc.,* 17 (for 1957—1959): 183—216.

Ingels, J.J.C., 1963. Geometry, paleontology, and petrography of Thornton reef complex, Silurian of northeastern Illinois. *Bull. Am. Ass. Petrol.Geol.,* 47: 405—440.

Jones, O.T., 1938. On the evolution of a geosyncline. *Q. J. Geol. Soc. Lond.,* 94: lx-cx (Proceedings).

Kay, M., 1947. Geosynclinal nomenclature and the craton. *Bull. Am. Ass. Petrol. Geol.,* 31: 1289—1293.

Kay, M., 1951. North American geocynclines. *Mem. Geol. Soc. Am.,* 48: 143 pp.

Kidwell, A.L. and Hunt, J.M., 1958. Migration of oil in Recent sediments of Pedernales, Venezuela. In: L.G. Weeks (Editor), *Habitat of Oil.* American Association of Petroleum Geologists, Tulsa, Okla., pp.790—817.

Krumbein, W.C. and Sloss, L.L., 1963. *Stratigraphy and Sedimentation* (2nd ed.). Freeman, San Francisco, London, 660 pp.

Kündig, E., 1959. Eugeosynclines as potential oil habitats. *Proc. World Petrol. Congr., 5th, New York, 1959* (1): 461—474.

Lowenstam, H.A., 1950. Niagaran reefs of the Great Lakes area. *J. Geol.,* 58: 430—487.

Terry, C.E. and Williams, J.J., 1969. The Idris "A" bioherm and oilfield, Sirte basin, Libya — its commercial development, regional Palaeocene geologic setting and stratigraphy. In: P. Hepple (Editor), *The Exploration for Petroleum in Europe and North Africa.* Institute of Petroleum, London, pp.31—48.

Weeks. L.G., 1952. Factors of sedimentary basin development that control oil occurrence. *Bull. Am. Ass. Petrol. Geol.,* 36: 2071—2124.

Weeks, L.G., 1958. Habitat of oil and some factors that control it. In: L.G. Weeks (Editor), *Habitat of Oil.* American Association of Petroleum Geologists, Tulsa, Okla., pp.1—61.

Chapter 2. **A SYNOPSIS OF PETROLEUM GEOLOGY**

Geology is concerned with observing facts about the earth, studying the relationships between these facts, and interpreting them in terms of natural processes in space and time. Some aspects of the science are speculative (an attribute shared with archaeology and astronomy) in the sense that the hypotheses that result from the studies are rarely confirmable — either because they relate to past events, or because they are intangible. Geology is a descriptive science because the diverse materials and phenomena cannot be interpreted until they have been properly described. It is an eclectic science in that it borrows from many other disciplines — biology, chemistry, and physics, and must increasingly borrow the mathematician's tools — in order to do the job properly.

The geologist's work falls into two general areas of activity: the description of present geology, and the interpretation of that geology in terms of past geology and geography. The emphasis is necessarily on description in the early stages, for it is the essential basis of interpretation. By describing the rock types found in an area, measuring their thicknesses, and drawing their outcrops on a map, the factual basis of the geology of the area is recorded. By measuring dips and strikes, and determining the sequence of strata, one acquires data for the interpolation between data points on the surface, and extrapolation from the surface into the subsurface. The interpretation of these data is another matter.

The provincialism of which geologists are accused (and sometimes accuse themselves) stems largely from the emphasis on descriptive geology. The infinite variety of geology makes each area unique; yet each area is but a local expression of basic processes that have general validity. New Zealand, for example, has much in common with California. The geology of the Devonian rocks of Belgium has much in common with that of western

Canada and Western Australia, for all three areas contain broadly contemporaneous organic reefs. Yet each is unique.

Petroleum geology shares these problems, because it is a general geology with a specific aim. The petroleum geologist's work also has descriptive and interpretative aspects, but the emphasis tends to remain on the descriptive stage, because the goal of petroleum geology is a deterministic model of an area. This emphasis reaches its peak in subsurface geological studies of producing petroleum fields.

It is commonly said that the petroleum geologist has the advantage of working without financial restraint. This is rarely, if ever, true. It is true that many areas are investigated using several disciplines, some of which (geophysics, drilling) are very expensive to apply; but these will be operating under some financial restraint. It is not so often said, but it is nevertheless true, that most petroleum geological work has a *time* restraint (which is also a financial restraint) and so may be based on inadequate data. Much of petroleum geology is carried out in regions of the world that would otherwise have waited for decades before investigation. Much of this work is carried out against time limitations, and so the danger of false inference is present. When such work finds its way into print, the conclusions are likely to be accepted by geologists with no local knowledge, working in other fields of activity. There are also competitive restraints. It would be invidious to mention specific published articles: but all geologists must have experienced the frustration of reading a paper that gives formation names or ages, but no lithologies; the stratigraphy of the petroleum-bearing sequence, but not of that underlying or overlying it. These errors of omission result from time (or other) restraints, not from stupidity. We are unlikely to detect errors of commission.

The great accumulation of factual data and the demands of specialization have ensured, unfortunately, that the geologist can only make his judgements on the basis of incomplete knowledge within a rather narrow field. Even within specialities, the limit of time and opportunity in a human life prevents his seeing and doing all he should see and do to provide a proper balance to his judgement. These are severe limitations, but they apply to all science today. In petroleum geology, there is a tendency to specialize in either surface (largely exploration) geology, or subsurface (largely production) geology. These two specializations are so different in outlook that there is a danger of the one not understanding the other fully.

Surface geology is concerned primarily with geology in the two horizontal dimensions, with extrapolation into the subsurface. Subsurface geology is concerned primarily with almost complete factual data in the vertical dimension, at separate points in the horizontal dimensions. The surface geologist deals with dry rocks: the subsurface geologist deals with the electrical response of rocks rather than the rocks themselves. The surface geologist thinks largely in terms of the solids in the rocks; the subsurface geologist, largely in terms of the fluids in the rocks. Each has much to learn from the other – but life is short. The great challenge to petroleum geologists of both specialities is that his geological skills are put to the test by drilling.

The great advances in geological thought during the 19th century are attributable largely to the construction of railways, canals, and coal mines. A study of petroleum geology suggests that the construction of boreholes in the 20th century has not contributed sufficiently to modern geological thought, and that some of the difficulties we encounter are due to the extension of the concepts developed from surface geology to the subsurface, and a failure to revise those concepts in the light of the borehole data. We shall return to this topic in Chapter 7.

Geological inference

Geological inference is a process of argument based on observation and induction. The nature of the argument may be logical, as when determining the relative ages of superimposed strata, or by analogy with observations made in areas where the evidence is more conclusive. The scale of the argument varies from the submicroscopic to the global. Conclusive geological arguments are those in which several different lines of argument lead to the same conclusions. They are unfortunately rare. Even the principle of superposition applies strictly only in a vertical sequence in one place. If applied carelessly to a diachronous unit, it leads to erroneous conclusions.

It has been noted by previous writers that there is more disagreement than agreement between geologists, and that consequently many of us are in error much of the time. One major cause, perhaps the major cause of disagreement is lack of understanding of all the disciplines involved – geology, biology, chemistry, physics. One ordinary man cannot know enough, and his ignorance of one facet of a problem means that his judgement is incomplete. Conflicting evidence is a cause for disagreement – but that too must be the result of ignorance.

Take for example the movement of oil through a permeable rock. Gravity segregation of gas, oil, and water – in order of increasing density with depth within a single reservoir – is demonstrable in very many petroleum accumulations; and when a well is put onto production, oil moves through the rock to the well. So there is no difficulty at all in accepting the migration of oil through permeable rocks. Yet, those familiar with capillary force insist that oil *disseminated* as a separate phase in water cannot easily be moved through the pore spaces. We know that significant quantities of oil are left in the pore spaces of a reservoir that is being depleted, and that it is very difficult to displace this residual oil with water, and impossible to displace all of it artificially with water. Most reservoirs show not the slightest trace of oil in the reservoir rocks below the oil/water interface; yet as this interface rises due to the displacement of produced oil by water, significant residual oil is left. In this fundamental topic of petroleum geology there is therefore conflicting evidence, and no general agreement amongst geologists – except that oil in one form or another has moved into the accumulation.

Many geological and petroleum geological inferences are based on associations. The association of lithologies in a sequence may be the basis for the correlation of rock units or for the interpretation of the environment in which the sediment was deposited; consistent association of a particular fauna with a lithology leads to the conclusion that the fauna is "facies-bound"; the association of petroleum with anticlines (rather than synclines) indicates accu-

mulation under the influence of gravity, with an upward component of movement of the less dense petroleum through the denser
formation water.*

Associations are notoriously difficult to use in geological (or
other) inference because a causal relationship does not necessarily
exist. Associations such as those between the consumption of
alcohol and teachers' salaries, or between Denmark's birthrate and
its stork population, are amusing. But would we find some geological associations amusing if we knew all the facts?

Consider the following common associations with depth:

(1) Temperature increases (with depth).

(2) Fluid pressure increases.

(3) Water salinity tends to increase.

(4) Water density tends to increase.

(5) Oil density tends to decrease in successive reservoirs in one
field.

(6) Clay (shale) density tends to increase.

These six associations with depth, seven items in all, lead to 21
consequent associations, which can be shown in a correlation
half-matrix (Fig.2-1). Some of these are clearly not causal relationships. For example, the association of increasing water density
with increasing temperature is demonstrably false (indirect) because water expands when heated and its density decreases. Is the
increase in water salinity with depth due to increasing temperature? ...or pressure? ...or both? Or is it perhaps related to the
increase in clay density — that is, with the expulsion of pore water
on compaction? Is the commonly observed decrease of oil density
with depth to be attributed to increasing temperature and/or
pressure, or the salinity of the water?

The increase in temperature is *caused* by none of the listed
factors; nor is the increase in clay density. It could be that the
only causal relationship in the table of Fig.2-1 is that between
water salinity and water density.

The association between petroleum accumulations and anticlines has been a guiding principle of petroleum exploration for

---

* "Formation" does not have a strict connotation in petroleum geology out
of its purely geological context.

	Depth	Temperature	Water pressure	Water salinity	Water density	Oil density	Clay density
Depth	1						
Temperature	+	1					
Water pressure	+	+	1				
Water salinity	(+)	(+)	(+)	1			
Water density	(+)	(+)	(+)	(+)	1		
Oil density	(−)	(−)	(−)	(−)	(−)	1	
Clay density	(+)	(+)	(+)	(+)	(+)	(−)	1

Fig.2-1. Correlation half-matrix of common associations with depth. Correlations are read by taking the intersection of the row of one element with the column of the other. Brackets here indicate a tendency.

nearly a century, and is considered to be well understood. The association between petroleum and evaporite sequences has been recognized for some decades, but it is not yet understood.

Two conclusions are evident: associations must be searched for causal relationships, and the significance of departures from normal associations must be assessed. Abnormality must not be dismissed as a freak, for in abnormality (as we shall see in Chapter 3) may lie the clues to the true causal relationships.

For example, in some petroleum fields in Venezuela and Indonesia the density of the oil in successive reservoirs increases with depth, or a trend of decreasing density is reversed. It is also observed in some of these that the salinity of the interstitial water decreases as the density of the oil increases. In other words, water salinity and oil density are apparently closely related − but again, closeness of association is not necessarily to be interpreted as a causal relationship, and causal relationships are necessary for understanding. It is thought that the real association is environmental, and that some of these anomalously heavy oils are generated from organic matter associated with a terrestrial environment, with fresher water. At the same time, this environmental influence is unlikely to be the only influence, because temperature demonstrably affects the diagenesis of organic matter to petroleum.

The goal of petroleum geology and the industry in general cannot be to drill every anticline (one is reminded of the definition of an engineer as one who can do for $1 what any fool can do for $2). The goal of petroleum geology must be to understand the processes so well that the speculative element in the industry is significantly reduced and finally eliminated. Cases of one company relinquishing an area on geological advice, only to watch another find oil there, are geological failures. Even if the goal is unattainable, it must be worth seeking if only for the contributions that the evidence of petroleum, as a natural material of the earth, make to geology as a whole. Petroleum geology is not just a technically-based variety of historical geology. It contributes significant ideas as well as significant data to the geological understanding of the earth — and it will certainly continue to do so.

Petroleum geology

Much of the experience of petroleum geology is well known to every student of geology. It has been acquired from the collective and cumulative experience of the industry, and centres logically around the three main processes — petroleum generation, migration and accumulation. However, the emphasis is placed in the reverse order. Entrapment is the heart of the industry. It is observable, definable, and measurable.

Exploration for petroleum is carried out essentially by looking for potential traps, then drilling into them to see if there is any petroleum. The experience of the industry is that petroleum occurs more commonly in *sedimentary basins* than in areas of thin and incomplete sedimentary sequences; more commonly in rocks of Mesozoic and Tertiary ages than in older or younger rocks; and more commonly in anticlinal traps than in other types of trap. Experience also indicates that petroleum is found more cheaply in areas where petroleum has been found before, and in sedimentary basins where petroleum has been found before.

Oil fields can be grouped in several ways: by structural type, by geological age, by geographic position, by depth, by petroleum characteristics, by reservoir characteristics, and so on. These are descriptive groupings. They may also be grouped according to the type of sedimentary basin in which they occur. This is also descriptive, for sedimentary basins are themselves of great variety and so individually unique.

Petroleum

The chemistry of petroleum is a subject in itself, and most of it is low on the petroleum geologists' list of priorities. However, what is summarized here should be regarded as minimum knowledge of the subject for a petroleum geologist, and this can be supplemented as required by reading (e.g., Levorsen, 1967, chapter 5) or by consulting a petroleum chemist.

Petroleum is a natural substance that occurs in the earth as a solid (or semi-solid), or a liquid, or a gas — or as mutual solutions. It is a *mixture* of hydrocarbons, usually with impurities (such as sulphur). Hydrocarbons are compounds of hydrogen and carbon atoms with a wide range of molecular structures. *Petroleum* is a collective term for hydrocarbons with impurities that does not specify their state (solid, liquid, or gas). To be more specific about their state, one must refer to solid petroleum (such as bitumen), oil, or gas. When one wishes to be more specific about the nature of the hydrocarbons, one refers to the dominant hydrocarbon *series* present. These are:

The *paraffins*, which are all open saturated chains with a general formula $C_n H_{2n+2}$. The gases of the paraffin series are *methane* (CH_4), *ethane* (C_2H_6), *propane* (C_3H_8), and *butane* (C_4H_{10}). The structures of methane and ethane are shown in Fig.2-2: the others are homologous. The liquids are *pentane* (C_5H_{12}), *hexane* (C_6H_{14}), and so on up to molecules with 15—20 carbon atoms, within which range the paraffins form waxy solids. The series continues with molecules with up to 60—70 carbon atoms.

The *aromatics* are closed unsaturated chains, or rings, with the general formula $C_n H_{2n-6}$; for example, *benzene* (C_6H_6) with the structure shown in Fig.2-2.

The *naphthenes* are unsaturated polycyclic chains, or rings, with the general formula $C_n H_{2n-12}$; for example, *napthalene* ($C_{10}H_8$) as shown in Fig.2-2.

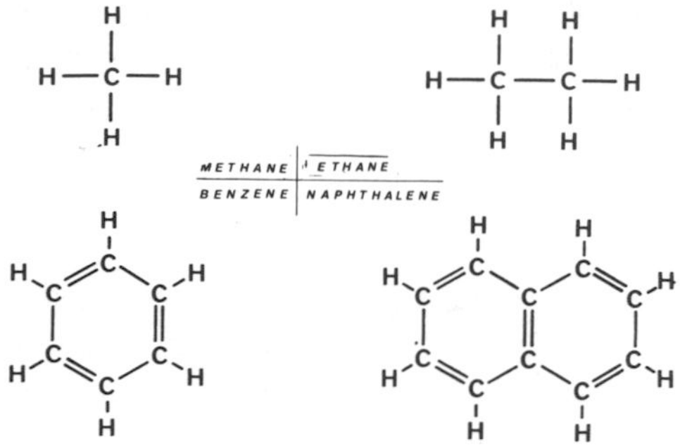

Fig. 2-2. Molecules of ethane, methane, benzene and naphthalene.

The *olefins* are not known to exist in the rocks, but they are a product of the refinery. This series consists of unsaturated chains, $C_n H_{2n}$.

The composition of crude oils in terms of hydrocarbons varies widely from area to area, from field to field, and even from reservoir to reservoir in one field. However, the elemental composition varies very little, with carbon ranging from about 82% to 87%, hydrogen from about 12% to 15%, with nitrogen, oxygen, and sulphur (commonly abbreviated to NOS) in minor amounts usually less than 5%.

Crude oils are classified generally as *paraffin base, asphalt* (or *naphthene*) *base,* or *mixed base,* depending on the residue. Paraffin base crudes contain paraffin wax in solution. The wax content of crude oils may be geologically significant, so the petroleum geologist should encourage its determination for all reservoirs.

Crude oil is almost invariably a rather dark, viscous liquid at the surface. But when we see it, it is "dead", cool, and without gas in solution. In the ground its colour is irrelevant; but its viscosity is highly relevant. For oil of any one series, its viscosity decreases with increasing temperature, and with increasing gas in solution. Its viscosity also increases with increasing density ("gravity" in the jargon), and with increasing numbers of carbon atoms in the molecule ("carbon number" in the jargon). The density of petroleum varies, but almost all oils have a density less than 1 g/cm^3, and most fall in the range 0.75—0.9 g/cm^3.

Hydrocarbons are variably soluble in water. In the paraffin

series, solubility is inversely proportional to carbon number. They are soluble in other hydrocarbons, and very soluble in chloroform, carbon tetrachloride, and carbon disulphide. This latter property is important to the geologist for testing rock samples for traces of petroleum. Crude oil discolours the solvent.

Crude oil and solid hydrocarbons are also fluorescent, as is the oil in solution in one of the solvents. When an oil-stained rock sample or cutting is examined under ultra-violet light, it fluoresces in greens or blues.

Crude oil is said to be *saturated* when no more gas can be taken into solution — or *unsaturated*. It may also be saturated, with an associated gas cap.

Petroleum gas is commonly a mixture of several hydrocarbons and exists in the subsurface as a separate accumulation, in association with an oil accumulation, in solution in oil, and in solution in the formation water. Gas is compressible, and under certain conditions of temperature and high pressure, some of the components may be liquid in the subsurface (their physical properties are then similar to those of oil). It is important as a substance in its own right as a fuel and as a feedstock for industrial chemical plants. It is also the prime source of energy in many oil reservoirs. Methane is the dominant constituent of natural gas, usually with smaller amounts of paraffins with higher carbon numbers. A gas may be *wet* and contain liquid oil vapours, or *dry*.

Solid hydrocarbons are relatively rare, and are perhaps best known from Pitch Lake in southwest Trinidad, where semi-solid bitumen is mined at the surface. There are other surface occurrences, such as that of the Bermúdez Pitch Lake in eastern Venezuela. They also occur as bitumen dykes. Bitumen is also valuable to the geologist in its *elastico-viscous* properties, for it demonstrably flows yet can be broken by a hammer.

Varieties of solid bitumen include albertite, elaterite, gilsonite, grahamite and wurtzillite. *Kerogen* is an important solid bituminous mineraloid to the petroleum geologist; however, its significance is still not fully understood. Its composition is variable, but consists principally of hydrogen, carbon, and oxygen. It occurs in "oil shales" and also with coals. Kerogen yields hydrocarbons on heating (it is a *pyrobitumen*) but only at temperatures well above

those encountered in oil reservoirs. It may be a primary petro-
leum-producing substance, or a residual after petroleum genesis
from another substance.

Water

Water is the most common fluid in pore spaces in sedimentary
rocks in the subsurface. It is found in many parts of the world
within a few metres of the surface; and in most parts of the world
within a few tens of metres of the surface. Water has been found
in the deepest wells drilled, and is probably only finally eliminated
as free water during metamorphism.

Water is important, of course, as a natural resource when it is
relatively free of dissolved solids. For the geologist, though, the
role of water in the rocks is of fundamental importance, equal to
that of the solid constituents. For the petroleum geologist, it
could almost be said that it is more important than the solid
constituents because of its association with petroleum. Geology
that ignores the water in the rocks is largely meaningless: one can
describe rocks without considering their water, but one cannot
understand them.

All water in the rocks contains some dissolved solids. These
solids, in terms of their dissociated ions, are commonly:

calcium	Ca^{2+}		carbonate	$CO_3{}^{2-}$	
magnesium	Mg^{2+}	cations	bicarbonate	$HCO_3{}^{-}$	anions
sodium	Na^+		sulphate	$SO_4{}^{2-}$	
potassium	K^+		chloride	Cl^-	

There is a long list of minor constituents that includes iron, alu-
minium, boron, fluoride, copper, silver, tin and vanadium (the last
mentioned also occurs associated with petroleum and in oil
shales).

The chemistry of groundwater, like that of petroleum, is a subject in itself. For general purposes, however, the geologist needs to
know the *salinity* of the water in a particular rock unit, usually
expressed in *parts per million* (p.p.m.) *total dissolved solids.* For
electrical log interpretation this may be converted to *NaCl equiv-*

alent — the solution of NaCl that would have the same electrical conductivity as the more complex solution.

The salinity of surface water varies from almost nil in many rivers and lakes to that of sea water, which is about 35,000 p.p.m. total dissolved solids. In the subsurface, however, salinities vary from very low in fresh water aquifers to well over that of sea water. Not only does the salinity commonly differ significantly from that of sea water, but also ionic composition. The relative proportions of the ions vary greatly. Hence it is an unjustifiable over-simplification to regard formation water as sea water buried with the rocks. Formation waters commonly contain 80,000 to 100,000 p.p.m. total dissolved solids; and salinities around 300,000 p.p.m. are known.

Variations in ionic composition (as we have noted) are considerable, and rarely reflect the composition of seawater. SO_4^{2-} is significantly low in most oil field brines, but commonly high near base metal sulphide deposits. CO_3^{2-} and HCO_3^- are unimportant in sea water and usually unimportant in oil field brines; but they are relatively important in many fresh waters. However, it must be remembered that the great bulk of formation water analyses comes from water associated with petroleum in the subsurface, and may not therefore be representative.

It is pointless to speculate on the origin of the salinity of formation water at this stage. Fresh groundwater near the surface may be regarded as *meteoric* (rain water that has infiltrated and percolated into the rocks), and much of the water of artesian aquifers (when fresh or brackish) may also be regarded as meteoric. Interstitial water that is regarded as original, in the sense that it was the medium in which the sediment was deposited, is called *connate* — but there are difficulties with this concept. The compaction of sediments results in important redistribution of the original interstitial water. Changes in salinity may be related to this redistribution. There are therefore not only the well-known difficulties of reconciling the composition of sea water with the compositions of the surface waters discharging into the sea, but also difficulties in reconciling the compositions of formation waters with those of sea water and fresh surface water.

The salinity of formation water is also of interest to the geologist because it affects its density. Hence the pressure exerted by a column of water is a function of its mean salinity. Precise quantitative treatment of these relationships is not practicable because neither salinity nor temperature is a strictly linear function of depth, even if the compressibility of water can be ignored at shallow depths (say, down to 3,000 m or 10,000 ft.). In the practical context, fluid pressure may be satisfactorily expressed as a linear function of depth and its density − or more than one function when the groundwater salinities are separable into more than one zone (e.g., fresh water near the surface, saline below).

Water also exists in sedimentary rocks as part of the molecular structure of some minerals (such as gypsum, $CaSO_4.2H_2O$, and montmorillonite, $Al_4Si_8O_{20}(OH)_4.nH_2O$). Under certain conditions of temperature and pressure, this water can be released to the interstitial water. The role of molecular water in geology is not yet fully understood, but it may have significance in both petroleum geology and structural geology through the influence its release could have on interstitial fluid pressures.

Generation of petroleum

The occurrences of petroleum in the world strongly suggest that petroleum rarely, if ever, originates in the reservoir in which it is found; but rather in other rocks, known as source rocks, from which the petroleum migrates to the trap.

The study of petroleum generation is hampered by the fact that it is not absolutely clear what the source rocks for most petroleum accumulations are. If the source rock cannot be identified with certainty, it cannot be studied with understanding.

There is general agreement that the main source of petroleum is the organic matter buried with a fine-grained sediment (usually a clay); and that diagenesis of this organic matter leads to a "protopetroleum" which, before or during migration, becomes modified by the physical and chemical environment − particularly by increasing temperature during burial − until it eventually becomes petroleum.

There is general agreement that the conditions at the depositional surface are critical for the preservation of organic matter, that aerated, oxidizing conditions are inimicable to the preservation of organic matter for subsequent alteration to petroleum. This must not be interpreted too qualitatively, because the amount of organic matter supplied to an environment is an important factor. One should view it rather as the difference between the supply of organic matter and the ability of the environment to destroy it. Large amounts of organic matter may lead to reducing conditions in an environment that would otherwise be oxidizing.

There is increasing evidence that terrigenous vegetable matter may lead to waxy oils, while marine organic matter, both animal and vegetable, leads to non-waxy oils; and that whether oil or gas is formed depends on the diagenetic history of the organic matter, with temperature an important factor.

The doubts and uncertainties that surround the processes of petroleum generation (and migration) arise from one main factor: many scientific disciplines are clearly required for the elucidation of the processes, but a man only has a limited capacity to master the knowledge he needs. Judgements therefore tend to be based on inadequate knowledge of geology, biology, chemistry, and physics.

Much of the evidence is apparently contradictory. Research into Holocene (Recent) sediments of the Orinoco delta at Pedernales indicates that petroleum of a sort is being generated at depths shallower than 60 m (200 ft.), some of it accumulating in a sand at a depth of about 35 m (120 ft.), in sediments probably less than 10,000 years old from ^{14}C dating (Kidwell and Hunt, 1958).

The data on clay compaction as a function of depth of burial, obtained by various authors, also suggest early migration of petroleum with the water expelled by compaction (see Fig.3-3, p. 56). Since compaction can only proceed with the expulsion of interstitial liquid, the decreasing *rate* of compaction with depth implies decreasing rate of liquid expulsion with depth — that is, more liquid is expelled during burial to 1,000 m (or feet) than during burial from 1,000 to 2,000 m (or feet), and so on. In other words, most of the liquid is apparently expelled at shallow depth; and if this liquid is the vehicle for primary migration out of the source rock, the more important part of primary migration quantitatively must also take place at shallow depth. Hence diagenesis of the organic matter to a fluid must also have taken place at a shallow depth.

Yet many of the petroleum accumulations can only have begun to be important after burial of the sediments to depths of at least one or two thousand metres (3—6,000 ft.) *after* the formation of a trap. Stratigraphic traps below an unconformity could normally only begin to accumulate petroleum after the deformation of the older rocks and the accumulation of the unconformable cap rock. This line of argument does not deny early genesis of petroleum by itself, for genesis must precede migration.

Research into the petroleum content of clays in the Los Angeles basin (California) tends to support a conclusion of late generation, because petroleum hydrocarbons were not apparently generated at shallow depth, and the composition of the hydrocarbons in the fine-grained rocks does not approach that of the accumulated petroleum until depths of about 4,000 m (12—13,000 ft.) (Philippi, 1965).

We therefore return to the problems of geological inference. Does the absence of petroleum at shallow depths in an area indicate that it was only generated deeper?... or is it that there are no source rocks at shallow depth? Should a source rock contain petroleum of the same composition as that expelled?... or do some components migrate more readily than others?... or does petroleum in the reservoir alter during burial? Does the presence of hydrocarbons at shallow depth in the Orinoco delta mean that it will become a significant accumulation, given the right conditions, in a few million years time?... or is this part of the immense quantities of petroleum that are considered to be lost through lack of a trap?

One conclusion is clear: we cannot reasonably postulate that petroleum generation is not going on today, for that would make this period of time unique in the last 600 million years of world history. Until the present-day source rocks can be identified with certainty and studied, the processes will necessarily remain rather speculative. Nevertheless, geological arguments can narrow the areas of doubt and unify to some extent the conflicting evidence (this we shall seek to do in Chapter 6). Above all, it must be remembered that the problems of petroleum in the rocks are fundamentally geological problems. No chemical or physical explanation can be satisfactory unless the geological explanation is also satisfactory. If a geologist feels in need of encouragement in this point of view, he should read some of the geological pronouncements of the great 19th-century physicist, Sir William Thomson (Lord Kelvin)!

Migration of petroleum

Migration of petroleum into accumulations is thought of largely in terms of permeability paths. It must also be thought of in terms of fluid potential gradients — that is, deviations from hydrostatic equilibrium in the fluids in the pore spaces of the rocks. Permeability is only a measure of the capacity of fluids to be transmitted, or transmissibility, through a rock. A sponge lying in a bath of water may be very permeable; but no water will flow through it if the water in the sponge is in hydrostatic equilibrium with that in the bath.

Migration paths may be long or short. Professional opinion on the matter is widely divided. Hypotheses vary from simple migration from the source rock into the adjacent reservoir rock, and through the reservoir rock to the trap; to multiple stage migration from a distant source, sometimes with intermediate trapping from which the petroleum is spilled by subsequent geological events. The cause of this diversity of opinion is partly ignorance: we do not know exactly what a source rock is, we do not know what the substances that are intermediate between source material and petroleum are, and we do not know precisely how they move through the rocks.

Migration is divided into two stages: *primary migration* from the source rock to a permeable rock; *secondary migration* from there to the trap, through one or more "carrier" beds.

Opinions differ widely on the state of petroleum during migration, whether in solution, in colloidal solution, or as a separate phase in water. Petroleum occurs in solution in formation waters; it occurs as emulsions in the production processes; and it occurs as a separate phase in the trap. Each possibility has its merits, and its problems.

Migration in aqueous solution has the merit of requiring least work for its transport through the rocks. The problems relate to the quantitative sufficiency of this process in view of the relatively low solubility of petroleum in water, and to the need for some physical or chemical change to be imposed upon the solution for the release of petroleum to a separate phase in (or on the way to) the accumulation.

At the other extreme, migration as a separate phase has the merit that this is the state found in the accumulation. The problems relate to the mechanical difficulty of transporting petroleum as a separate phase when it is disseminated through the pore spaces with water (and disseminated it must be at some stage between generation and accumulation). This difficulty is particularly great if primary migration through a fine-grained source rock as a separate phase is postulated.

Transport in a colloidal state has the merit that it reduces the difficulties of the alternatives — but it also has a problem relating to the need for an agent to emulsify the petroleum and an agent to de-emulsify it.

Combinations have also been proposed, particularly transport as a separate phase, with residual petroleum being dissolved in the formation waters.

From the great diversity of processes proposed, the only conclusions that would receive general support from petroleum geologists would be the following.

(1) Clays are the principal source rocks of petroleum, so primary migration takes place in clays. (Important carbonate source rocks have been postulated in some areas, notably in the Middle East.)

(2) Petroleum in one form or another is expelled from clay source rocks during compaction, and migrates through permeable rocks under the influence of gravity (and the hydrodynamic field) to the trap — or the surface.

Entrapment of petroleum

The accumulation of petroleum in a trap is accomplished when the physical properties and geometry of the rocks prevent further migration. Since petroleum is less dense than water, the barrier to further migration is, in general, such that it prevents upward, or an upward component of, migration.

The main forms of petroleum traps are well known: they consist of the *anticlinal* trap, the *fault* trap, and the *stratigraphic* trap. The entrapment of petroleum in *anticlines* was one of the first principles of petroleum geology, and it has dominated petroleum-geological thinking. Its essential features are (Fig.2-3): (a) a geometric closure — that is, the structural contours form closed rings; (b) a reservoir rock that has permeability (which implies porosity); and (c) a fine-grained, or relatively impermeable cap rock that overlies the reservoir and seals it.

One may be a little more specific and state that the closure must be on the top of the reservoir and the bottom of the cap rock, because there are many anticlines in which the geometry of the individual rock units changes with depth.

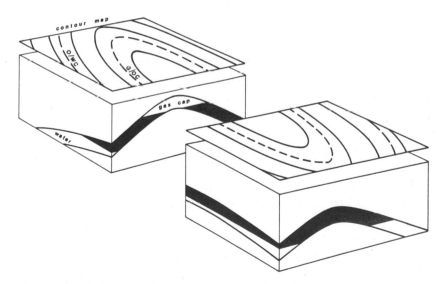

Fig.2-3. Block diagram of petroleum in an anticlinal trap.

Entrapment may be in a single reservoir, or in multiple reservoirs in the same anticline. A single reservoir accumulation is sometimes referred to as a "pool", but the terminology is not standard over the world. The general term for an accumulation from which production has started is a *field* — oil field or gas field, as the case may be.

The nature of the petroleum and its composition vary from one field to another; and they may vary from one reservoir to another in the same field. Variation between petroleums of different reservoirs is commonly from heavy oil with little or no gas near the surface, through intermediate oils, to light oils with gas, gas and condensates at depth.

Within a reservoir, oil will lie on water; and the interface — the *oil/water contact* (O/WC or OWC) — is a horizontal, or near-horizontal surface. If free gas is present when the reservoir is discovered, it will lie on the oil and the *gas/oil contact* (G/OC or GOC) will also be a horizontal, or near-horizontal surface. Gas that segregates as a result of changes in the physical properties of the reservoir during production will not necessarily have a horizontal interface with the oil because the accumulation will depend on the *effective permeability* of the reservoir to gas, and this may not be uniform.

The oil/water and gas/oil contacts of different reservoirs in the same field are usually at different depths below datum. Occasionally the oil/water contact of two or more reservoirs is found at the same depth below datum. When this happens, it is usually argued that these reservoirs are connected in some way, leading to a common plane of physical equilibrium. Gas/oil contacts may also coincide, but they are more difficult to assess unless they can be shown to be original gas/oil contacts that have not been affected by production.

The quantity of petroleum, in terms of the volume of oil or gas *in place* in the reservoir also varies from reservoir to reservoir. Reservoirs are rarely full, in the sense that the petroleum column rarely extends down to the point at which it would spill out of the trap ("spill point"). They are never full in the sense of occupying all the available pore space, because petroleum does not displace all the water in the pore spaces. However, if the reservoir exists by virtue of cracks, joints, and fissures, the total volume of these may be very nearly filled with petroleum due to their large volume in relation to the enclosing surface area and the consequent lack of water adhering to the rock surfaces.

The sizes of anticlines and anticlinal accumulations vary widely. The Middle East is famous for anticlines that extend for several hundred kilometres (two or three hundred miles) and accumulations 100 km long (60 miles) — such as Kirkuk in Irak. One can hardly defend a statement that half the world's petroleum reserves are contained in non-typical fields; but it is nevertheless true that the other half of the world's reserves are contained in fields of more modest dimensions, on the whole. It is difficult to arrive at meaningful figures for the dimensions of typical petroleum accumulations. The sizes (area or volume) of known petroleum accumulations are log-normally distributed, with very many small fields and very few large ones (Kaufman, 1963). A significant proportion of the petroleum reserves to date are in relatively few very large accumulations. There are many profitable fields with an area of less than 20 km^2 (say, 8 square miles).

The *area* occupied by a petroleum accumulation is important mainly for its influence on the chances of finding it, but it also influences the economics of producing it. A thin extensive reservoir is more expensive to develop than a thicker and less extensive reservoir with the same porosity and permeability, and with the same volume of original petroleum in place.

The *volume* of petroleum in a field, and its distribution in different reservoirs, is clearly important. The volume of *oil in place* (or gas in place) in a reservoir is estimated by estimating the total volume of rock that contains oil, multiplying this by the best estimate of mean porosity, and then multiplying the product by the best estimate of the proportion of oil in the pore spaces (the oil saturation). The volume of *recoverable oil* is obtained by multiplying the oil in place by an estimate of the *recovery factor*. (The volumes of gas are given at a standard temperature and pressure, such as 15°C and 760 mm of mercury, the standard always being stated.) During production these estimates are revised by reservoir engineers on the basis of performance, new data, trends, and theory.

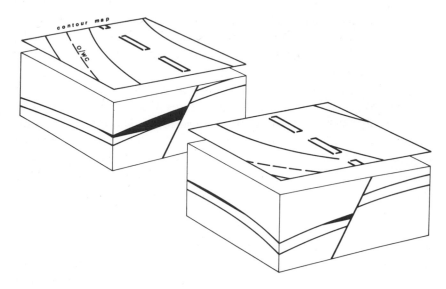

Fig. 2-4. Block diagram of petroleum in a fault trap.

The entrapment of petroleum by a *fault* (Fig. 2-4) involves: (a) an inclined reservoir; (b) a cap rock; (c) a fault that forms an up-dip barrier across the reservoir either by virtue of the fine-grained, relatively impermeable material in the fault plane itself, or by virtue of such material being in juxtaposition across the fault; and (d) some barrier in the reservoir along the fault, to prevent lateral migration.

As with anticlinal traps, fault traps may include single or multiple reservoirs; and the oil/water contacts of multiple reservoirs are usually at different levels, but may be the same. Displacement of a fluid contact in the same reservoir (lithological) unit across a fault is taken as evidence of fault-trapping; and conversely, observation of different fluid contacts in the same lithological unit is regarded as evidence of an intervening sealing fault.

The accumulation of petroleum in *stratigraphic* traps (Fig. 2-5) consists essentially of a restraint on further migration arising from stratigraphic causes, such as: (a) permeability or porosity changes in the reservoir rock; (b) convergence of rock units; (c) isolated rock units of porosity and permeability different from adjacent units; (d) an unconformity providing the barrier, usually by trun-

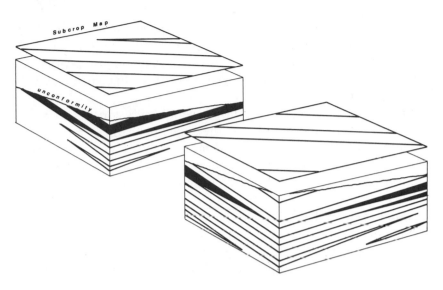

Fig.2-5. Block diagram of petroleum in a stratigraphic trap.

cation of the reservoir rock by a fine-grained or relatively impermeable rock unit.

Examples of stratigraphic traps include lenticular sand units
entirely surrounded by clay, sand units that "shale out" laterally,
and organic reefs (such as coral reefs) that are enclosed laterally
and above by clays and/or evaporites.

In practice it is rarely possible to assign a petroleum accumulation exclusively to a single class of trap. Most accumulations may
be classed as anticlinal traps, but few anticlines are unfaulted and
few stratigraphic traps other than organic reefs are unfolded (Organic reefs are usually purely stratigraphic traps with no folding.)

Geophysics

Geophysics is the study of the physical properties of the earth
and the study of the earth through its physical properties. It is
concerned with the distribution of matter in and around the earth,
particularly that within the earth as revealed by its physical
properties — the force of gravity and its variation from place to

place; the strength and direction of the magnetic field and their variations from place to place; the occurrence of earthquakes and the propagation of their energy, and the propagation of artificially generated elastic waves (seismic waves) through the earth (seismology).

As applied to economic geology, geophysics consists of measuring the physical properties of the rocks beneath an area (gravity, magnetism, radioactivity), and measuring the response of the rocks to artificially generated energy fields (seismic, electric or electro-magnetic). The scale of such investigations varies from the global to the very local (such as the measurement of the velocity of sound in the wall of a borehole). The application of geophysical techniques to the search for petroleum has not only been of immense importance to the petroleum industry, it has also provided an important stimulus to the broader development of the science of geophysics. It is the practical application, largely, that has kept geophysics closely related to geology.

Gravity

Newton's law of gravity states that "any two particles of matter attract one another with a force directly proportional to the product of their masses and inversely proportional to the square of the distance between them". This law may be expressed by the equation:

$$F = G \frac{m_1 m_2}{d^2}$$

where F is the force of attraction between two particles (or bodies) of masses m_1 and m_2, d is the distance between them (or their centres of gravity), and G is the constant gravitation the value of which is found empirically to be $66.7 \cdot 10^{-9}$, the attraction in dynes between two spherical gram masses the centres of which are 1 cm apart. The dyne is that force that produces an acceleration of 1 cm per second per second on a mass of 1 g: an acceleration of 1 cm per second per second is known as a "gal" (after Galileo). This is rather large for practical purposes, so the common unit of acceleration due to gravity is the *milligal* (gal·10^{-3}).

There is a mutually attractive force between all matter in, on, and around the earth. At any one point on the surface of the earth, this force (and hence also the acceleration due to this force, denoted by g) may be regarded as having three main components: (a) a mean value due to the mass of the earth; (b) a counter force (centrifugal) due to the earth's rotation; and (c) a local variation due to the topography.

Gravity surveys consist in the first place of measuring the value of g at many points in an area. These values can be plotted on a map, and contoured. Such a map indicates the pattern and rate of change of g over the area; but it has little value to the geologist because it includes anomalies due to the earth's rotation and to irregularities in the topography of the area.

The regional effect due to the latitude of the area can be calculated, and this pattern eliminated from the first map by subtraction. There are two components to this regional effect: the latitude of the observation point (the centrifugal force is nil at the Poles, greatest at the Equator) and the elevation of the observation point above a datum surface (usually sea level). When these effects are removed, the resulting map still reflects the influence of topography. This may be insignificant when the area is flat; but large hills or valleys materially affect the measured value of g. (The reader will remember that Airy deduced a significant gravitational attraction between the Himalaya and a plumb-bob during the triangulation of the northern Indian subcontinent, and that the discrepancy between observation and theory led to the postulate of isostasy.)

In practice the anomalies due to elevation above sea level are removed by the application of two component corrections. The first, known as the "free-air" correction, considers the effect of elevation without solid material between sea level and the observation point. The second, or "Bouguer" correction, considers the attraction of the material between the observation point and sea level that was omitted for the free-air correction. Topographic effects are included in the Bouguer correction if necessary.

The end result is a map of residual gravity values, known as the

Bouguer anomaly map. The patterns and rates of change of the Bouguer anomaly are attributable to variations in mass in the earth under the area, and are interpreted in terms of rock-types and structures. Areas of low values of residual gravity are interpreted as areas deficient in underlying mass: those of high values, areas of greater underlying mass. Thus a syncline may be indicated by a gravity "low" due to the extra thickness of relatively unconsolidated rocks, while an anticline may be indicated by a gravity "high" due to the elevation of more compacted material in the core of the anticline to shallower depths. However, the evidence of gravity must be interpreted in geological terms, and the interpretation must make sense geologically — to the extent that all the relevant data can be assessed.

Seismics

When elastic waves (energy waves, seismic waves) are propagated in the ground by means of an explosion or other shock they spread out in all directions through the rocks — and eventually dissipate. The velocity of propagation depends partly on the type of wave generated (compression, shear, or L waves), and partly by the nature of the materials through which the wave passes. In general, the velocity of a wave is very much slower through the surface layer than it is through the more consolidated material below the surface layer, with the result that if an elastic wave is generated at point *A* in Fig.2-6, the first wave to arrive at a detector (seismometer or geophone) has passed through rocks below the surface. The greater the distance between the shot point and the geophone, the deeper the path or ray of the wave that arrives first because the greater velocity at depth more than compensates for the greater distance the wave has to travel. Thus if a line is shot with multiple geophones (or a series of shots fired with an increasing distance to the geophone), the "first arrival" at each geophone is an indication of the nature of the rocks through which the waves have passed. This is the principle of *refraction* shooting.

It is important for understanding to realize that although all diagrams show straight or slightly curved lines to represent the paths of seismic waves, these lines merely represent successive

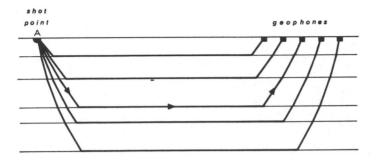

Fig.2-6. Seismic refraction paths (diagrammatic) when each stratum is less dense than the one underlying it.

points on the wave front that eventually become the first arrival. This wave front is not spherical, because the velocity of propagation is not equal in all directions. Different rock materials, as already noted, propagate elastic waves at different velocities. In any one material, this velocity is approximately proportional to the porosity.

The interpretation of a line of refraction shooting is more in terms of material and the depths of materials than structure, and the result is an indication of the sequence of rocks below the line shot. The successive lines shot in a grid pattern over an area contribute to a broad structural interpretation in the same way that a series of geological sections also leads to a structural interpretation of the area. The closeness of the lines affects the accuracy and detail discernible in the finished map.

More detailed structural information is obtained from *reflection* shooting, in which the elastic waves are partly reflected by surfaces of contrasting density, and these reflections are detected by the geophones and recorded on a seismogram. A "good reflector" is a surface that reflects a significant proportion of the energy that arrives at it — much as there are good and poor echoes to be obtained in the hills.

Again, the velocity of wave propagation depends on the nature of the rock sequence; but instead of concentrating on first arrivals, the whole pattern of energy detected by the geophone over several seconds is recorded on a seismogram, and the characteristic pat-

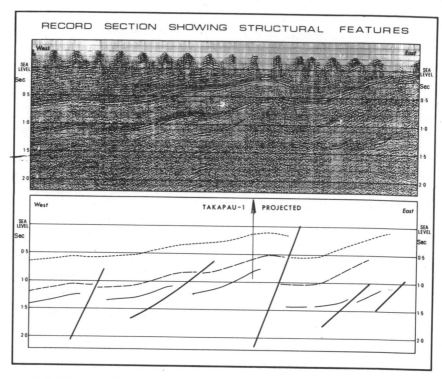

Fig.2-7. Seismic reflection profile. (Courtesy of Beaver Exploration Australia N.L., from W.C. Leslie and R.J.S. Hollingsworth, 1972, *The APEA Journal*, 12: p.42.)

terns recorded by each geophone are correlated. Hence more than one reflection may be identified on the seismograms. The elapsed time between the firing of the shot and the receipt of a reflection is a measure of the depth of that reflector below the level of the shot line. The composite seismogram of a single line may be directly interpreted in terms of "marker" horizons and structure, for folds and faults are commonly evident (Fig.2-7). The depth scale in such diagrams is *time* (seconds), but a conversion formula is usually included with which one may obtain an approximate depth. Precise depths require specific computations.

The processing of seismic data is nowadays done by computer, the speed of which enables the geophysicist to insert different values for the parameters, and to try various combinations of variables. There are also techniques for processing the records to enhance meaningful signals and reduce the "noise" or meaningless signals. The end product for the geologist is a seismic contour map with contours on a reflector, or a bed of characteristic velocity (refraction shooting). Drilling to structures first defined by seismic surveys has confirmed that seismic surveys carried out under good conditions can result in maps of considerable accuracy and detail. The positions of faults are not always reliable, but the general pattern is commonly a valuable indication of the structure of the area.

Selected bibliography

Buckley, S.E., Hocott, C.R. and Taggart, M.S., 1958. Distribution of dissolved hydrocarbons in subsurface waters. In: L.G. Weeks (Editor), *Habitat of Oil*. American Association of Petroleum Geologists, Tulsa, Okla., pp.850—882.

Bullen, K.E., 1963. *An Introduction to the Theory of Seismology* (3rd. ed.). Cambridge University Press, Cambridge, 296 pp.

Dobrin, M.B., 1960. *Introduction to Geophysical Prospecting* (2nd. ed.). McGraw-Hill, New York, N.Y., 446 pp.

Forsman, J.P. and Hunt, J.M., 1958. Insoluble organic matter (kerogen) in sedimentary rocks of marine origin. In: L.G. Weeks (Editor), *Habitat of Oil*. American Association of Petroleum Geologists, Tulsa, Okla., pp.747—778.

Hunt, J.M., and Jamieson, G.W., 1958. Oil and organic matter in source rocks of petroleum. In: L.G. Weeks (Editor), *Habitat of Oil*. American Association of Petroleum Geologists, Tulsa, Okla., pp.735—746.

Kaufman, C.M., 1963. *Statistical Decision and Related Techniques in Oil and Gas Exploration*. Prentice-Hall, Englewood Cliffs, N. J., 307 pp.

Kidwell, A.L. and Hunt, J.M., 1958. Migration of oil in Recent sediments of Pedernales, Venezuela. In: L.G. Weeks (Editor), *Habitat of Oil*. American Association of Petroleum Geologists, Tulsa, Okla., pp.790—817.

Levorsen, A.I., 1967. *Geology of Petroleum* (2nd. ed.). Freeman, San Francisco, Calif., 724 pp.

Nettleton, L.L., 1940. *Geophysical Prospecting for Oil*. McGraw-Hill, New York, N.Y., 444 pp.

Philippi, G.T., 1965. On the depth, time and mechanism of petroleum generation. *Geochim. Cosmochim. Acta*, 29:1021—1049.

Staff of British Petroleum Co., Ltd., 1970. *Our Industry Petroleum*. British Petroleum Co., Ltd., London, 528 pp.

Staff of Royal Dutch/Shell Group, 1966. *The Petroleum Handbook* (5th ed.). Shell International Petroleum Co., Ltd., London, 318 pp.

Thomson, Sir William (Lord Kelvin), 1868. On geological time. *Trans. Geol. Soc. Glasg., 3:1—28*.

Thomson, Sir William (Lord Kelvin), 1877. Presidential address, mathematics and physics. *Notices Abstr., Br. Ass. Adv. Sci., Glasg., 1876*, pp.1—12.

Chapter 3. COMPACTION OF SEDIMENTS AND ITS CONSEQUENCES

Summary

(1) Compaction is a diagenetic process that begins on burial and may continue during burial to depths of 9,000 m (30,000 ft.) or more. Compaction increases the bulk density of a rock and reduces its porosity.

(2) Sands compact with little loss of porosity or permeability. The deformation is largely elastic, and reversible if the load is removed.

Clays compact with serious and permanent loss of porosity and permeability. The deformation is largely plastic and irreversible.

Carbonates compact to varying degrees, depending on the proportion of plastic material. Some behave like clays, but most appear to suffer very little mechanical compaction. Compaction by solution processes is probably important.

(3) Compaction can proceed only with the expulsion of interstitial liquid. In a homogenous lithology this takes place upwards across the bedding planes, in the direction of the fluid potential gradient.

(4) If clays alternate with more permeable beds, compaction creates fluid potential gradients both upwards and downwards, from the more compactible lithology to the more permeable, and fluid is expelled both upwards and downwards. The downward potential gradient makes the caly a perfect barrier to upward migrating fluids; hence lateral migration must take place in the more permeable, intercalated, beds.

(5) Abnormal interstitial fluid pressures result when a compactible rock is loaded faster than the corresponding rate at which expulsion of fluids can maintain stress equilibrium between solids and liquids in the rock. A rock with abnormal fluid pressures is

mechanically weaker than it will be when the pressure is reduced to normal by expulsion of fluids.

(6) The transition zone from normal to abnormal fluid pressures is an important zone of upward fluid migration; and there may be a similar, but inverted, zone at the bottom of the abnormally pressured rock unit, with important downward fluid migration.

(7) The maximum depth of burial at which an over-pressured rock unit acquired its pressure anomaly can be estimated. This depth is also a measure of liquid expulsion, and hence the degree of compaction.

(8) Abnormal fluid pressures in permeable beds constitute a drilling hazard, and can lead to a blowout. Warning of abnormal pressures is usually given, however, by a significant increase in drilling rate — due partly to reduced mechanical strength of the rock and retarded compaction, and partly to reversal of the fluid potential gradient across the bottom of the hole (from downwards to upwards).

Compaction of sediments

The compaction of sediments under the gravity load of overlying sediments is a fundamental geological process, and so necessarily a central theme of petroleum geology. It affects stratigraphic relationships, groundwater movement and salinity, migration of petroleum (and perhaps also the migration of some of the metals), and the mechanical strength of the rock. All sediments compact to some degree, and in doing so, some of their properties are changed. Most obviously they become more dense, less porous, and less permeable; and the unit becomes less thick. The mechanical strength of a rock increases with compaction, and it becomes less "drillable". Compaction normally increases with depth due to the increase in load, but there are important exceptions when this *trend* may be halted and even reversed in sequences in which the interstitial fluid pressures are abnormally high.

Compaction is a diagenetic process that begins with, or very soon after deposition. When granular material, such as a quartz sand, is laid down in water with gentle agitation, the arrangement

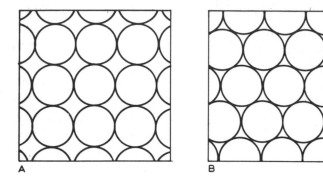

Fig.3-1. Inefficient (A) and efficient (B) packing (idealized).

of the grains in the accumulating sediment approaches an "efficient" packing (Fig.3-1). Any shocks received by the accumulating sand agitate it further and tend to improve the efficiency of the packing, so increasing the bulk density and reducing the porosity of the sediment. It is hard to imagine an environment free from shocks, for they may be generated by earthquakes, thunder or surf. Loading by burial does not significantly improve the efficiency of the packing of elastic material, such as quartz sand, but extreme loading by burial to great depths may lead to mechanical fracturing of the grains, or to solution at the points of contact. The nature of the deformation depends on the nature of the material and the magnitude and duration of the forces applied to it. Some materials suffer plastic deformation under stress.

Porosity and bulk density are related parameters of a rock. It is usually more instructive to think of bulk density of a sedimentary rock as the sum of two partial densities:

$$\rho_{bw} = f\rho_w + (1-f)\rho_g = \rho_g - f(\rho_g - \rho_w) \qquad (3\text{-}1)$$

where ρ_{bw} is the bulk density of the rock saturated with fluid of density ρ_w, ρ_g is the grain density, and f the porosity ($0 \leqslant f < 1$). There are advantages for the present discussion in expressing this relationship in terms of specific weights:

$$\gamma_{bw} = f\gamma_w + (1-f)\gamma_g = \gamma_g - f(\gamma_g - \gamma_w) \qquad (3\text{-}1a)$$

where γ_{bw} is the specific weight of the rock saturated with fluid of specific weight γ_w, γ_g is the specific weight of the grains (all in consistent units of either kg/cm^2 per m or psi/ft.) and f is the porosity as before. In general, the specific weight multiplied by the depth gives the pressure in that material at that depth.

Eq.3-1 and 3-1a show that as the porosity changes from 1 (no grains) to 0 (no fluid), the bulk wet density changes linearly from ρ_w to ρ_g, and the bulk wet specific weight changes linearly from γ_w to γ_g (Table 3-I). There is also a practical advantage in thinking of these parameters in this way: as grain size gets smaller, porosity becomes increasingly difficult to measure, but bulk density easier.

TABLE 3-I

Variation of bulk wet density and bulk wet specific weight of quartz sand with porosity *

Porosity	ρ_{bw} (g/cm³)	γ_{bw} (kg/cm² per m)	γ_{bw} (psi/ft.)
0.35	2.09	0.209	0.91
0.30	2.17	0.217	0.94
0.25	2.25	0.225	0.98
0.20	2.33	0.233	1.01
0.15	2.41	0.241	1.04
0.10	2.49	0.249	1.08

* Interstitial water density, 1.06 g/cm³; grain density, 2.65 g/cm³.

Compaction of sediment results in a reduction of porosity. But when a sediment is saturated with a relatively incompressible fluid, such as the liquids water or oil, porosity can only be reduced by the expulsion of a commensurate part of that liquid. Liquid can only be expelled if it is free to move away. The rate of compaction is therefore influenced by the compressibility of the fluid and by the rate at which liquid can be expelled — which in its turn is consequent liquid movement. Compaction and hydraulic conductivity are related, for the hydraulic conductivity of a specific rock type generally decreases with increasing compaction. Both are related to the load, and rate of loading, and must therefore be considered in the broad geological context. Porosity and permeability are also related in a general way; but porosity is only one parameter of permeability, which depends also on the geometry of the pore spaces. The Kozeny equation is sometimes useful (see Glossary): it shows that the permeability of a given porous rock varies with $f^3/(1-f)^2$.

Sands, as we have seen, compact by re-arrangement of the grains soon after deposition and burial. Quartz is essentially an elastic material that deforms under moderate stress, but which recovers its original shape when the stress is removed. Compaction of a quartz sand under a gravitational load of overlying sediments results in some reduction of porosity due to the deformation of the quartz grains, but this effect is minor compared with the natural variations in porosity, and hence bulk density, due to variations in grain shape and sorting. There is rarely a trend of decreasing porosity in quartz sands with depth that can be attributed to compaction under load because environmental influences give rise to large variations in porosity which obscure the compactional effect. Some linear compaction trends, however, have been observed (Maxwell, 1964).

Clay, on the other hand, is essentially a plastic material the grains of which deform under stress, but which do not recover their original shape when the stress is removed. The early stages of the compaction of an accumulating clay may include an important element of grain re-arrangement, because the porosity of a fresh clay-mud at the surface may be 80% or more. When a substantial degree of grain contact has been achieved, plastic deformation of the clay particles begins. This deformation not only results in the reduction of porosity, but also in the increase of the area of grain-to-grain contacts. Permeability is thus seriously reduced by both the reduction of porosity and the constriction of the pore spaces.

The compaction of clay beds under gravity loading also leads to significant reduction in bed thickness. This feature is well known in the context of drape structures, where the amount of compaction is proportional to the thickness of the clay bed. Thickness reduction is the result of volume reduction due to the expulsion of interstitial fluid by gravity. Several methods of calculating the thickness loss due to compaction have been described; but the underlying premise of most of these is that the compaction of clay is a function of depth only. We shall seek to show later that this premise is of doubtful validity for any but very thin clays and very old (e.g., Palaeozoic) clays. We therefore confine ourselves for the moment here to considerations divorced from depth.

Consider the compaction of a unit cube of water-filled clay from 30% to 12½% porosity. Porosity — the ratio of pore volume to bulk volume — is not a convenient parameter for these calculations. Easier is the *void ratio** — the ratio of pore volume to grain volume — which is the ratio $f/(1-f)$. The initial unit cube with 30% porosity has a void ratio of 0.43 (Fig.3-2). When compacted to 12½% porosity, the void ratio becomes 0.143. If we now make

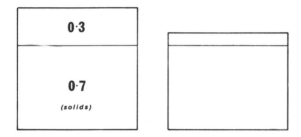

Fig.3-2. Compaction of unit volume of clay with 30% porosity to 12½% porosity results in the expulsion of 0.2 units of water.

the assumption that the total grain volume remains constant at 0.7 units (an assumption that may prove untenable when the diagenetic history of clays is better understood) the volume of liquid retained is 0.7 × 0.143 = 0.1 units. The bulk volume of the initial unit cube is therefore reduced to 0.8 by the expulsion of 0.2 units of water. These figures are proportional to thickness when compaction is under a gravity load. The immense volumes of water expelled will be appreciated when it is considered that 1 km³ of water-saturated clay compacted from 30% porosity to 12½% porosity expels 0.2 km³ of water. This is equal to the *total* pore

---

* The symbol for void ratio is conventionally e: it is not used here because of ambiguity with the Napierian e, which is retained in conformity with many of the works to which reference is made.

volume of 1 km^3 of sand with 20% porosity. This is why there are difficulties in the concept of connate water (p.31).

The compaction of carbonate rocks is less well understood. Carbonates are prone to chemical alteration and solution; but the effects of these diagenetic changes on the compaction phenomenon of increasing bulk density with depth are not clear. Many carbonates appear to suffer no appreciable compaction, for delicate original structures are commonly found well preserved. On the other hand, some lime muds apparently behave like clays. McCrossan (1961) found that the dry density of some Devonian clays in Canada increased with $CaCO_3$ content as well as with depth; and the higher the $CaCO_3$ content, the smaller the relative compaction. If stylolites are but a special case of compaction of carbonates under load, a loss of both fluid and solid (in solution) may occur.

Mechanical compaction is certainly not the only diagenetic process affecting rocks during burial. Chemical and physico-chemical processes may affect both the mineral constituents and the interstitial fluids. However, if attention is confined for the time being to the movement of fluids in the rocks, mechanical compaction appears sufficient to explain the observed and deduced effects, and is a valuable — even essential — simplification.

Several workers have determined clay (or "shale") densities, and plotted them against depth (notably Hedberg, 1926, 1936; Athy, 1930a; Dickinson, 1953). Let us anticipate the arguments and confine our attention to Athy's curve, which was based on Palaeozoic clays in Oklahoma and is therefore considered to represent the stability achieved over a considerable span of time. Athy plotted *dry* bulk densities against depth and found that the resulting curve could be represented by an empirical equation of the form:

$$D = B + A(1 - e^{-bx})$$

where D is the density (dry bulk), B is the density of clay at the surface, A is the maximum increase in density possible, b is a constant, and x the depth of burial. This curve is plotted in Fig.3-3 in terms of *wet* bulk density (which we shall use in further discussion) and implied porosity.

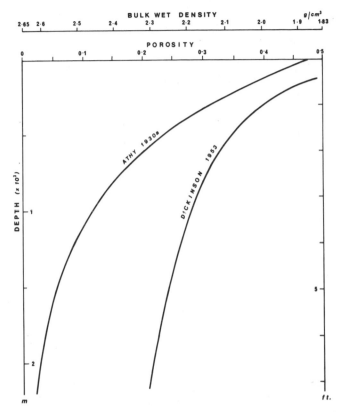

Fig.3-3. Athy's and Dickinson's clay compaction curves plotted in terms of bulk *wet* density and porosity.

This equation of Athy's was re-expressed by Rubey and Hubbert (1959, p.176, eq.15):

$$f = f_o \, e^{-cz}$$

where f is the porosity at depth z, f_o the initial porosity with a numerical value of 0.48 from Athy's data, and c a constant. (We shall return to this equation in Chapter 6.) By simple differentiation:

$$\frac{df}{dz} = -c \, f$$

and we deduce that the rate of loss of porosity with depth is directly proportional to the porosity at that depth.

While these empirical relationships are useful, they must not be accepted too readily at face value, because the important dimension of time is excluded. The curve is an instantaneous curve representing the density and porosity of clays at depth z *now*. Interpretation in terms of compaction history requires caution: we shall return to this topic.

Fluids

Interstitial fluid pressure

It is a matter of common observation, amply confirmed around the world, that, as one penetrates the upper layers of the continents, porous rocks are found to be completely filled or saturated with fluid (usually water or brine), and that the water is under a pressure that is a linear function of the specific weight of the water and the depth at which the pressure measurement is made:

$$p_e = \gamma_w z \qquad\qquad (3\text{-}2)$$

where p_e is the pressure in kg/cm^2 (or psi), γ_w is the specific weight of the water in kg/cm^2 per m (or psi/ft.), and z the depth of measurement in metres (or feet — consistent units being used throughout). γ_w is the pressure *gradient*.

Eq.3-2 implies that if the water were free to rise in a borehole, it would reach the surface. However, it is a generalization. It is a generalization because γ_w varies with the salinity of the water and with its temperature; and because the level $z = 0$ is usually taken to be the surface of the ground, when it should be taken as the static water level, or water table. It is a generalization because the specific weight of the water varies from the exceptional, and usually superficial value of 0.1 kg/cm^2 per m (0.433 psi/ft.) to about 0.109 kg/cm^2 per m (0.47 psi/ft.), corresponding to a salinity of about 130,000 p.p.m. total dissolved solids. In some areas, the interstitial brine is even more saline, with a corresponding increase in its specific weight. Interstitial fluid pressures that conform with those expected from the specific weight of the

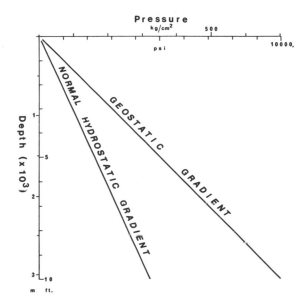

Fig.3-4. Normal hydrostatic pressure gradient and geostatic pressure gradient.

interstitial water in eq.3-2 are known as *normal hydrostatic pressures,* with a *normal hydrostatic gradient* (Fig.3-4).

These observations indicate that the interstitial water is a separate phase from the solid, and that the pore spaces in the rocks that contain fluid with normal hydrostatic pressures are connected to the surface — however tortuously. The grains of sediment may be regarded as being contained within a water reservoir with as much validity as the more usual statement that the rocks contain water. The sediments of many environments may logically be regarded as having been deposited in a water reservoir.

However, it is also a matter of observation (though not so common) that fluid pressures are sometimes encountered in the subsurface that do not correspond with a normal hydrostatic gradient. Occasionally they are significantly lower; but this abnormality is usually attributable to a level $z = 0$ that is significantly lower than the ground surface. Pressures that are higher than normal hydrostatic have been measured in many areas, and these are observed to have a limiting pressure approximately equal to the pressure exerted by the water-saturated overburden:

$$p_{max} \rightarrow \bar{\gamma}_{bw} z \qquad\qquad\qquad\qquad (3\text{-}3)$$

where p_{max} is the fluid pressure at depth z, and $\bar{\gamma}_{bw}$ is the mean bulk wet specific weight of the overburden.

Again, this is an empirical relationship that generalizes the limiting pressure. It is a generalization because the bulk wet specific weight of the overburden varies with lithology, the degree of compaction, and the specific weight of the interstitial fluids. While bearing in mind that variations in the bulk wet specific weight of the overburden are geologically significant in some contexts, let us accept for the present argument a representative value of 0.23 kg/cm^2 per m (1 psi/ft.). This is the *geostatic gradient,* and it is also shown graphically as a straight line (Fig.3-4).

Eq.3-3 indicates that when fluid pressures are abnormally high, the liquid phase is not independent of the solid phase. There is more validity for regarding the water as contained in the rocks, because an unrestrained liquid with pressure p_a at depth z would have a pressure of $p_a - p_e$ at the surface, and the effect would be artesian.*

The difference between normal hydrostatic pressures and pressures that approach the geostatic, then, is a matter related to the containment of the fluid in the rocks, and is therefore related to the hydraulic conductivity, or overall permeability, of the rocks and the overburden over the area. In other words, it is related to the lithologies of the rocks.

An important part of petroleum geology concerns itself with the porosity and permeability of sedimentary rocks. A petroleum reservoir must be permeable and porous; but it must be contained by some barrier if the petroleum is not to escape. The seal, or cap rock, is regarded as impermeable (though it may well be porous). However, no sedimentary rock is ideally impermeable: it is the

---

* Cause must be distinguished from effect in making the analogy with groundwater aquifers. We are also making a distinction between confined and unconfined groundwater; but the cause of abnormal pressures in a confined artesian aquifer is that the level $z = 0$ of a normal hydrostatic gradient lies above ground level away from the intake area.

force of capillarity rather than the impermeability of a fine-grained rock that makes the seal effective to petroleum. When water is the only liquid phase, a clay (for instance) will only be a perfect barrier under certain conditions.

When a clean, well-sorted sand is compacted, there is some loss of porosity and permeability; but the permeability will remain effectively high for the dispersal of fluids expelled by compaction. Thus a thick sequence of clean sands suffering compaction on account of loading by younger sediments has interstitial fluid pressures that correspond closely to the normal hydrostatic gradient for the interstitial fluid.

The compaction of a clay, on the other hand, results from a plastic deformation of a porous and permeable material, and leads to loss of porosity and a permanent and significant loss of permeability. This loss of permeability results largely from the increase in the areas of grain-to-grain contacts and the corresponding constriction of the pore spaces. So the very processes leading to the expulsion of interstitial fluid (reduction of porosity) lead also to a reduction in the ability of the material to expel its fluids (reduction of permeability). The quantitative determination of permeability in clays is not easy. It is not certain that Darcy's law applies to very low permeabilities: the viscosity of water in some clays may be higher on account of molecular attraction; the effective porosity may be reduced by a stationary film of water over the clay particles; there is a preferential expulsion of the more saline solutions; and there may be other effects. The commonly observed increase in "shale" or clay densities with increasing depth indicates that a clay retains some permeability until the compaction process is complete.

Clearly, then, the interstitial fluid pressure in a thick clay sequence is affected by the dimension of time. If sufficient time has elapsed, the expelled fluids will have dispersed and the pressures in the interstices will be normal hydrostatic. If insufficient time has elapsed, the inperstitial fluid pressures will be abnormal to some degree, with the geostatic pressure as a limiting pressure. Since fluids can only move in a hydrodynamic situation, it follows that the compaction processes set up a *fluid potential gradient* down which the fluid tends to migrate. The permeability of the material in the direction of the gradient determines whether this potential gradient shall be large or small.

Mechanical aspects of fluids in porous rocks

Geologically, one sees that the overburden is normally supported through the solid grains of the rocks in water; and the deformation of these grains under the load depends on the mechanical properties of the grain material, or the lithology. Fluid pressures in the interstices of the rocks also depend on the lithology. The more compactible the lithology, the more interstitial liquid that must be expelled for compaction to take place. The more permeable the lithology, the greater the ease of fluid dispersal. In general, the permeable rocks suffer elastic deformation under stress: the compactible rocks suffer plastic deformation under stress, and are also less permeable. If the rate of loading does not exceed the corresponding rate at which fluids can be expelled, then normal hydrostatic pressures exist in the fluids. If the rate of loading exceeds the corresponding rate at which fluids can be dispersed, compaction will be retarded, the fluid that cannot escape takes part of the load, and abnormal pressures exist in the fluids in the rock.

Geologists may therefore be in intuitive agreement with Terzaghi, Hubbert, Rubey, and others who have shown with more rigour that the total stress in a water-saturated rock is divided between the effective compressive stress transmitted through the solids and the interstitial fluid pressure:

$$S = \sigma + p \tag{3-4}$$

where S is the vertical component of total stress (the overburden pressure), σ the effective stress in solids, and p the fluid pressure, σ is the stress that compacts a rock: it is quantitatively equal to the difference between the overburden pressure and the fluid pressure.

As a porous rock is loaded, so the load is taken first by the interstitial liquid which, as it escapes, transfers the load progressively to the grain-to-grain contacts. Hence compaction can only proceed while liquid can leak from the system, and the interstitial liquid pressure is a measure of the balance between the load and the leakage (for leakage there is, however slow it may be).

Hubbert and Rubey (1959, p.142) introduced a useful parameter, λ, which can be written:

$$\lambda = p/\bar{\gamma}_{bw} z \tag{3-5}$$

and is the ratio of fluid pressure to geostatic pressure at depth z. Since the geostatic gradient, or mean bulk wet specific weight of the overburden, may be taken as 0.23 kg/cm^2 per m (1 psi/ft.) for many practical purposes, approximations are:

$$\lambda' = p \ (\text{kg/cm}^2)/0.23 z \ (\text{m})$$

or:

$$\lambda' = p \ (\text{psi})/z \ (\text{ft.})$$

λ is a dimensionless parameter with a maximum value of about 1, and a common minimum value of about 0.43 (corresponding to normal hydrostatic pressure in fresh water and an overburden specific weight of 0.23 kg/cm^2 per m). When $\lambda = 1$, the overburden is supported not on rock but on water. Since an abnormal pressure may be regarded as the sum of two partial pressures — the normal hydrostatic and an incremental pressure:

$$p_a = p_e + p'$$

λ may also be considered as the sum to two components,

$$\lambda = \frac{\gamma_w z}{\bar{\gamma}_{bw} z} + \frac{p'}{\bar{\gamma}_{bw} z}$$

Hence, when fluid pressures are normal hydrostatic, the stress distribution between solids and liquid is in equilibrium, and λ then takes its equilibrium value, which we shall denote by λ_e,

$$\lambda_e = \gamma_w z/\bar{\gamma}_{bw} z = \gamma_w/\bar{\gamma}_{bw} \tag{3-5a}$$

The value of λ_e usually lies between about 0.45 and 0.55, depending on the water salinity and the overburden lithologies.

Following the argument of Rubey and Hubbert (1959, pp.173—

175) we may substitute our eq.3-5 into eq.3-4 and, re-arranging, obtain:

$$\sigma = S - \lambda \bar{\gamma}_{bw} z \qquad (3\text{-}6)$$

and noting that S is the overburden pressure, $\bar{\gamma}_{bw} z$, write:

$$\sigma = (1 - \lambda)\bar{\gamma}_{bw} z \qquad (3\text{-}6a)$$

This also shows, of course, that the stress in solids, σ, decreases as λ increases towards unity. A rock with abnormal fluid pressures at depth z has a stress in solids that is equal to the stress in solids in an identical rock at some shallower depth of burial, under equilibrium conditions. This depth Rubey and Hubbert called the *equilibrium depth*, z_e. So, under equilibrium conditions:

$$\sigma = (1 - \lambda_e)\bar{\gamma}_{bw} z_e \qquad (3\text{-}7)$$

Thus the solid stress, σ, in an abnormally pressured rock at depth z can be equated to the solid stress in the rock under equilibrium conditions at a shallower depth, z_e. From eq.3-6a and 3-7 we obtain:

$$(1 - \lambda)\bar{\gamma}_{bw} z = (1 - \lambda_e)\bar{\gamma}_{bw} z_e$$

and, re-arranging:

$$z_e = \frac{(1 - \lambda)}{(1 - \lambda_e)} z \qquad (3\text{-}8)$$

Denoting the expression $(1 - \lambda)/(1 - \lambda_e)$ by δ (Chapman, 1972), we may write:

$$\delta = \frac{z_e}{z} = \frac{(1 - \lambda)}{(1 - \lambda_e)} \qquad (3\text{-}8a)$$

δ is non-dimensional, and commonly takes values between 0 (when $\lambda = 1$) and 1 (when $\lambda = \lambda_e$). When stress equilibrium has been maintained by leakage of fluid from the rock, δ is equal to unity, and the equilibrium depth equals the actual depth ($z_e = z$). When no leakage has occurred, δ is equal to zero, and the equilibrium depth is the surface of deposition. δ may therefore be interpreted as a dimensionless measure of the expulsion of fluids

TABLE 3-II

Conversion tables for λ and δ for various common values of λ_e

$\lambda_e = 0.44$		$\lambda_e = 0.47$		$\lambda_e = 0.5$	
λ	δ	λ	δ	λ	δ
0.44	1	0.47	1		
0.5	0.89	0.5	0.94	0.5	1
0.6	0.71	0.6	0.75	0.6	0.8
0.7	0.54	0.7	0.57	0.7	0.6
0.8	0.36	0.8	0.38	0.8	0.4
0.9	0.18	0.9	0.19	0.9	0.2
1.0	0	1.0	0	1.0	0
δ	λ	δ	λ		
1.0	0.44	1.0	0.47	*Note:* for most	
0.8	0.55	0.8	0.58	practical uses the	
0.6	0.66	0.6	0.68	table above will	
0.4	0.78	0.4	0.79	serve.	
0.2	0.89	0.2	0.89		
0.0	1	0.0	1		

since deposition. Values of δ for common values of λ_e and λ are tabulated in Table 3-II.

For example, the fluid pressure measured in a thin sand in a clay unit was found to be 635 kg/cm^2 (9,030 psi) at 3,250 m (10,660 ft.). Assuming a geostatic gradient of 0.23 kg/cm^2 per m (1 psi/ft.) and a hydrostatic gradient of 0.106 kg/cm^2 per m (0.46 psi/ft.), the value of λ is found to be 0.85, and that of λ_e, 0.46. The value of δ is therefore:

$$\delta = \frac{(1-0.85)}{(1-0.46)} = \frac{0.15}{0.54} = 0.28$$

and the equilibrium depth is:

$$z_e = 0.28 \times 3,250 \ = 910 \ m$$
(or: $z_e = 0.28 \times 10,660 = 3,000$ ft.).

Discussion of the geological significance of the equilibrium depth and related parameters must be postponed until the geological data of zones of abnormal fluid pressures have been considered.

Fluid migration

Fluid migration involves the concepts of fluid potential gradients and permeability. Permeability is a specific measure of the transmissibility of fluid through the pore spaces of a rock. Whether or not the fluid in a rock moves depends primarily on whether or not there is a fluid potential gradient in that rock, for no rock can be regarded as ideally impermeable. The direction of movement depends on the direction of the fluid potential gradient. Statements such as "migration of fluids in clays is lateral because the lateral permeability is greater than the vertical permeability" are therefore erroneous.

In a clay rock that is compacting under a uniform gravity load, the vertical component of total stress is a function of overburden thickness, and the surfaces of equal potential energy are essentially horizontal. The vertical component of stress in solids is a function of both the total stress and the fluid pressure (eq.3-4), and these equipotential surfaces are also essentially horizontal. Lack of equilibrium between solids and liquids therefore induces fluid potential gradients normal to the equipotential surfaces in the fluids, and the interstitial fluid tends to migrate vertically towards the nearest permeable outlet — which may be the depositional surface, or a permeable sand that is in stress equilibrium (with normal hydrostatic fluid pressures). This migration is across the bedding because this is the direction of the fluid potential gradient. Clay units in nature may be of the order of tens of thousands of metres in lateral dimensions, tens or a few hundreds of metres thick. The principal component of the fluid potential gradient will only be lateral near the margins of such units, that is, near facies changes that involve changes of permeability, or near faults that throw more permeable beds against the clay. (In every case, of course, the permeable unit must have relatively unrestricted pore channels to the surface.)

The compaction of an alternating sequence of sands and clays, for example, leads to the expulsion of interstitial liquids from the clays to the sands — or more generally, from the compactible to the permeable lithology. Provided the hydraulic conductivity to the surface is sufficient for the dispersal of this liquid, the measurable pressures within the permeable beds will coincide with the normal hydrostatic gradient for the density of the water.

Within the clays, however, the interstitial fluid is at a higher potential because of the restricted fluid flow; and this difference of potential creates both upward and *downward* fluid potential gradients, and the fluid will tend to migrate both upward and downward towards the intercalated permeable beds. These flows are not quantitatively equal, for the amount of fluid flow depends both on the fluid potential gradient and the permeability. Flow will continue in both directions until the potential gradient is eliminated in one direction. The clay will compact from the top downwards, and from the bottom upwards, because as the fluid pressure changes, so does the stress in solids (σ). Compaction is a function of σ. The tendency towards reduced porosity down the fluid potential gradient is also a tendency towards reduced permeability, so the compaction processes of clays in an alternating sequence tend to seal the fluids in the calys (Fig.3-5). There is also evidence of cementation near the top of abnormally pressured clays as a result of precipitation of salts from solution during migration down the fluid potential gradient (Boatman, 1967; Fertl and Timko, 1970; Weaver and Beck 1971). Such cementation

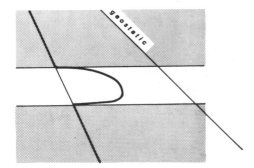

Fig.3-5. Pressures in compacting clay between two permeable beds with normal hydrostatic pressures.

must also reduce the permeability of the rocks and so tend to seal the fluids in the abnormally pressured zone.

As soon as a compacting bed acquires a downward fluid potential gradient, with a downward flow of fluid, it becomes a *perfect* barrier to the upward migration of fluids. Upward-migrating fluids from the next deeper compacting bed must then either disperse by lateral migration in the permeable bed, or the permeable bed will also acquire an abnormal fluid pressure. Thus lateral migration of fluids in permeable beds is significant during the compaction of alternating compactible and permeable beds. General upward migration can only be postulated when a single lithology is being compacted below the surface, or when a thick permeable bed overlies a compacting, relatively impermeable bed.

In the geological context, the permeable beds are associated with environments of higher energy, near the marine margins of physiographic basins, and tend to "shale out" away from the margins. Fig.3-6 shows a schematic cross-section through a dominantly regressive sequence. From this it will be clear that the fluids of expulsion migrate towards the marine margin of physiographic basins in the permeable beds preserved in the sedimentary basins.

The formation of a relatively impermeable sheath around clay units is of considerable geological significance. The upper part of

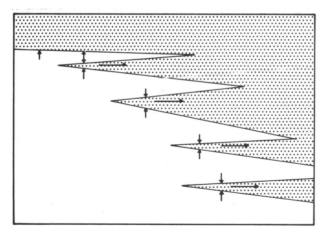

Fig.3-6. Schematic cross-section through regressive sequence. (Vertical scale greatly exaggerated.) Arrows indicate directions of fluid migration.

an accumulating clay bed may have very high porosity, and through this part pass the fluids expelled by compaction. Such a clay unit is compacting from the bottom to the top. But as soon as this clay bed is buried under a permeable bed, such as a sand, the upper layer of the clay begins to compact under the load, so retarding further expulsion of fluid. The rate of loading then also changes significantly, not only because the permeable unit may accumulate more rapidly than the clay but also because the specific weight of the accumulating sediment may increase from 0.16 or 0.17 kg/cm^2 per m during clay accumulation to a figure of the order of 0.21 kg/cm^2 per m (0.9 psi/ft.), corresponding to a porosity of about 35% in sand. The load additional to the water column above the upper surface of the clay may be of the order of 0.1 kg/cm^2 per m of permeable bed accumulated (0.45 psi/ft.). This load will be taken at least in part by the interstitial fluid in the clay. Thus a change of facies in the accumulating sediment affects the mechanical properties of the sediments — particularly the clays — already accumulated.

The geology of abnormal fluid pressures

In Chapter 2 it was suggested that in the study of any phenomenon, important clues are probably to be found in the abnormalities, the deviations from general patterns. Abnormal interstitial fluid pressures in the subsurface constitute an important deviation from the general tendencies of normal hydrostatic pressures in the pore fluids and increasing compaction with depth.

Abnormal fluid pressures were sometimes encountered and successfully drilled in the days of cable tool drilling (see Keep and Ward, 1934). As more and deeper drilling was carried out, so the occurrence became more common. It was Dickinson (1953) who demonstrated beyond reasonable doubt that the occurrence of abnormal pressures in the Gulf Coast province of North America was stratigraphically controlled, and to be related to facies rather than depth. Abnormal pressures were found to occur in sands that were inferred to be discontinuous, lenticular bodies; or discontinuous sand bodies on account of the faulting of a tongue of sand

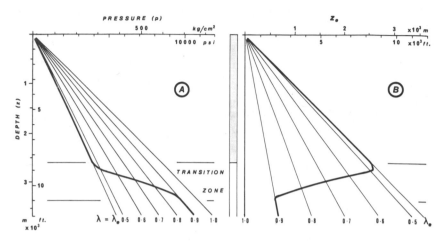

Fig.3-7. Plots of fluid pressure (A) and equilibrium depth (B) against depth. (After Chapman, 1972, p.792, fig.1 and 2.)

against a clay. These sands occur in the clayey sequence below the dominantly regressive younger sands.

Drilling into abnormal pressures in the subsurface has shown that below the normal pressures there is a transition zone in which: (a) the rate of increase of fluid pressure may vary, but is almost invariably greater than the rate of increase of the geostatic pressure (Fig.3-7A); in other words, λ increases with depth in the transition zone; (b) the mechanical strength of the rock decreases as λ increases, and the penetration rate increases; (c) there is a limit to the value of λ. The absolute limit is 1, but many areas appear to have a lower maximum value of about 0.9 (e.g., in the Gulf coast province of North America); and (d) the bulk density of the clays decreases with depth (or another parameter, such as sonic velocity, changes in such a way that reduction of bulk density with depth can be inferred).

It is necessary to consider in some detail the geological significance of these observations, and the nature of the transition zone.

The characteristics of the transition zone can be shown graphically by plotting observed or estimated interstitial fluid pressures against depth, on a chart that includes the values of λ (Fig.3-7A). This plot shows how the fluid pressures change from normal hydrostatic towards the geostatic. The rate of change of the fluid pressure with depth must have geological significance, and intuitively one would suggest that this is related to the hydraulic conductivity of the rocks. Relatively high hydraulic conductivity would lead to a low rate of change, or a thicker transition zone: low hydraulic conductivity would lead to a high rate of change, or thinner transition zone. The lithological column should therefore also be included in the plot of pressures versus depth.

If we now consider the relationship between the interstitial fluid pressures and the equilibrium depth and plot the equilibrium depth (z_e) against depth z (Fig.3-7B) it will be seen that while the value of z_e increases with z through the sequence that is normally pressured (the zone of present-day stress equilibrium) the transition zone is marked by a reversal of this trend, and here the equilibrium depth decreases with increasing depth. The rate of change of this parameter with depth in the transition zone varies, of course, with the rate of change of pressure and λ. This reversal of the equilibrium depth trend is also commonly associated with the reversal of the bulk density trend in clays, as indicated by cuttings or by the formation density log, the reversal of sonic velocity trends in clays with depth, and the reversal of the "shale" resistivity trends with depth. At the bottom of the transition zone, the equilibrium depth increases again with depth, but on a gradient determined by the value of λ. The trends of the other parameters likewise change.

What does this reversal of equilibrium depth mean geologically? The concept of equilibrium depth, as defined by Rubey and Hubbert, is a notional or imaginary depth at which the effective stress in solids, σ, would equal the actual stress in solids in a rock with abnormal interstitial fluid pressures at a greater depth, z. In the special case where a load is applied to a rock after normal compaction at depth z, then the equilibrium depth is indeed notional. But when clay sediments are compacted under a gravity load, and their compaction has been retarded by the limited leakage of pore water, this notional depth acquires some degree of reality.

The compaction of a clay rock is generally accepted to be essentially plastic and irreversible; so it cannot be accepted that

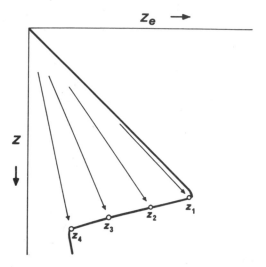

Fig.3-8. Postulated development of $z-z_e$ relationship during burial (diagrammatic). (After Chapman, 1972, p.793, fig.3.)

the compaction history of an abnormally pressured clay rock includes a reversal of the trend of increasing bulk density and decreasing porosity with depth. It certainly cannot be accepted that the compaction history of a clay in terms of the $z-z_e$ relationship has followed the heavy line in Fig.3-8, through points z_1, z_2, z_3, and z_4. This history must rather be represented *qualitatively* by the arrows for each point in Fig.3-8, for a rock now abnormally pressured at depth z can only have had normal hydrostatic fluid pressures at depth z_e if there has been no leakage from the rock during burial from depth z_e to depth z.

In the example shown in Figs.3-7, the bottom of the transition zone (highest value of λ) is at 3,353 m (11,000 ft.) and the equilibrium depth is 622 m (2,040 ft.). The pressure in the interstitial fluids is 696 kg/cm^2 (9,900 psi). We conclude that the *maximum* depth at which this clay lost stress equilibrium under a gravity load was 622 m. What interpretation is to be put on rocks within the transition zone, such as that at 2,987 m (9,800 ft.) with an interstitial fluid pressure of 492 kg/cm^2 (7,000 psi) and an equilibrium depth of 1,582 m (5,190 ft.)? By the same argument, this clay has never been in stress equilibrium since burial to that depth — but this does not mean that it was in stress equilibrium *until* burial to that depth. The difference between the pressures at 3,353 m and 2,987 m cannot be accounted for by the difference of 366 m of overburden, because the pressure difference is 204 kg/cm^2, not 0.23 × 366 = 84 kg/cm^2. This difference must therefore be attributed to leakage of interstitial fluid from the clay, which has the effect of increasing δ and increasing z_e, the equilibrium depth. The equilibrium depth, through the parameter δ ($=z_e/z$) is therefore a measure of the leakage that has occurred from a rock since initial accumulation, and the best measure is obtained at the base of the transition zone, where the maximum value of λ is reached.

The maximum value of λ (as distinct from its limiting value) at the base of the transition zone in the Louisiana Gulf Coast is about 0.9 at 3,000 to 3,700 m (10,000–12,000 ft.). The corresponding value of δ is (1–0.9)/(1.0–0.465) = 0.2. This indicates that the abnormally pressured clays now at depths between 3,000 and 3,700 m acquired their abnormality at depths of burial of the order of 600–800 m (2,000–2,600 ft.) *or shallower.*

If such shallow depths of abnormal fluid pressures are indicated for the past, it is reasonable to expect some confirmation from present day sediments at shallow depth. Leaving aside California, New Zealand and Trinidad, where tectonic activity obscures the evidence, shallow abnormal interstitial fluid pressures are reported from the island of New Guinea and from the Orinoco delta. Drilling in the North Coast basin of West Irian, on the north coast of the island of New Guinea, encountered abnormal pressures at about 1,300 m (4,000 ft.). Although the pressure data are unreliable, equilibrium depths of the order of 800 m (2,600 ft.) are indicated at about 1,800 m (5,900 ft.) and it is unlikely that the base of the transition zone was reached (Visser and Hermes, 1962, p.230: see p.160 of this volume for further discussion). In the Gulf of Papua, at the south eastern end of the island, unspecified abnormal pressures are reported at a depth of about 640 m (2,100 ft.) in Pliocene mudstones (Spinks, 1970). In the Orinoco delta, investigations into the Holocene (Recent) sediments at Pedernales revealed clays with abnormal interstitial fluid pressures within 30 m (100 ft.) of the surface (Kidwell and Hunt, 1958).

It therefore seems clear that a clay loses stress equilibrium soon after burial — or more specifically, when it is loaded by a permeable sediment. A thick clay may not achieve stress equilibrium during a geologically significant span of time.

Given that the equilibrium depth has a real meaning in sediments that are compacting under the gravity load of overlying sediments, it is pertinent also to examine the lithologies of the sequence of thickness z_e above the base of the transition zone. This is an estimate of the overburden lithologies when the base of the transition zone was buried to depth z_e. If this sequence is essentially of rocks of low hydraulic conductivity, early acquisition of abnormal pressures is indicated. This concept is valid as an approximation because compaction has generally been retarded in the transition zone, and because the data from which λ and δ are computed usually lack precision.

The long history of retarded mean compaction also implies necessarily that there has been retarded mean fluid expulsion. This implication is essential for the understanding of primary migration of petroleum from clay source rocks (Chapter 6).*

The maximum value of λ

There is no difficulty in accepting that λ has a limiting value of 1 (as distinct from its maximum value). But we have seen that when $\lambda = 1$, the value of δ is zero and the equilibrium depth is zero — there has been no leakage of fluid from the sediment. Since some leakage of fluid from sediments certainly occurs because rocks are not ideally impermeable, it seems that purely sedimentary loading cannot lead to a maximum value of λ equal to its limiting value. If compaction, however slight, increases the value of σ above zero, eq.3-4 indicates that the fluid pressure cannot equal the geostatic pressure. Again, since the amount of leakage is a factor that determines the maximum value of λ, and this leakage is a function of the hydraulic conductivity of the rocks in the hydrodynamic field, there can be no unique maximum value for λ.

Consider the following conceptual model of the development of

---

* See Postscript (p.267).

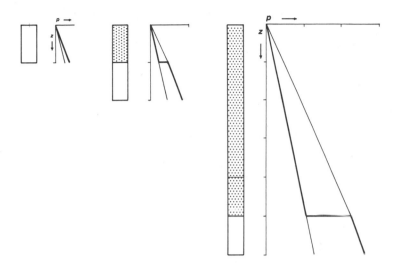

Fig.3-9. Model of pore pressure development in a clay bed buried under permeable sand.

a thick sedimentary sequence. Let us assume that no fluid leaks from the clays, but that sands maintain normal hydrostatic pressures unless a seal is expressly postulated. Fig.3-9 shows such a model development. We will assume that clay has a mean bulk wet specific weight of 0.185 kg/cm^2 per m (0.8 psi/ft.), and that that of the sand is 0.225 kg/cm^2 per m (0.98 psi/ft.) corresponding to a mean porosity of 25%.

First, 500 m (1,600 ft.) of clay is accumulated; and since no fluid leakage is postulated, the pressure gradient in this clay will be geostatic, $\lambda = 1$, $\delta = 0$, and $z_e = 0$ throughout. The interstitial fluid pressure at the base of the clay is 93 kg/cm^2 (1,323 psi). (Do not confuse λ with the approximation λ' that is based on $\gamma_{bw} = 0.23$ kg/cm^2 per m.)

If this clay is now buried under 500 m of sand, λ remains 1 throughout the clay, δ remains zero. The fluid pressure at the base of the clay, now at 1,000 m, is increased to 205 kg/cm^2 (2,916 psi); and that at the top to 112 kg/cm^2 (1,593 psi). But the interstitial fluid pressure at the base of the sand is normal hydrostatic, say 53 kg/cm^2 (754 psi).

Loading this sequence with a further 2,000 m (6,600 ft.) of

permeable sand increases the fluid pressures in the clay (now 2,500 to 3,000 m below the surface) to 562–655 kg/cm². In the clay, λ remains 1 and δ remains zero. At the base of the sand, now at 2,500 m, the interstitial fluid pressure is hydrostatic, that is, 265 kg/cm² (3,769 psi), and $\lambda = \lambda_e$. In other words, the top of the clay has an equilibrium depth of zero, the base of the sand one of 2,500 m (because the solids are in stress equilibrium with the liquid). A fluid potential gradient exists across the lithological boundary.

If liquid now begins to leak from the clays, flowing down the fluid potential gradient, the top of the clay begins to compact, and the value of λ will be reduced by an amount commensurate with the amount of leakage, and the value of δ and hence z_e will increase. This leakage creates a transition zone from the normal hydrostatic to the geostatic gradient. The thickness of the zone is governed by the hydraulic conductivity of the compacting clays in the zone, and the fluid potential gradient across it.

Fig.3-10 shows the development of a thick alternating sequence under the same model conditions. If the second bed of clay seals

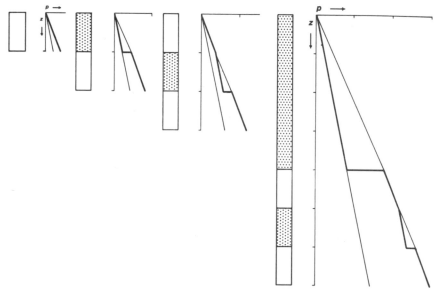

Fig.3-10. Model of pore pressure development in alternating sequence.

the fluids in the underlying 500 m of sand, burial under 2,000 m of permeable sand will have the following effects. In the clays, the value of λ remains 1 throughout, and δ remains zero. The interbedded sand will have interstitial fluid pressures with a normal hydrostatic *gradient,* but displaced towards the geostatic by the load additional to the water, $(\gamma_{bw} - \gamma_w) z$, which will become, on final burial in this example $543 - 265 = 278$ kg/cm^2 (3,954 psi). The fluid pressure in the sand at 2,500 m will be 543 kg/cm^2 (7,723 psi); and at 3,000 m, it will be $543 + 53 = 596$ kg/cm^2 (8,477 psi). The value of λ at the top of the sand is 1; and at the bottom it is $596/655 = 0.91$. Hence λ decreases with depth in a thick permeable bed that is abnormally pressured.

At the interface between the intercalated sand and the lower clay there is the curious situation of an apparent fluid potential difference that cannot give rise to a fluid flow unless fluid can leak from the sand. The pressure at the bottom of the sand cannot be

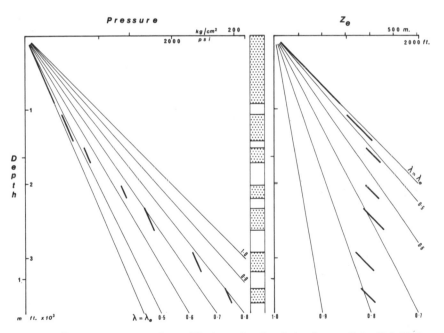

Fig.3-11. Pore pressure and equilibrium depth plot of a well in Trinidad. (From data kindly supplied by Bataafse Internationale Petroleum Maatschappij N.V., The Hague.)

increased without the pressure at the top exceeding the geostatic pressure at that depth.

If fluid now leaks from the system, the values of λ will tend to be reduced, and there will be two transition zones, one in each clay unit. If the leakage also occurs through the intercalated sand, two separate clays that are abnormally pressured will eventually remain.

These models are artificial, and differ from reality in at least one important respect: in nature, the leakage of fluid is continuous, even if very slow. However, the parameters governing the rate of leakage are too variable and too complex to allow quantification at this stage. Smith (1971) has constructed a mathematical model of clay compaction; but nature is more complex. While artificial, the models are related to reality: Fig.3-11 shows an interesting example of the pressure–depth relationships in a sand/clay sequence in a well in Trinidad.

Drilling through zones of abnormal pressures

The transition zone

The rate of penetration in drilling is a function of the weight on the bit, the rate of rotation, the bit-tooth geometry, the properties and hydraulic energy of the mud, the fluid potential gradient across the bottom of the hole, and, of course, the mechanical strength or "drillability" of the rock at the bottom of the hole. When all controllable factors are kept constant, the main influences on the penetration rate are the last two – the fluid potential gradient across the bottom of the hole, and the mechanical strength of the rock.

When drilling into the transition zone, from normal hydrostatic to abnormal fluid pressures, both these parameters change, and both change towards promoting the penetration rate. This increase in penetration rate, called a "drilling break" in the jargon, is often dramatic; and unless there is convincing evidence to the contrary, it *must* be taken as a warning of abnormal interstitial fluid pressures in the rocks.

Normal procedure is to stop drilling as soon as a "break" is detected, pull the bit back above the depth at which the break occurred, shut down the pumps slowly, and observe the mud level in the hole and in the suction tanks. Whatever action is indicated by these observations, at some time early in the operation it will be necessary to circulate "bottoms up" to sample the mud from the bottom of the hole for contamination by fluids, and to examine the cuttings.

Lack of inflow into the borehole is not of itself diagnostic. Drilling breaks can and do occur in clays that give no measurable flow of fluid. Indeed, it is clear that abnormal pressures will always begin in the more compactible and less permeable beds. The purpose of pulling the bit back is to avoid the danger of the hole's collapsing onto the bit as a result of a reversal of the fluid potential gradient into the borehole. Such collapse will be detected when feeling for bottom before resuming drilling.

The petroleum geologist must not be an idle spectator during these operations. It must be assumed that if drilling is resumed, there will be fluid influx into the borehole as soon as a permeable bed is penetrated, and the well will "kick". Casing is normally set when the well kicks. There are two good reasons for this procedure. First, carrying a heavy mud in open hole through normally pressured permeable beds involves an unacceptable risk of wall-sticking (when the pressure differential between the mud column and the formation fluids holds the pipe to the wall of the hole — see Glossary). Wall-sticking in this situation cannot be resolved by reducing the mud wieght, because the fluids in the transition zone will flow before the pressure differential at the stuck pipe can be sufficiently reduced. Secondly, there is little real security in having the casing deeper. To drill deeper without casing involves the risk of an uncontrollable blowout, with fluids repressuring normally pressured permeable units on account of the fluid potential gradient between them. Perhaps more fundamentally, the competence of the rocks *decreases* in the transition zone (eq.3-4) and may be reduced to the competence of rocks at depths of the order of 600 m (2,000 ft.) (eq.3-8). These are incompetent by any standards, and casing cemented into them provides little real security. These considerations apply with even greater force when it is desired to set a liner, for the security of the liner depends on the cement bond in the casing below the hanger.

With casing set at the top of the transition zone, it is usually possible to drill safely towards the bottom of the transition zone.

Beneath the transition zone

Zones of abnormal interstitial fluid pressures are essentially lithological units that are compactible, and have inherently low hydraulic conductivity. There is therefore no justification for assuming that once abnormal pressures have been reached in the subsurface they will continue in depth. If a thick clay unit overlies a porous and permeable sand, with effective pore-space continuity to the surface, such a sand will contain fluids at normal hydrostatic pressures.

The mechanical difficulties of drilling through thick abnormally pressured sequences, and the expense, usually result in the termination of drilling while in the transition zone, or a short distance below it. There are few published examples of drilling through the abnormally pressured unit into normal, or near normal hydrostatic pressures below. Nevertheless, it will be apparent from the discussion so far, that the base of an overpressured clay is highly significant in the context of fluid migration, for it is a total barrier to the upward migration of fluids.

The lower part of an abnormally pressured clay unit has a transition zone that is the mirror-image of the transition zone at the top of the unit. In the lower transition zone, the rock parameters tend towards equilibrium with depth. The fluid potential gradient is downwards, the clay is compacting from the bottom upwards, tending to seal the fluid pressures in, and its mechanical strength increases downwards as the value of λ decreases. The drilling break that accompanies penetration of the upper transition zone has its counterpart in a sharp reduction of penetration rate, warning of a return to more normal pressures.

Tectonic loading of sediments

So far we have discussed only the mechanical compaction of

sediments under the gravitational load of the overlying sedimentary column. However, the deformation of sediments by tectonic forces is an observational fact, and it is thought to be a contributary (if not the principal) factor in the generation of abnormal interstitial fluid pressures in California, New Zealand, Trinidad, and near the Himalaya. Clearly, lateral compression of fluid-saturated porous rocks can generate abnormal pressures of the same order, and with the same limits, as those generated under a gravity load. The stratigraphic control will be as important as it is under gravity loading. Three comments suggest themselves:

(1) The value of λ can more nearly approach unity if the rate of tectonic loading exceeds the corresponding rate of leakage.

(2) Abnormal pressures may exist at a shallower depth in rocks of relatively higher hydraulic conductivity, if the rate of loading is fast enough.

(3) δ retains the significance it has in gravity loading, but the concept of the equilibrium depth is notional.

Consider a thick sequence of sedimentary rocks of variable lithology and compactibility that has achieved stress equilibrium throughout by the leakage of fluid. If this sequence is now loaded tectonically at a rate faster than the corresponding rate of fluid leakage, abnormal fluid pressures will result, and λ may reach high values approaching unity. The δ values would be correspondingly low, indicating relatively little fluid leakage *under that load.* The equilibrium depth would be a notional depth.

However, if we accept again the evidence that clays compact by plastic deformation, and that this process is irreversible, the trend of increasing bulk density of clays (decreasing porosity) with depth will not be altered significantly by the tectonic load. In any transition zone that develops by leakage of fluid from a compactible to a permeable bed, compaction will tend towards equilibrium for the load, and there may be a slight reversal, or change, of the trend of increasing bulk density with depth. However, the low permeability induced by the compaction that occurred prior to tectonic loading would apparently lead to a very ill-defined transition zone, and the absolute bulk densities would indicate depths of burial much greater than the notional equilibrium depth. In other words, it would appear that abnormal pressures generated by tectonic loading after normal gravity compaction would be characterized by bulk density or shale travel time plots that will be inconsistent with the plot of equilibrium depth versus true depth.

In practice, areas of active tectonic deformation are commonly areas of rapid contemporaneous sediment accumulation, and the abnormal pressures generated are indistinguishable from those generated by gravity loading alone. In California and New Zealand, for example, the contemporaneity of tectonic deformation and sedimentation and sediment accumulation is observable. Both areas also have clay diapirism.

(*Note:* Other possible, even probable causes of abnormal interstitial fluid pressures are discussed in works included in the list of references and selected bibliography. Osmosis and clay diagenesis are important topics. Thermal expansion of water (see p.24) may also contribute a component of abnormality to the pressure, but this effect may be largely counteracted by the corresponding decrease in viscosity.)

Selected bibliography

Athy, L.F., 1930a. Density, porosity, and compaction of sedimentary rocks. *Bull. Am. Ass. Petrol. Geol.*, 14:1—24.

Athy, L.F., 1930b. Compaction and oil migration. *Bull. Am. Ass. Petrol. Geol.*, 14:25—35.

Boatman, W.A., 1967. Measuring and using shale density to aid in drilling wells in high-pressure areas. *J. Petrol. Technol.*, 19:1423—1429.

Bredehoeft, J.D. and Hanshaw, B.B., 1968. On the maintenance of anomalous fluid pressures, I. Thick sedimentary sequences. *Bull. Geol. Soc. Am.*, 79:1097—1106.

Burst, J.F., 1969. Diagenesis of Gulf Coast clayey sediments and its possible relation to petroleum migration. *Bull. Am. Ass. Petrol. Geol.*, 53:73—93.

Chapman, R.E., 1972. Clays with abnormal interstitial fluid pressures. *Bull. Am. Ass. Petrol. Geol.*, 56:790—795.

Dickinson, G., 1953. Geological aspects of abnormal reservoir pressures in Gulf Coast Louisiana. *Bull. Am. Ass. Petrol. Geol.*, 37:410—432.

Fertl, W.H. and Timko, D.J., 1970. Occurrence of cemented reservoir roof rock and geopressure caprock and its implication in petroleum geology and geohydrology, *Am. Inst. Min. Metal. Petrol. Eng., Publ.*, SPE 3085, 5 pp.

Gretener, P.E., 1969. Fluid pressure in porous media — its importance in geology: a review. *Bull. Can. Petrol. Geol.*, 17:255—295.

Hanshaw, B.B. and Bredehoeft, J.D., 1968. On the maintenance of anomalous fluid pressures, II. Source layer at depth. *Bull. Geol. Soc. Am.*, 79:1107–1122.

Hanshaw, B.B. and Zen, E—an, 1965. Osmotic equilibrium and overthrust faulting. *Bull. Geol. Soc. Am.*, 76:1379–1386.

Heard, H.C. and Rubey, W.W., 1966. Tectonic implications of gypsum dehydration. *Bull. Geol. Soc. Am.*, 77:741–760.

Hedberg, H.D., 1926. The effect of gravitational compaction on the structure of sedimentary rocks. *Bull. Am. Ass. Petrol. Geol.*, 10:1035–1072.

Hedberg, H.D., 1936. Gravitational compaction of clays and shales. *Am. J. Sci.*, 31 (5th. ser.):241–287.

Hubbert, M.K. and Rubey, W.W., 1959. Role of fluid pressure in mechanics of overthrust faulting, I. Mechanics of fluid-filled porous solids and its application to overthrust faulting. *Bull. Geol. Soc. Am.*, 70:115–166.

Keep, C.E. and Ward, H.L., 1934. Drilling against high rock pressures with particular reference to operations conducted in the Khaur field, Punjab. *J. Inst. Petrol. Technol.*, 20:990–1026.

Kidwell, A.L. and Hunt, J.M., 1958. Migration of oil in Recent sediments of Pedernales, Venezuela. In: L.G. Weeks (Editor), *Habitat of Oil.* American Association of Petroleum Geologists, Tulsa, Okla., pp.790-817.

Kok, P.C. and Thomeer, J.H.M.A., 1955. Abnormal pressures in oil- and gas reservoirs. *Geol. Mijnb., N.S.*, 17:207–216.

Magara, Kinji, 1968. Compaction and migration of fluids in Miocene mudstone, Nagaoka Plain, Japan. *Bull. Am. Ass. Petrol. Geol.*, 52:2466–2501.

Maxwell, J.C., 1964. Influence of depth, temperature, and geologic age on porosity of quartzose sandstone. *Bull. Am. Ass. Petrol. Geol.*, 48:697–709.

McCrossan, R.G., 1961. Resistivity mapping and petrophysical study of Upper Devonian inter-reef calcareous shales of central Alberta, Canada. *Bull. Am. Ass. Petrol. Geol.*, 45:441–470.

Perry, E. and Hower, J., 1970. Burial diagenesis in Gulf Coast pelitic sediments. *Clays Clay Minerals*, 18:165–177.

Powers, M.C., 1967. Fluid-release mechanisms in compacting marine mudrocks and their importance in oil exploration. *Bull. Am. Ass. Petrol. Geol.*, 51:1240–1254.

Rittenhouse, G., 1971a. Pore-space reduction by solution and cementation. *Bull. Am. Ass. Petrol. Geol.*, 55:80–91.

Rittenhouse, G., 1971b. Mechanical compaction of sands containing different percentages of ductile grains: a theoretical approach. *Bull. Am. Ass. Petrol. Geol.*, 55:92–96.

Rubey, W.W. and Hubbert, M.K., 1959. Role of fluid pressure in mechanics of overthrust faulting, II. Overthrust belt in geosynclinal area of western Wyoming in light of fluid-pressure hypothesis. *Bull. Geol. Soc. Am.*, 70:167–206.

Skempton, A.W., 1970. The consolidation of clays by gravitational compaction. *Q. J. Geol. Soc. Lond.*, 125 (1969) :373–411.

Smith, J.E., 1971. The dynamics of shale compaction and evolution of pore-fluid pressures. *J. Int. Ass. Math. Geol.*, 3:239–263.

Spinks, R.B., 1970. Offshore drilling operations in the Gulf of Papua. *J. Aust. Petrol. Explor. Ass.*, 10:108–114.

Visser, W.A. and Hermes, J.J., 1962. Geological results of the exploration for oil in Netherlands New Guinea. *Verh. K. Ned. Geol.-Mijnb. Genoot. (Geol. Ser.)*, 20:1–265.

Weaver, C.E. and Beck, K.C., 1971. Clay water diagenesis during burial: how mud becomes gneiss. *Geol. Soc. Am., Spec. Pap.*, 134 :96 pp.

Weller, J.M., 1959. Compaction of sediments. *Bull. Am. Ass. Petrol. Geol.*, 43:273–310.

Chapter 4. GROWTH STRUCTURES

Summary

(1) Growth structures are folds and faults in which variations of rock unit thickness show a close relationship to the structure itself. They result from diastrophism that took place during sediment accumulation, burial, and compaction.

There is an element of interpretation in a short definition of growth structures. The structures that result from differential compaction are not strictly growth structures.

(2) Growth faults (there are numerous synonyms, most common of which are *contemporaneous* and *depositional*) are faults in which the thicknesses of rock units in the downthrown block are greater than those of the same units in the upthrown block.

(3) Both blocks of a growth fault, in general, had a capacity to accumulate sediment, both were subsiding relative to baselevel, but the downthrown block subsided faster than the upthrown block, and so had a capacity to accumulate a greater thickness of sediment.

(4) The fault plane of growth faults is usually curved in plan and in section, concave to the basin and concave up. The throw of a growth fault generally increases with depth on account of the thickness contrast across it; but antithetic faults may reduce the throw.

(5) Growth anticlines are anticlines in which rock units thicken from the crest towards the flanks. They grew while sediment was being accumulated, buried, and compacted. The whole area of the anticline, in general, was subsiding; but the flanks subsided faster than the crest, and so accumulated a greater thickness of sediment.

Presumably growth synclines can be formed.

(6) These processes can and do lead to local stratigraphic hiatus, the recognition of which can be extremely difficult — but essen-

tial, of course, for the correct interpretation of such areas

(7) Growth structures probably result from diapirism (or incipient diapirism) at depth and may therefore be underlain by sediments with abnormal interstitial fluid pressures (Fig. 5-1A and 5-2).

(8) Sedimentary basins can be regarded as growth structures on a large scale.

Definitions and terminology

Growth structures are structures in which the variations in sedimentary thicknesses show a close relationship to the structure itself. They are interpreted as being the result of diastrophism that was contemporaneous with sedimentation. Growth structures are normally thought of as faults or anticlines, but they may also be monoclines — and presumably synclines. They are local variations in the development of a sedimentary basin, but the sedimentary basin itself is a growth structure in the broadest sense.

It is difficult to define growth structures without including the interpretation of them in the definition. *Drape,* or *supratenuous* folds are not growth structures in spite of the fact that the sedimentary thicknesses may show a close relationship to the underlying "structure". Likewise, *contemporaneous deformation,* as used by Billings (1954) and subsequent writers, refers more to the deformation of unconsolidated sediments by slumping and sliding than to folding and faulting on the scale of petroleum accumulations.

The terminology of growth faults is confused. There is little doubt that *concurrent* fault (Tiddeman, 1890) has priority, when applied to a fault that has a thicker sedimentary sequence on the downthrown side than on the upthrown side. Currie (1956) used both *concurrent* and *contemporaneous*; Liechti et al. (1960) used *deposititonal,* following common U.S. Gulf Coast usage; Ocamb (1961) used *growth*; but Hardin and Hardin (1961) stated that *contemporaneous* has "some claim to priority". In addition to these, *synsedimentary, progressive, Gulf Coast type,* and other synonyms have been used. Dennis (1967) accepted *growth* fault for the *International Tectonic Dictionary,* and recommended that all synonyms be dropped.

Since *concurrent* can hardly be revived with any hope of acceptance, and the multiplicity of synonyms can serve no useful purpose, we bow to the *International Tectonic Dictionary* here, and accept *growth fault* as the term for a fault that separates correlative sequences of different thicknesses, with the thicker sequence on the downthrown side.

The terminology for growth structures other than faults has not received much attention. It is desirable to use the same adjective for analogous geological features, and *growth structure* is in common usage amongst petroleum geologists. However, "structure" is a wide term that is not synonymous with "anticline". We therefore use the term *growth structure* to embrace all structures that affected contemporaneous sedimentation and sediment accumulation; *growth fault* and *growth anticline,* or other specific terms, for structural features that affected contemporaneous sediment accumulation.

Growth faults

A growth fault may be defined as a fault that separates two correlative sequences, the thicker of which is on the downthrown side (Fig.4-1). It is interpreted as a fault that was moving during the accumulation of those rock units that show a thickness contrast across the fault. The throw of a growth fault generally increases with depth over the interval or intervals of thickness contrast (because of the thickness contrast); but antithetic faults reduce the throw with depth. The diagnostic feature is therefore the contrast in thickness: the increase of throw with depth is a result of this, and is not in itself diagnostic.

Growth faults occur in many — perhaps most, possibly all — sedimentary basins of the world, and in rocks of all ages. Tiddeman's brief description of the Craven Fault in England (Tiddeman 1890) is apparently the first description of a growth fault. This fault affected Lower Carboniferous (Mississippian) sedimentation; and Tiddeman clearly recognized its significance. Dron (1900)

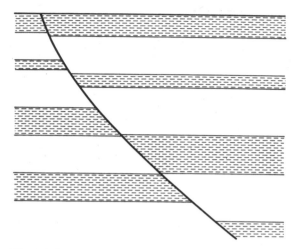

Fig.4-1. Diagrammatic section across a growth fault.

later recognized a similar Lower Carboniferous fault in Scotland. Williams (1962, p.67) figures growth faults that affected Ordovician sedimentation in Scotland. Younger examples, however, are much more common. The reason for this is unlikely to be that the process was more common in the younger sedimentary basins (although this may be partly true), but rather that growth faults are more easily recognized in the subsurface from borehole data than on the surface from outcrop data; and drilling emphasis is on the younger sedimentary basins.

Growth faults are important in the Gulf Coast province of North America and many of the "down-to-the-basin" faults there are growth faults. They are commonly extensive, with a tendency to be curved in plan and to be generally parallel with the basin margins and the depositional strike. They may form *en echelon*. Locally, they may be conjugate, forming graben. They are commonly associated with flexures ("roll-overs" in the jargon) and antithetic faults — both on the downthrown side. In section, the fault surface commonly flattens with depth, but may also be sinuous. They are reported more commonly in post—Eocene beds in the Gulf Coast province, but they also affect Mesozoic and Palaeozoic sediments.

In the Los Angeles basin, post-Cretaceous growth faults have been interpreted as reverse faults (McCulloh, 1960; Shelton 1968). The upthrown blocks were sometimes eroded, while the downthrown blocks accumulated sediment.

By extension of these concepts, the San Andreas and associated faults of California, and the Alpine fault of New Zealand, are growth transcurrent faults that have affected sedimentation (and are still affecting it). However, a transcurrent fault with significant lateral displacement, while clearly having a potential to influence sedimentation over a span of time, is a phenomenon that is peripheral to this discussion.

Emphasis on the Gulf Coast province in the literature should not be interpreted as meaning that growth faults are more common there than elsewhere. They occur in northwest Europe, in the Vienna basin (Janoschek, 1958), in the Po basin of Italy (Rocco and Jaboli, 1958); in Bengal they have been detected by seismic work (Sengupta, 1966), and in Nigeria by seismic and drilling (Short and Stäuble, 1967). Further east, growth faults have been recognized extensively in Borneo, both in the subsurface and on the surface, in sediments of Late Cretaceous and Tertiary ages (Liechti et al., 1960). In South America they occur in the eastern Venezuela basin (Renz et al., 1958). They also occur in Australia (Hosemann, 1971; James and Evans, 1971). Growth faults are associated with growth anticlines, and these occur even more widely than growth faults.

The nature of growth faults

The quality of correlation across a growth fault varies from poor to excellent. This must be seen as a measure of the degree to which the movement of the fault affected sedimentation. Where rock unit correlation across a growth fault is good, the process was clearly one of transport of sediment across a subsiding depositional surface, with a greater potential for sediment accumulation on the more rapidly subsiding downthrown block. The continuity of lithologies implied in good correlation suggests that the supply of sediment generally exceeded the capacity of the area to accumulate is. It is quite clear that deposition of sediment from *suspension* in the water cannot lead to the observed results by itself, because there is no reason why the rate of deposition from suspension should be different across a subsurface feature. Hence bottom transport is essential, *even for the deposition of clays.* The excess if sediment over the local capacity to accumulate it is potentially a *regressive* situation that implies a tendency for facies to migrate seaward.

The concept of a growth fault involves the displacement of unconsolidated sediments. Therefore, at depth, the processes of compaction lead to the deformation of the fault surface. The overall effect is that of reducing the dip of the fault with depth. The observed order of fault-dip reduction is from about 70° to about 40°. In detail, however, the deformation of the fault surface by compaction is complicated. In an alternating sequence of lithologies of variable compactibility, the deformation will be greater across the more compactible beds. Such irregularities due to alternating compactibility could not survive fault movement, and one must visualize a smoothing effect with, perhaps, a zone of disturbance on either side of the fault surface.

Sinuosity in the fault surface in cross-section may lead to "satellite" faults that are synthetic in character — the result of the relief of stresses caused by movement along an uneven surface. These faults will not generally be growth faults, and there will be no thickness contrast across them (but they may become growth faults with further movement).

Since the rate of change of compaction in the more compactible lithologies decreases with depth generally (with the reservations noted in the previous chapter) so the rate of change of dip of a growth fault generally decreases with depth. Normal fault movement along a curved fault surface tends to separate the two blocks at and near the surface. This tendency to separate is thought to be the principal cause of slumping near the fault on the downthrown side, and to cause the larger flexures or "roll-overs", and antithetic faulting, against the growth fault on the downthrown side (Fig.4-2). Differential compaction due to fluid migration through the fault surface also contributes to this (see *Fluid migration,* (p. 93).

No growth fault can show a thickness contrast across it over the entire fault surface in depth because when movement begins,

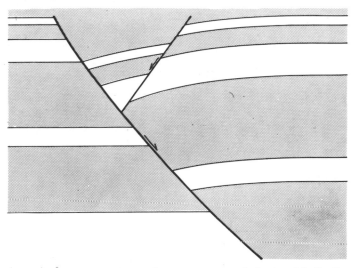

Fig.4-2. Diagrammatic section across growth fault with "roll-over" and anti-thetic fault.

sediments are displaced that have already accumulated and are in the process of compaction. At depth the fault may be absorbed in a thick clay unit, if the stresses induced in the clay unit by the movement do not exceed the limit at which the clay unit fails by fracture.

Once a growth fault has developed and existed during the accumulation of a considerable thickness of sediment, compaction processes alone must tend to perpetuate it to some extent, provided the supply of sediment continues. Nevertheless, growth faults may die out upwards (Fig.4-3). Above that level, there is no fault and no abrupt change of sediment thickness laterally. A growth fault may become reactivated after a period of quiescence, and there is then no thickness contrast across the fault in those sediments that accumulated during the period of quiescence.

Reservoir rocks not only show volumetric contrasts across a growth fault, but commonly also a contrast in porosity and permeability. The slower rate of accumulation on the upthrown side of the fault may lead to better winnowing of the sands there, so that the permeability tends to be higher in the upthrown block. Porosity may also be higher in the upthrown block on account of

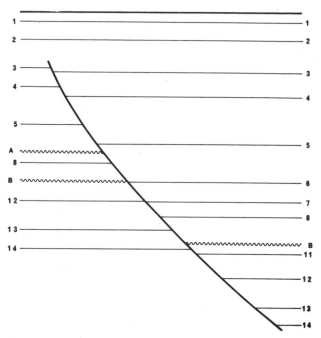

Fig.4-3. Diagrammatic section across complex growth fault. Fault movement began after accumulation of marker 12, and ceased after accumulation of marker 3.

the winnowing out of clay material, but better sorting of the sand reduces its porosity.

The relative activity of a growth fault is assessed by the ratio of the correlative bed thicknesses across the fault. A plot of the ratio of upthrown thickness to downthrown thickness (or downthrown to upthrown), or of the Standard Stratigraphic Sequence to downthrown thickness (see p. 239 and Fig. 4-4), will not only reveal the history of the fault movement against the time scale of accumulated sediment, but also, in areas with more than one growth fault, the relative activity and times of movements of each fault in relation to the others.

It is essential to bear in mind that while stratigraphic continuity in both blocks of a growth fault is common, it is not the only expression of a growth fault. The potential to accumulate sediment is related to the rate of subsidence and the rate of sediment

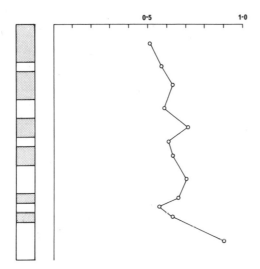

Fig.4-4. Plot of ratio of upthrown to downthrown block thicknesses. The inverse is also commonly used.

supply. Many growth faults indicate quite clearly that *both blocks* were subsiding relative to baselevel, but that one block was sub-siding faster than the other. The stratigraphic sequence in the upthrown block is evidence of this; and this sequence is commonly the sequence of the downthrown block of another growth fault. The evidence of other growth faults indicates intermittent sedi-ment accumulation — sometimes over the whole area, sometimes restricted to accumulation on the downthrown block. It is the relative accumulation of sediment that is diagnostic.

Growth faults have various expressions, ranging from faults where erosion of the upthrown block is contributing sediment to the downthrown block, to faults across which detailed correlation is possible, even within rock units. Far more difficult is the case where intermittent reduction in the rate of subsidence over an area resulted in non-deposition (i.e., non-accumulation) on the up-thrown side, and continued, but reduced accumulation on the downthrown side (Fig.4-3). The difficulty lies in recognizing the breaks in the stratigraphic sequence.

A stratigraphic hiatus* associated with a growth fault may

---

* *Hiatus* plural *hiatus*: pedantry seems preferable to ugliness! Hiatus are breaks in the stratigraphic sequence.

easily be misinterpreted as a fault — a misinterpretation that will be plausible because of the association with a known fault. The misinterpretation of hiatus will introduce a spurious complexity into the geological interpretation that not only confuses the geologist but, in a producing field, confuses also the reservoir engineer and affects reserve estimates and production planning.

The many possible variations on the theme of variable rate of sediment accumulation include a stratigraphic hiatus that has different "values" across the fault. A hiatus is analogous to a rock unit, and may change across the growth fault in the ways a rock unit may change. It may have different numerical values (thickness missing) across the fault while representing identical portions of the stratigraphic sequence; or it may represent a greater proportion of the stratigraphic sequence on the upthrown side than on the downthrown side (Fig.4-3).

The association of growth faults with antithetic and synthetic faults, and stratigraphic hiatus may therefore present problems of interpretation of intimidating complexity. There is no certain way of distinguishing stratigraphic hiatus from faults in boreholes (see Chapter 11). It is essentially a geological problem, the solution of which lies in part in the degree of association between "gaps" in the sequence and their stratigraphic levels. A hint may also be found in those areas where rock units are generally of comparable thicknesses in the same block. Reduction in the rate of sediment accumulation may show as a hiatus in the upthrown block and as thinner beds in the downthrown block at that stratigraphic level.

Reverse growth faults would seem to be unlikely; but most of the difficulties that spring to mind at first are found not to be real difficulties. These apparent difficulties stem from the common misconception (aided by the terminology) that a fault separates a block that has been raised from one that has been lowered. As we have seen, the movement is relative, and both may have been downwards relative to baselevel. Topographical expression of growth faults at the surface is not a necessary consequence of fault movement provided there is an adequate supply of sediment.

The compaction processes would deform the fault "plane" or surface of a reverse growth fault in the same way that they deform the fault surface of a normal growth fault. The dip of the fault surface would decrease with depth. But whereas the opposing blocks of a normal fault tend to be separated at the surface and at shallow depth by the movement of the fault, the movement of a reverse growth fault would tend to force them together, and a horizontal component of compressive stress would be induced in the relatively incompetent shallower beds. These stresses would presumably lead to a zone of disturbance adjacent to the fault.

In general, it is clear that all faulting that takes place at the surface has a potential to influence the deposition of sediment and its accumulation. When related to the development and evolution of a sedimentary basin, such faults may move − intermittently, perhaps − over significant spans of geological time. Fault movement can rarely (if ever) be regarded as an instantaneous event. A fault is one form of adjustment to the forces acting on a rock mass. Instantaneous forces can only be visualized in catastrophic situations. Whether a fault moved during the accumulation of sediment in a sedimentary basin, or subsequently, the movement must have occupied a span of time, and brought rocks of different lithologies together during that time.

It matters to the petroleum geologist when a fault moved, because it may be a significant event in the migration of fluids and the accumulation of petroleum.

Fluid migration

The migration paths of fluids expelled from clays by compaction near growth faults may be very complex because, apart from the normal vertical fluid potential gradients generated by the compaction processes, horizontal fluid potential gradients may be generated across growth faults from compactible to permeable beds (Fig.4-5). Furthermore, these horizontal gradients may change during the development of a growth fault as the beds of the downthrown block are moved progressively deeper across the succession in the upthrown block.

Lateral fluid expulsion from compactible beds near the fault surface to permeable beds across the fault result in the accelerated compaction of the compactible bed near the fault. This process

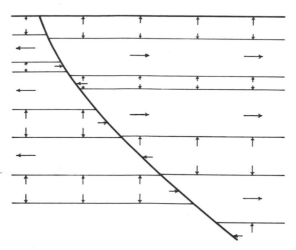

Fig.4-5. Directions of fluid migration around a growth fault (cf. Fig.4-1).

contributes to the deformation of the rocks adjacent to the fault surface, and may contribute to the flexures and "roll-overs".

However, two facts must be born in mind. An alternating sequence of compactible and permeable beds that is being faulted by a growth fault may have a relatively strong regional hydrodynamic field, with fluid migration in the permeable beds towards the marine margins of the physiographic basin. Secondly, the relationship of contrasting lithologies across the fault probably changes along the fault. A permeable bed may intercommunicate with several other permeable beds on the other side of the fault. This is clearly true for faults with a throw that varies along its strike.

Growth anticlines

Growth anticlines are anticlines in which the thicknesses of rock units are greater on the flanks than on the crest (Fig.4-6). Isopach maps over growth anticlines may be viewed as structural contours on the bottom of the isopached interval below the top of the interval as datum plane (see Fig.10-3, p. 222). More than one rock unit may show this feature, and the development of the growth

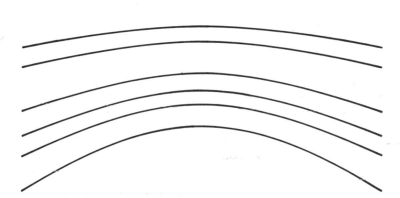

Fig.4-6. Diagrammatic section through a growth anticline.

anticline against the time scale of accumulated sediments may be revealed by cumulative isopaching, in maps and in cross-sections, as shown in Fig.10-5. Growth anticlines are commonly closed, oval or dome-like.

"Drape structure" is not synonymous with "growth anticline". Differential compaction, however, may contribute to growth anticlines by the greater compaction of thicker compactible units on the flanks. It is also possible that the compactible units have been more compacted on the deeper flanks, under the greater sedimentary load. Hence the isopach results may tend to underestimate the growth of the structure as a whole. This growth is perhaps better indicated by the relatively incompactible units.

Growth anticlines presumably have analogous growth synclines; but these are not normal targets for drilling, so little is known of them. Growth monoclines are the essence of a sedimentary basin.

Growth anticlines occur even more widely than growth faults, but this is perhaps not surprising because they are essentially variations in the deposition and accumulation history of a basin. They occur extensively in the Gulf Coast province and most of the larger basins of North America; in Venezuela and other areas of South America; in Europe; in Nigeria; in the Middle East; in the younger basins of Southeast Asia, including Borneo and New

Guinea; and in Australia. They have received little attention in the literature, yet they are commonly figured. Experience suggests that many of the petroleum-bearing anticlines have a "growth" component, and that many were initiated as growth anticlines.

As with growth faults, growth anticlines are best understood in terms of differential subsidence relative to baselevel. The whole area of the growth anticline was subsiding, but the area that was the crest was subsiding more slowly than the flank area. Hence the flank areas had a capacity to accumulate a greater thickness of sediment. Again, one must see the sediment as being transported across the depositional surface, not deposited from suspension, for one cannot postulate such patterns of deposition from suspension.

Growth anticlines range from those that show continuity of rock units across it, with differences confined to thickness (and perhaps permeability and porosity), through those that influenced sedimentation to such a degree that different facies occur in the crestal areas from the flank areas, to those in which rock units may be discontinuous across the crestal area. Reservoirs may therefore vary not only volumetrically, but also in reservoir properties. As with growth faults, these are variations on a theme of differential subsidence.

It is important to bear in mind that the growth of an anticline only affects those sediments that were accumulating during the growth period. This is analogous to the intermittent movement of a growth fault. All sediments accumulated in the area prior to the beginning of growth of the anticline, and all sediments accumulated during periods of quiescence, will show either no thickness variations, or variations that are not related to the structure. (This statement requires two qualifications: it applies to sediments above the agent or cause of growth; and the processes of compaction tend to perpetuate growth anticlines, as they do growth faults.) One must therefore distinguish between the periods of growth on the time scale of accumulated sediment, and the folding of sediments into an anticline subsequently to the accumulation of sediment. The time or times of deformation may be revealed by the younger sediments.

Growth anticlines may be faulted by growth faults that are contemporaneous. The simultaneous deformation of a structure by folding and faulting requires careful analysis. Qualitatively, the deformation of the curved fault surface of a growth fault by contemporaneous growth of the anticline may be important, in that it sets up stresses that may be relieved by further faulting, or by slumping. Quantitatively, such deformation of the fault surface may be insignificant, because it will usually be far finer than the rather coarse control afforded by boreholes.

The deformation of a growth anticline by contemporaneous growth faulting is, of course, significant in terms of the geometry of the anticline and the geometry of the reservoirs. The growth component of faulting may obscure the growth component in the anticline, so that its recognition depends on the recognition of convergence of stratigraphic units towards the crest within fault blocks.

The proper use of isopach maps and sections is essential for the elucidation of even simple growth structures. For instance, the axis of minimum sediment accumulation may change position during the development of a growth anticline. Such shifts of position or changes of shape can rarely be seen in structural maps or sections. These techniques are discussed in Chapter 10.

We cannot leave the subject of growth anticlines without mention of an alternative hypothesis for the thinning of stratigraphic units; that is, mechanical attenuation of the beds due to the enlargement of their area, or stretching, over a growing anticline. Confidence in the sedimentation hypothesis rests largely on the analogy with growth faults, the evidence of which is not consistent with mechanical attenuation of the sediments because of the abrupt changes of thickness across the fault. Mechanical attenuation is not mutually incompatible with sedimentary thinning; and model studies have shown attenuation of layers over a growing diapir. The key to the problem may lie in the thinning of individual beds of similar lithology. If clays, for example, show consistent and greater thinning than sands or limestones, then attenuation may be suspected. On the other hand, if the patterns of thinning are variable and not associated with lithology, sedimentary thinning may be the dominant cause. The problem is complex and the evidence ambiguous.

Fluid migration

Growth anticlines do not generally modify the patterns of primary fluid migration significantly. In a large, symmetrical, unfaulted anticline with a long history of movement during the deposition of alternating compactible/permeable rocks, there will be significant lateral fluid migration through the permeable rocks, with a tendency for this to be radially away from the crestal area in the absence of another hydrodynamic field. This radial tendency, however, will normally be subordinate to the regional hydrodynamic field imposed by the compaction of the sediments of varying lithologies which, as we have seen, will normally be towards the marine margins of the physiographic basin where more permeable lithologies were or are accumulating.

Causes of growth structures

Growth structures are related to the development of a sedimentary basin. Indeed, they make a valuable contribution to the understanding of sediment accumulation. Most sedimentary basins can be regarded as large-scale growth structures, and all have important analogies with growth structures. Growth structures are not, therefore, oddities.

In the Gulf Coast province of North America, growth structures are reported rather more frequently in rocks of post-Eocene age, in the sandier part of the sequence. They appear to be related to the rate of sedimentation and to the nature of the sediment. The growth faults sometimes die out downwards in the thicker clay units. Some growth structures also appear to be associated with salt domes. In Northwest Europe, they occur in sandy sequences and carbonates, and are associated with salt domes. In Venezuela, Nigeria, and Borneo, they occur in sandy sequences, and there is no known association with salt domes. In Australia they occur mainly in sandy sequences, and there is no known association with salt.

As discussed in Chapter 2, one of the persistent problems facing a geologist is that of perceiving cause and effect in associations. In the present problem, the association with more sandy sequences may well result from the fact that these are the potential reservoirs and are therefore penetrated by more boreholes; and that the contrasting lithology is a valuable, if not essential feature for the recognition of growth structures. A growth fault in a clay sequence, or a limestone sequence without interbedded clays or other contrasting lithology, might well not be recognized for lack of definable rock units.

The observed occurrence of growth structures over salt-domes cannot be denied; and all the other associations have a possible – even probable –geological significance. But perhaps the most significant geological association is that between young growth structures and deeper, thick clay sequences with abnormal interstitial fluid pressures – i.e., *regressive sequences.*

Abnormally pressured clays, as we have seen, are mechanically weak, with low equivalent viscosity. They are also less dense than normally pressured, normally compacted clays and may be less dense than some sands. These properties of low equivalent viscosity and low relative density, shared with salt, suggest that diapirism or incipient diapirism is the underlying cause of growth structures.

If this postulate is correct, it follows that the association between growth structures and the type of sediment accumulated is indirect, for the causal relationship is between the sequence of sediment accumulated, its rate of accumulation and diapirism.

Regressive periods during the development of sedimentary basins are significant events in geological history that record the extension of land areas. In marine environments they lead to the accumulation of permeable rocks on thick, relatively impermeable clays. The rate of loading during sand accumulation may be significantly higher than during the accumulation of the clays – both on account of more rapid accumulation and on account of the higher specific weight of sand. Abnormal pressures are generated in the clays to some extent.

The significance of the regressive phase is that mechanical instability, retarded fluid expulsion, potential source rocks and potential reservoir rocks are brought together in space and time. The significance of growth structures is that they form soon after the accumulation of the potential reservoir rocks, and are therefore potential petroleum traps. To understand their significance, we must examine the nature of diapirism.

Selected bibliography

Billings, M.P., 1954. *Structural Geology.* (2nd ed.) Prentice-Hall, New York, N.Y. 514 pp.

Carver, R.E., 1968. Differential compaction as a cause of regional contemporaneous faults. *Bull. Am. Ass. Petrol. Geol.,* 52:414—419.

Cebull, S.E., 1970. Low-angle growth faults in the Eastern Venezuela basin. *Bull. Am. Ass. Petrol. Geol.,* 54:730—734.

Cloos, E., 1968. Experimental analysis of Gulf Coast fracture patterns. *Bull. Am. Ass. Petrol. Geol.,* 52:420—444.

Currie, J.B., 1956. Role of concurrent deposition and deformation of sediments in development of salt-dome graben structures. *Bull. Am. Ass. Petrol. Geol.,* 40:1—16.

Dennis, J.G., 1967. *International Tectonic Dictionary English Terminology. Am. Ass. Petrol. Geol., Mem.,* 7: 196 pp.

Dron, R.W. 1900. The probable duration of the Scottish coalfields. *Trans. Inst. Min. Eng.,* 18:194—212.

Hamblin, W.K., 1965. Origin of "reverse drag" on the downthrown side of normal faults. *Bull. Geol. Soc. Am.,* 76:1145—1164.

Hardin, F.R. and Hardin, G.C., 1961. Contemporaneous normal faults of Gulf Coast and their relation to flexures. *Bull. Am. Ass. Petrol. Geol.,* 45:238—248.

Hosemann, P., 1971. The stratigraphy of the basal Triassic sandstone, north Perth basin, Western Australia. *J. Aust. Petrol. Explor. Ass.,* 11:59—63.

James, E.A. and Evans, P.R., 1971. The stratigraphy of the offshore Gippsland basin. *J. Aust. Petrol. Explor. Ass.,* 11:71—79.

Janoschek, R., 1958. The inner-alpine Vienna basin. In: L.G. Weeks (Editor), *Habitat of Oil.* American Association of Petroleum Geologists, Tulsa, Okla., pp.1134—1152.

Koinm, D.N. and Dickey, P.A., 1967. Growth faulting in McAlester basin of Oklahoma. *Bull. Am. Ass. Petrol. Geol.,* 51:710—718.

Liechti, P., Roe, F.W. and Haile, N.S., 1960. The geology of Sarawak, Brunei and the western part of North Borneo. *Bull. Geol. Surv. Dept. Br. Terr. Borneo,* 3: 360 pp.

McCulloh, T.D., 1960. Gravity variations and the geology of the Los Angeles basin of California. *Prof. Pap. U.S. Geol. Surv.,* 400—B:B320—B325.

Ocamb, R.D., 1961. Growth faults of south Louisiana. *Trans. Gulf-Coast Ass. Geol. Soc.,* 11: 139—175.

Quarles, M., 1953. Salt-ridge hypothesis on the origin of the Texas Gulf-Coast type of faulting. *Bull. Am. Ass. Petrol. Geol.,* 37:489—508.

Renz, H.H., Alberding, H., Dallmus, K.F., Patterson, J.M., Robie, R.H., Weisbord, N.E. and MasVall, J., 1958. The Eastern Venezuela basin. In:

L.G. Weeks (Editor), *Habitat of Oil,* American Association of Petroleum Geologists, Tulsa, Okla., pp.551—600.

Rocco, T. and Jaboli, D., 1958. Geology and hydrocarbons of the Po basin. In: L.G. Weeks (Editor), *Habitat of Oil.* American Association of Petroleum Geologists, Tulsa, Okla., pp.1153—1167.

Sengupta, Supriya, 1966. Geological and geophysical studies in western part of the Bengal basin, India. *Bull. Am. Ass. Petrol. Geol.,* 50:1001—1017.

Shelton, J.W., 1968. Role of contemporaneous faulting during basinal subsidence. *Bull. Am. Ass. Petrol. Geol.,* 52:399—413.

Short, K.C. and Stäuble, A.J., 1967. Outline of geology of Niger delta. *Bull. Am. Ass. Petrol. Geol.,* 51:761—779.

Stanley, T.B., 1970. Vicksburg fault zone, Texas. In: M.T. Halbouty (Editor), *Geology of Giant Petroleum Fields. Am. Ass. Petrol. Geol., Mem.,* 14:301—308.

Thorsen, C.E., 1963. Age of growth faulting in southeast Louisiana. *Trans. Gulf-Coast Ass. Geol. Soc.,* 13:103—110.

Tiddeman, R.H., 1890. On concurrent faulting and deposit in Carboniferous times in Craven, Yorkshire, with a note on Carboniferous reefs. *Rept. Br. Ass. Advan. Sci.,* 1889, pp.600—603.

Walters, J.E., 1959. Effect of structural movement on sedimentation in the Pheasant-Francitas area, Matagorda and Jackson counties, Texas. *Trans. Gulf-Coast Ass. Geol. Soc.,* 9:51—58.

Weber, K.J., 1971. Sedimentological aspects of oil fields in the Niger delta. *Geol. Mijnb.,* 50:559—576.

Williams, A., 1962. The Barr and Lower Ardmillan series (Caradoc) of the Girvan district, southwest Ayrshire, with descriptions of the Brachiopoda. *Mem. Geol. Soc. Lond.,* 3:267 pp.

Chapter 5. DIAPIRS AND DIAPIRISM

Summary

(1) Diapirs, in the context of petroleum geology, are intrusions of sedimentary material, primarily salt and clay, into the overlying sedimentary sequence. The deformation of the sediments around and above a diapir creates potential petroleum traps.

(2) Diapirs are initiated by unequal loading of a layer of material of relatively high plasticity (low equivalent viscosity). The common diapiric materials — salt and abnormally pressured clay — may be less dense than normally compacted sediments overlying them. Hence, once a diapir is initiated (particularly a salt diapir), the forces of buoyancy tend to elongate the deformation vertically.

(3) The upward movement of a diapir is relative to the surrounding sediments. The accumulation of a sedimentary sequence over a diapir indicates that it is subsiding with the development of a sedimentary basin. It is only an absolute upward movement if the relative movement is faster than the subsidence of the surrounding sediments.

(4) The differential subsidence between a diapir and its surrounding area creates a potential for growth structures, which contributes further to the variations of loading on the diapiric mother bed.

(5) The elastico-viscous, or rheid properties of the diapiric material change with time and position. Salt becomes less viscous with increasing temperature. Clay becomes less viscous with increasing values of λ, the ratio of fluid pressure to overburden pressure.

(6) A diapir commonly, but not invariably, shows a gravity minimum. This indicates a deficiency of mass.

(7) Elastic failure of the overburden by faulting may accom-

pany diapiric development; but diapiric development may also inhibit subsidence locally at the depositional surface, and so lead to local stratigraphic hiatus.

(8) Clay diapirism is necessarily contemporaneous with the expulsion of fluids from the clay by compaction. It is therefore of particular significance in petroleum geology.

Diapirs

Diapirs are essentially intrusions of deeper material into the overlying material of the earth's crust. The processes of diapirism are dynamic, and lead to structures that range from minor displacements of plastic material to major intrusions of large volumes of material through considerable thicknesses of overlying rocks (Fig.5-1). For clarity, the stages of diapirism that precede penetration may be referred to as *incipient* diapirism (incipient diapirs). In plan, diapirs tend to acquire a more or less circular outline; in section, the amplitude may achieve dimensions of thousands of metres. The scale of diapiric and incipient diapiric structures ranges from centimetres (e.g., load casts) to kilometres. They commonly occur in groups, or in lines, or in lines of groups. They may be intimately associated with folding and faulting. They

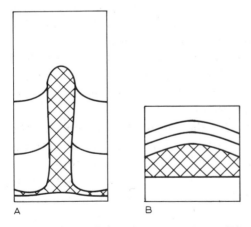

Fig.5-1. Diapir (A) and incipient diapir (B).

demonstrate that certain rock materials under stress will flow as a quasi-fluid or a viscous solid. The materials of diapirs include ice, peat, evaporites (especially salt), clays, marls, occasionally sands, and some igneous rocks.

Confining our attention to diapirs of sedimentary rock material, we find them only in sedimentary basins, in rocks of most geological ages from Proterozoic to Holocene (Recent), and in all continents except Antarctica (so far). They are common in the petroleum provinces of the Gulf Coast of the United States and offshore in the Gulf of Mexico, the Middle East, the Caucasus and adjoining regions to the north of the Caspian Sea, and northwest Europe (Braunstein and O'Brien, 1968). They may be equally common in non-petroleum provinces that have not received the same intensity of geological and geophysical investigation. Current research indicates salt diapirism in sedimentary sequences off the continental shelf of west Africa, with water depths to 4,000 m (13,000 ft.) (Beck, 1972).

Diapirs commonly (but not invariably) occupy areas of gravity minima. A local gravity minimum over a diapir indicates a deficency of mass despite the intrusion of deeper material to shallower depths.

Salt diapirs

Salt diapirs occur under large areas of the Gulf Coast province of North America, northwest Europe, Russia, and around the Arabian or Persian Gulf. The expression of these is very varied; some have reached the surface, or are at very shallow depth. Salt diapirs may form the cores of diapiric anticlines, or take the self-explanatory shape of salt *pillows.* More pronounced forms are known as salt *domes, plugs,* or *stocks.*

The mining of salt domes near the surface has shown that the salt is intensively deformed, with complicated flow patterns (rather than folds) but very rare faults. The external form, however, tends to be more regular. Many salt domes, particularly those at shallow depth, have developed a cap rock, which consists mainly of anhydrite or gypsum. The cap rock is the less soluble residue from leaching of the salt by circulating groundwater. Salt

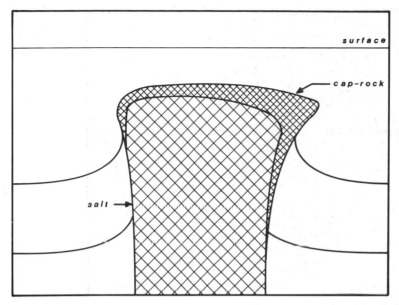

Fig.5-2. Diagrammatic section across well-developed salt diapir. (After various authors.)

domes may be sheathed in a thin layer of anhydrite or clay "gouge". The cap rock sometimes contains sulphur in commercial quantities; and the sulphur is associated, probably biogenically, with oil-bearing diapiric structures.

While a salt-dome is usually roughly circular in plan, the cap rock commonly extends laterally over a wider area than that occupied by the main part of the dome. The main part of the dome may be more or less cylindrical, or narrowing downwards towards the mother layer of salt from which the dome was supplied. Characteristically, the upper surface of the mother layer is deformed near the salt-dome into a *rim syncline,* rim sink, or peripheral sink. A well-developed salt dome may therefore have a profile as depicted in Fig.5-5-2.

Structurally, salt domes are important for two reasons. First, the deformation of the overlying sediments and the sediments through which the dome has penetrated may lead to petroleum accumulations trapped either by the anticlinal form or by truncation of a reservoir by the relatively impermeable salt. Such accu-

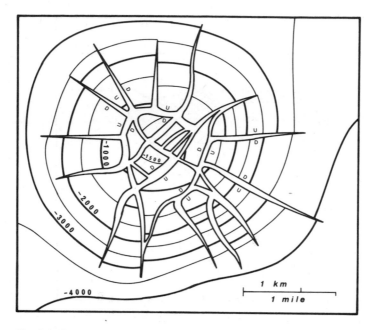

Fig.5-3. Stratum contour map on Wilcox sand, just above salt of Clay Creek dome, Texas. Contours in feet. Contour interval, 500 ft. (150 m approximately). (After T.J. Parker and A.N. McDowell, 1953, *Bull. Am. Ass. Petrol. Geol.*, 35, p.2085, fig.8.)

mulations may also be affected by faulting that resulted from the deformation. Secondly, three or more salt domes in a group may form an anticlinal trap by virtue of their rim synclines. The structure of the sediments over and around a salt dome is usually extremely complex. Strata tend to be variably inclined, and faulted with predominantly radial faults that die out away from the dome (Fig.5-3). There is no means of knowing whether lateral continuity of particular rock units existed prior to their penetration by the salt; but local hiatus are common in strata overlying domes, and they are commonly associated with growth features discussed in the preceding chapter.

Some salt diapirs in the Gulf Coast province of North America are also intimately associated with clay diapirs, both as a single structure and as separate structures.

Clay diapirs

Clay does not seem to develop into such clearly defined diapirs as salt. The expressions of clay diapirism are typically two: diapiric cores to anticlines, and mud-volcanoes. Anticlinal clay diapirs occur very widely — usually as incipient diapirs, without penetration — and one suspects that many more would be recognized of the lithology were as distinctive as salt. Clay diapirs known at the surface are perhaps about as numerous as salt diapirs at the surface. In depth, however, demonstrable clay diapirs are relatively rare.

The younger clay diapirs in the subsurface characteristically contain interstitial fluids at abnormal pressures. These are contained in a "sheath" or gouge of compacted shale, in a manner analogous to the abnormally pressured clay units discussed in Chapter 3. Dips measured in boreholes are commonly regular but steep in diapiric clay. The physical properties of diapiric clay are those associated with other abnormally pressured clays — high porosity and low bulk density *relative to normally compacted clays,* low mechanical strength and low equivalent viscosity. These properties suggest that the mother layer is an abnormally pressured clay unit with retarded compaction; that is, a gravity loaded rather than a tectonically loaded clay.

Mud-volcanoes occur commonly in younger sedimentary basins around the world. They are reported from Trinidad and northern South America, the Gulf Coast province of North America, Asia Minor, West Pakistan, Burma, Indonesia, Borneo, New Guinea, and New Zealand. The principle of uniformitarianism requires us to postulate that they also occurred in older sedimentary basins; but subsequent geologic events have obscured them.

Salt water is the main fluid in mud-volcanoes, but gas (mainly methane or carbon dioxide) and petroleum also occur. The fluid is usually warm, and the activity intermittent. Where the heat can be attributed to the elevation of material from a deeper point on the geothermal gradient, some indication of the depth of "origin" can be obtained. The evidence of boreholes is that the geothermal gradient is rather higher in abnormally pressured clays than in other sedimentary rocks. The fluid is clearly the fluid of expulsion

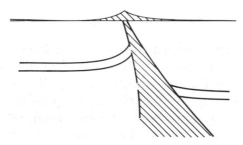

Fig.5-4. Mud volcanism and clay diapirism associated with a fault (diagrammatic).

from the clay; and the intermittent activity is probably to be related to the rupturing of compacting layers of clay and their subsequent sealing by further compaction.

Most mud-volcanoes can be considered as clay diapirs at the surface, and activity will continue until the fluid is expelled. The bedding of the clay is commonly largely destroyed, and rock material may be included that has demonstrably been brought from another formation at depth. Some mud-volcanoes have apparently resulted from clay intrusion up a fault plane — but it is not easy to determine the causal relationship (Fig.5-4). It seems likely that the diapirism caused the fault in many cases.

Generalizations

Diapirs, of whatever sedimentary material, are characteristically overlain by a sequence of sediments that is, of course, younger than the material of the diapir. The accumulation of sediments must be taken as clear evidence that the depositional surface over the diapir was *subsiding* during periods of sediment accumulation. If the growth of a diapir is reasonably accurately represented by Fig.5-5, which is consistent with the geological observations reported in an extensive literature, the rocks now penetrated by the diapir were once continuous across it, like those that have not yet been penetrated. If the growth of a diapir is regarded as accelerating, there may come a time when there is absolute upward movement at a sufficient rate to inhibit sediment accumulation over it, and stratigraphic continuity will be broken. This is essen-

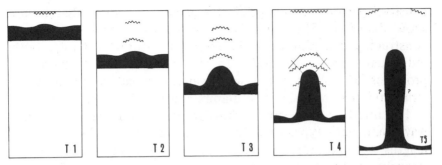

Fig.5-5. Growth of a salt diapir from a subsiding mother layer, with time. The question marks at *T5* denote the writer's uncertainty about the development of deformation from *T4* to *T5*.

tially the concept of "downbuilding" proposed by Barton (1933).

Diapirism is a process that takes place under gravity during the accumulation of sediment in a sedimentary basin. Its significance for the petroleum geologist is that it is a process that deforms sedimentary rocks while they are compacting, during fluid expulsion from the more compactible lithologies. Clay diapirism is probably the more significant, for the clay may itself be a source rock of petroleum, and clay diapirism is essentially contemporaneous with fluid expulsion from the clay.

Diapirism

Diapirism, like many geological processes, is not easily reduced to simple statements of cause and effect. There is, however, general agreement on the main factors that contribute to diapirism — even if there is disagreement on the relative importance of each.

The main factors are: (a) low equivalent viscosity in the material that contributes to, and forms, the diapir; (b) the load on the mother layer, and the variations of the load in space and time; (c) the bulk density of the diapiric material relative to that of the overburden; and (d) the thickness of the mother layer — but this is perhaps more a matter of scale.

None of these factors by itself necessarily leads to diapirism. Not all salt layers feed diapirs, for example; and there are many density inversions with depth in the geological column that do not show diapirism. Physical and mathematical models have been constructed that reproduce the essential features of diapirs, both individually and collectively. In the physical models there are problems of scaling; but a wide variety of substances leads to structures that resemble real diapirs and incipient diapirs closely.

The interface between overburden and mother layer becomes wavy, and both types of models have suggested that some wavelengths become more strongly amplified than others. The more strongly amplified wavelength, which Biot and Odé (1965) called the dominant wavelength, is affected by the viscosity ratio and the thickness ratio of the overburden and mother layer. Overburdens of higher viscosity tend to be deformed with a longer dominant wavelength, and the rate of diapiric growth is slower. As the thickness ratio is increased, Biot and Odé found that the rate of growth was significant for ratios with values of 1—5 (overburden/ mother layer) and that the dominant wavelength was about 10— 20 times the thickness of the mother layer. The relative density contrast affects the rate of development, but not the dominant wavelength.

Most physical models have to be started artificially; and mathematical models must assume an initial deformation of the interface between the mother layer and the overburden. But this need not detain us, because rock units in a sedimentary sequence must not be regarded as a Dickensian geological cake, and the interfaces between rock units are rarely if ever horizontal planes. Furthermore, diapirism is a dynamic process that takes place during the sedimentary evolution of a sedimentary basin, and this is a factor that cannot easily be incorporated into models. Both physical and mathematical models lead to results consistent with each other and with nature.

Consider a vessel (Fig.5-6) in which a liquid is overlain and contained by two identical, frictionless pistons. The interface between the pistons and the liquid is a plane because the vertical forces acting through each piston are equal. If one piston is now loaded with a weight W and the other with a weight $2W$ (merely a device to remind one that in nature a whole area may be loaded, but unequally) the more heavily loaded piston will sink relative to

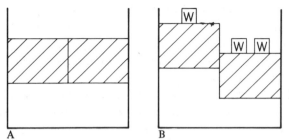

Fig.5-6. Simple model of diapirism.

the less loaded piston, displacing a weight W of liquid to the volume under the less loaded piston (Fig.5-6B).

If this is a valid, though simple model of diapiric process with a relatively rigid overburden, low equivalent viscosity and unequal loading are the two essential factors in *incipient* diapirism. The density of the liquid relative to that of the pistons is irrelevant.

However, it so happens that the common materials with low equivalent viscosity — particularly salt, and, under certain circumstances, abnormally pressured clay — are also less dense than the average overburden.

The mean density of the overburden has been assumed to be 2.3 g/cm^3 for a specific weight of 0.23 kg/cm^2 per metre (1 psi/ ft.), and this is a useful figure for general purposes. In detail, however, overburden density depends on lithology and porosity. Table 3-I (p. 51) lists porosities of clean quartz sands and the equivalent bulk wet densities and specific weights; and from this it is seen that the assumed mean bulk wet density corresponds to that of a quartz sand with a porosity of about 22%. There are difficulties in using clay compaction curves to represent overburden densities, both because clays may not achieve compaction equilibrium by the time diapirism begins, and because clay is rarely the dominant lithology. A thick clay may load a salt layer: but clay loading is largely meaningless in the context of clay diapirism. It must also be remembered that curves such as Athy's and Dickinson's (Fig.3-3) are almost certainly not valid for a very thick clay sequence at the time of diapirism for in practice such curves are constructed from clay density measurements as they occur in a sequence that includes other lithologies, and the curve is interpolated over the sand intervals. Indeed, Dickinson's curve is based on clays in a sedimentary column that consists mainly of sands. Dickinson (1953) appreciated this and showed that the error in taking clay compaction curve data for estimating over-burden *pressure* is negligible.

However, we wish to examine the matter of relative densities in diapirism; and to do this, the model chosen is that of a regressive sequence of sediments in which the permeable facies loads the compactible, or a sequence in which clastic sediments load salt. We therefore retain the figures of ρ_{bw} = 2.3 g/cm^3, γ_{bw} = 0.23 kg/cm^2 per m (1 psi/ft.) realizing that this may be on the high side in many areas.

Salt has a bulk density of about 2.2 g/cm^3 for a specific weight of 0.22 kg/cm^2 per m (0.95 psi/ft.), and this is relatively insen-sitive to depth. Salt is therefore less dense than a quartz sand overburden with a mean porosity of 28% or less. Salt loaded by clay is a matter to which we shall return when clay bulk densities have been discussed.

Clay has a variable bulk density, as we have seen, that depends on both depth and interstitial fluid pressure. It is therefore more useful to think of clay bulk densities in terms of z_e, the equilib-rium depth. Taking Athy's curve (Fig.3-3), as representing the equilibrium state of clay compaction, the bulk wet density of clay reaches 2.3 g/cm^3 when z_e is about 550 m (1,800 ft.). Assuming the minimum value of δ to be 0.2, density inversion with an overburden of 2.3 g/cm^3 can exist down to real depths of about 2,750 m (9,000 ft.). Thereafter, the clay is more dense than the overburden. If, on the other hand, Dickinson's curve is more realis-tic than Athy's during the period of diapirism, then the clay reaches a bulk density of 2.3 g/cm^3 when z'_e is about 2,000 m (6,500 ft.), and a density inversion may exist to a real depth of about 10,000 m (33,000 ft.). *Salt* loaded by clay has no density inversion until z_e is equal to about 400 m (1,300 ft.) from Athy's curve, or 1,100 m (3,600 ft.) from Dickinson's. The real depths of inversion (clay or salt) may therefore be down to 2,000–5,500 m (6,600–18,000 ft.) but the deeper part of the range is unrealistic in terms of clay thickness.

A density inversion may therefore exist in both clay and salt sequences over the common depths of petroleum accumulations, regarded by Weeks (1958, p.22) as between 750 and 2,750 m (2,500–9,000 ft.). It should be noted in passing that while the overburden/salt interface is well defined, the overburden/clay interface in a mechanical sense is less well defined, for as a clay compacts from the lithological boundary, the mechanical boundary also moves down.

The vertical forces acting on an incipient diapir by virtue of the differing specific weights of the diapiric and overburden material are of the form

$$S' = (\gamma_{\text{diapir}} - \gamma_{\text{overburden}})h \qquad\qquad (5\text{-}1)$$

where S' is the vertical component of stress in the diapir, γ the mean specific weights, and h the mean height of the incipient diapir measured, of course in units consistent with those of the specific weights. If the specific weight of the diapir is greater than that of the overburden, the vertical component of stress in the diapir is compressive, opposing the transfer of material from the mother layer into the diapir. In this case, equilibrium under an unequal load can be restored by the transfer of material from the more heavily loaded to the less heavily loaded area. If the specific weight of the diapiric material is less than that of the overburden, the vertical component of stress in the diapir is tensional, tending to draw out the diapir in the vertical dimension. In this case, the diapir is mechanically unstable because the tensional stress tends to increase the vertical dimension, h, which in turn increases the tensional stress in the diapir.

The *effect* of these forces depends on the size of the forces and their time-rate of application, and on the mechanical properties of the rocks containing the forces.

The concept of rock deformation by quasi-plastic processes is familiar to all geologists. It is evident in folded strata, and in many common materials. Pitch, for example, behaves as an elastic (brittle) solid when struck with a hammer, but will deform in a plastic manner, as a viscous solid, when subjected to lesser deformational forces over a longer time. These properties, which are inferred for all natural materials in some degree, were embodied by Carey (1954) into the concept of *rheidity,* which he defined as the ratio of viscosity (a measure of resistance to viscous flow − dyne-second per cm^2, or Nsm^{-2}) to rigidity (a measure of resistance to elastic deformation − dyne per cm^2, or Nm^{-2}) multiplied by an arbitrary factor of 1,000. This ratio has the dimension of time (sec). The rheidity of a given material decreases with increasing temperature. While too little is known of the physical properties of salt and clay in the subsurface to use the concept of rheidity quantitatively, the concept is nevertheless useful in emphasizing the dimension of time in the deformation of rocks.

In the matter of diapirism, the development of a diapir is influenced by the rheidity of the overburden as well as that of the diapiric material − the rheidity of the overburden being longer than that of the diapiric material. Time is necessary for the stresses induced in the diapir to deform the overburden. Hence the development of a diapir is likely to be out of phase, as it were, in the dynamic situation of burial and loading of the mother layer and the diapir (or incipient diapir) that prevails during the development of a diapir. Penetration of the overburden occurs when the time-rate of application of force exceed the rheid "capacity" of the overburden.

It seems reasonable to conclude that the development of a diapir is an accelerating process when the bulk wet density of the diapiric material is less than that of the overburden; that the rate of extension of the dimension of height above the mother layer increases as the diapir grows, until, perhaps, the overburden deforms elastically under the stress, and penetration occurs.

The qualitative aspect of unequal *loading* need not detain us, for it is hard to visualize a situation in a developing sedimentary basin that would lead to equal loading. There are, however, some pertinent geological aspects.

Consider a simple sedimentary basin that is accumulating littoral and inner neritic sands in one part, and outer neritic clays in the adjacent areas (such as is occurring today on the U.S. Gulf Coast and around the Niger delta). The distribution of the sands is controlled largely by sea currents; but the sediments commonly form rather well-defined zones related to the source of the sediments, the currents, and the energy of the environment generally. The rate of loading of the sediments depends both on the rate of supply and the rate of subsidence. During a regressive phase, the area of sand accumulation tends to move out over the area of clay accumulation, and, as has been discussed earlier, the combined effect of increased rate of loading and loading by permeable material is significant in the compaction of the clay in initiating compaction from the top of the clay. The area in which regressive permeable lithologies overlie clay is therefore an obvious area of unequal loading that can also lead to abnormal interstitial fluid pressures in the clay. It is thus also an area of mechanical instability. A subsequent transgressive phase does not rectify this inequality of loading — indeed, it will probably increase it.

This situation has also been reproduced in Ramberg's model experiments, which showed a preferential zone of diapirism along the margin of a discontinuous load (Ramberg, 1967). When the dimension of time is introduced into this phenomenon, a depositional regressive phase is seen to have the potential to induce diapirism at the margin of the permeable regressive sediments; but as the regression proceeds, incipient diapirs tend to be left behind and loaded more heavily. Thus the intensity of diapirism tends to decrease in the direction of regression. This feature is relevant to folding of regressive sequences that decreases in intensity away from the land area — as in the northwestern basin of Borneo (Schaub and Jackson, 1958, p.1335).

Flow of diapiric material

Throughout the discussion so far, the term "equivalent viscosity" has been used. This conventional qualification arises because "viscosity" (unqualified) refers to Newtonian viscosity in which the velocity of flow at a point is proportional to its distance from the static boundary of the fluid, and this is not known to be a characteristic of flow in rocks.

Carey (1954) argued that the conventional classification of matter into fluids and solids has a dividing line that shifts towards the solid side as the dimension of time increases, so that forces acting on a material for a short time may produce results that indicate that the material is a solid, while lesser forces acting on the same material for a longer time produce results that indicate that the material is a fluid.

The dynamic forces in the sedimentary column may act for periods of time greatly in excess of the rheidity of the materials. These materials may then be regarded, both generally and mathematically, as fluids. This concept is implicit in the scaling of physical models (Hubbert, 1937), for viscosity has a dimension of time. Properly scaled model materials resemble fluids much more than the geological materials they represent.

The formation of a diapir involves the displacement of diapiric material from the mother layer to the diapir under dynamic forces acting over long spans of time. The flow lines in the mother layer around a well-developed diapir are centripetal, and the material moves down an energy gradient analogous to the fluid potential gradient around a producing water well. If the mother layer is horizontal, the pressure in the mother layer adjacent to the diapir is less than that further away — for this is a necessary condition of flow.

The peripheral sink, or rim syncline, around a diapir is therefore to be regarded as an expression of the potential energy of the mother layer analogous to the drawdown of the water table around a producing water well (Ramberg, 1967). This sink is terminated on the inside by the upward drag of the diapir. This is clear for a well-developed diapir.

In stages of incipient diapirism, unequal loading of a potential mother layer (with low equivalent viscosity) creates a disequilibrium that may be restored by flowage from the more heavily loaded areas to the less heavily loaded areas. With clay diapirism in mind, this is generally away from the marine depositional margin of the physiographic basin. Locally, however, differences will exist, some of which will be minor, others more important. Since subsidence may locally increase the potential to accumulate sediments, a further inequality of loading may follow consequentially on initial inequality.

Conclusions

Salt diapirism under the gravitational load of overlying sediments deforms those sediments. In general, this occurs during compaction of these sediments (at least in part), and is thus contemporaneous with fluid expulsion from them. The deformation creates traps for any petroleum generated and expelled from a source rock; and ultimately, such accumulations may be displaced to the flanks of a salt diapir when penetration of the overburden takes place. Since the salt itself has no known causal association with petroleum, petroleum accumulation due to salt diapirism must be regarded as a coincidence in which the deformation of potential reservoir rocks happens to take place near source beds during their compaction.

Clay diapirism, both from an observational and a theoretical point of view, is a process that can begin soon after loading by burial under a permeable sequence of sediments. Mud-volcamism in general is clay diapirism that expresses itself at the surface; incipient clay diapirism at depth is inferred in many areas of the world. The apparent rarity of penetrative clay diapirs at depth (but see Gilreath, 1968) and their occurrence at shallow depths is consistent with relative density considerations, for the density inversion between clays and sands is greatest above equilibrium depths of about 500 m (about 1,500 ft.). The instability of clay under load may remain until the clay is buried to depths greater than those at which petroleum is commonly found. Such instability, and the structures resulting from it, are necessarily contemporaneous with the expulsion of the bulk of the interstitial fluids of a clay. In the geological context, such loading occurs typically during regressive phases of the development of a sedimentary basin, when thick clays or marls are loaded by a prograding permeable sequence of sediments. In the petroleum context, this instability is necessarily contemporaneous with the diagenesis of organic matter in clay source rocks. Hence, if the clay is whollyor partly a source rock, diapiric structures are formed contemporaneously with petroleum generation and its primary migration from the source rock, and petroleum may accumulate at a point lower on the fluid potential gradient between the clay and the surface. The association between growth structures, clay diapirism, and petroleum accumulations is therefore inferred to be a close one, of major significance in the geology of petroleum.

Selected bibliography

Arrhenius, Sv., 1912. Zur Physik der Salzlagerstätten. *Medd. K. Vetenskapsakad. Nobelinst.*, 2 (20):7–25.

Athy, L.F., 1930. Density, porosity, and compaction of sedimentary rocks. *Bull. Am. Ass. Petrol. Geol.*, 14:1–24.

Barton, D.C., 1933. Mechanics of formation of salt domes with special reference to Gulf Coast salt domes of Texas and Louisiana. *Bull. Am. Ass. Petrol. Geol.*, 17:1025–1083.

Beck, R.H., 1972. The oceans, the new frontier in exploration. *J. Aust. Petrol. Explor. Ass.*, 12 (2):7–28.

Biot, M.A. and Odé, H., 1965. Theory of gravity instability with variable overburden and compaction. *Geophysics*, 30:213–227.

Bornhauser, M., 1969. Geology of Day dome (Madison Country, Texas) – a study of salt emplacement. *Bull. Am. Ass. Petrol. Geol.*, 53:1411–1420.

Braunstein, J. and O'Brien, G.D. (Editors), 1968. *Diapirism and Diapirs. Am. Ass. Petrol. Geol., Mem.*, 8:444 pp. (All the papers are worth reading.)

Carey, S.W., 1954. The rheid concept in geotectonics. *J. Geol. Soc. Aust., 1* (for 1953):67–117.

Dickinson, G., 1953. Geological aspects of abnormal reservoir pressures in Gulf Coast Louisiana. *Bull. Am. Ass. Petrol. Geol.*, 37:410–432.

Gilreath, J.A., 1968. Electric-log characteristics of diapiric shale. In: J. Braunstein and G.D. O'Brien (Editors), *Diapirism and Diapirs. Am. Ass. Petrol. Geol., Mem.*, 8:137–144.

Hubbert, M.K., 1937. Theory of scale models as applied to the study of geologic structures. *Bull. Geol. Soc. Am.*, 48:1459–1520.

Kerr, P.F. and Kopp, O.C., 1958. Salt-dome breccia. *Bull. Am. Ass. Petrol. Geol.*, 42:548–560.

Kerr, P.F., Drew, I.M. and Richardson, D.S., 1970. Mud volcano clay, Trinidad, West Indies. *Bull. Am. Ass. Petrol. Geol.*, 54:2101–2110.

Lehner, P., 1969. Salt tectonics and Pleistocene stratigraphy on continental slope of northern Gulf of Mexico. *Bull. Am. Ass. Petrol. Geol.*, 53:2431–2479.

Murray, G.E., 1968. Salt structures of Gulf of Mexico basin – a review. In: J. Braunstein and G.D. O'Brien (Editors), *Diapirism and Diapirs. Am. Ass. Petrol. Geol., Mem.*, 8:99–121.

Nettleton, L.L., 1934. Fluid mechanics of salt domes. *Bull. Am. Ass. Petrol. Geol.*, 18:1175–1204.

Nettleton, L.L., 1955. History of concepts of Gulf Coast salt-dome formation. *Bull. Am. Ass. Petrol. Geol.*, 39:2373–2383.

Omara, S., 1964. Diapiric structures in Egypt and Syria. *Bull. Am. Ass. Petrol. Geol.*, 48:1116–1125.

Parker, T.J. and McDowell, A.N., 1955. Model studies of salt-dome tectonics. *Bull. Am. Ass. Petrol. Geol.*, 39:2384–2470.

Ramberg, H., 1967. *Gravity, Deformation and the Earth's Crust as Studied by Centrifuged Models.* Academic Press, London, New York, 214 pp.

Roach, C.B., 1962. Intrusive shale dome in South Thornwell field, Jefferson

Davis and Cameron Parishes, Louisiana. *Bull. Am. Ass. Petrol. Geol.*, 46:2121–2132.

Schaub, H.P. and Jackson, A., 1958. The northwestern oil basin of Borneo. In: L.G. Weeks (Editor), *Habitat of Oil*. American Association of Petroleum Geologists, Tulsa, Okla., pp.1330–1336.

Selig, F., 1965. A theoretical prediction of salt dome patterns. *Geophysics*, 30:633–643.

Trusheim, F., 1957. Über Halokinese und ihre Bedeutung für die strukturelle Entwicklung Norddeutschlands. *Z. Dtsch. Geol. Ges.*, 109:111–158.

Weeks, L.G., 1958. Habitat of oil and some factors that control it. In: L.G. Weeks (Editor), *Habitat of Oil*. American Association of Petroleum Geologists, Tulsa, Okla., pp.1–61.

Chapter 6. THE GENERATION AND MIGRATION OF PETROLEUM

Summary

(1) Petroleum is primarily a product of the diagenesis of fundamental organic compounds contained in organic matter accumulated with sediment under anaerobic conditions in a low-energy environment.

(2) The diagenesis takes place during burial under the influence of heat and pressure — probably in the presence of clay catalysts.

(3) Clays are important source rocks of petroleum, but not all clays are source rocks. Thicker clays (say, more than about 50 m) are more important than thinner clays because: (a) mean fluid expulsion from thicker clays is retarded; and (b) larger quantities of fluid are retained under higher temperatures and much higher pressures for a longer time.

(4) It is not known whether petroleum migrates in aqueous solution or as a separate phase in water. It is probably taken into solution initially, transferred to the outer layers of the clay unit with the pore water where, under the influence of decreasing pressure, and/or a catalyst, it is released from solution (at least in part) and accumulates.

(5) It is then probably expelled from the clay to permeable rocks as a slug by capillary force, aided by the fluid potential gradient.

(6) Petroleum migrates through permeable rocks under the influences of gravity and the hydrodynamic field until it can migrate no further and accumulates in a trap or disperses at the surface.

(7) In regressive sequences reservoirs tend to overlie the source rock: in transgressive sequences, they tend to underlie the source rock. Migration paths through regressive sequences are probably

short; those after expulsion from transgressive source rocks may be long.

(8) Variations in the composition of petroleum in accumulations is probably to be attributed more to the temperature-pressure conditions during burial, during expulsion from the source rock, and during its subsequent history, rather than to the nature of the original organic matter. Nevertheless, it has been suggested that some broad distinctions, particularly that of wax content, may be attributable to the nature of the organic matter.

Origin of oil

The evidence of petroleum generation and migration lies mainly in the two fields of geology and chemistry. The geological evidence, which is the more fundamental, is largely circumstantial. The chemical evidence involves considerations that are beyond the capacity of many geologists (including the present writer) to appreciate fully — and it seems reasonable to suppose that those who understand the chemical aspects fully may not understand the geological. The problem remains, however, a geological one fundamentally.

Empirically we note that hydrocarbons are common in the solar system. Hence we cannot rule out a primeval origin in the subcrustal evolution of the earth as a planet. Nevertheless, petroleum is strongly associated with sedimentary rocks, and most known occurrences in igneous rocks can be ascribed to nearby sedimentary rocks. The geological evidence is strong that the origin of petroleum lies in the biosphere, and in the very upper layers of the lithosphere. From this point on, the evidence is not always clear — which accounts for the fact that after nearly 100 years of study, a completely satisfying integrated theory of petroleum generation and migration has not yet been achieved. Hydrocarbons are common in the biosphere; but chemists tell us that they are not like the hydrocarbons of petroleum. Petroleum-like hydrocarbons are only found in the subsurface — or on the surface as a result of migration from the subsurface in the form of seeps, or contained in rocks now exposed at the surface.

The circumstantial evidence that clay rocks and marls are the site of the original material of most petroleum is overwhelming. All the great petroleum provinces of the world are intimately associated with clays or marls. Some of these accumulations are apparently *entirely* enveloped in clays; and in some of these, the quantity of petroleum accumulated is irreconcilable with an origin in the reservoir rock itself because the petroleum occupies almost all the available pore space. Permeable and porous sediments rarely contain measurable quantities of hydrocarbons near the surface: but most clays do, and the deeper clays often contain petroleum-like hydrocarbons (although they may still differ in some respect from those of accumulated petroleum).

The chemical evidence is strong that petroleum has an organic origin. Both geological and chemical evidence points to animal and vegetable organic matter accumulated in clays or fine grained carbonate rocks as being the principal source material for petroleum in general. However, the rather surprising fact is that while petroleums differ in their composition from place to place, there is no obvious relationship between the composition of petroleum and the age of the rocks in which they are found. In other words, the significant changes in the life forms on earth during the last 600 million years or so have not led to significant differences in the composition of petroleum through time. This, and analytical evidence, suggests that the original matter from which petroleum was generated consisted of fundamental organic compounds, such as protein (amino acids), fats, waxes, humus, and the like.

The nature of this material is indicated by geological evidence to be clastic, because the evidence of many clays in association with petroleum is that the grains were in transport along the depositional surface, a proportion being accumulated. But it is not clear whether the organic matter was adsorbed to clay minerals, or existed as separate clastic organic material. This writer tends to the view that it was a separate clastic material that survived on account of its arrival in an anaerobic environment on the depositional surface, or on account of its rapid burial to an anaerobic environment. These survival conditions are not mutually exclusive. In many areas of the world — perhaps most — petroleum is associated with unusually rapid sediment accumulation (not necessarily over a continuous, long span of time) during a regressive phase of the development of the sedimentary basin (e.g., Gulf Coast province of North America, Nigeria, Southeast Asia). In others, the rate of sediment accumulation appears to be secondary to the existence of anaerobic conditions of the depositional surface (e.g., Upper Devonian of the Western Canada basin).

The common association between petroleum, growth structures, and regressive sequences requires the facies that is favourable for the preservation of organic matter to be close to the facies of permeable clastics, for we cannot accept extensive lateral migration in clay rocks on present information. And the many prolific accumulations in the intertonguing zone between clays and permeable clastics suggest that the favourable source facies is very close to the permeable facies. Not all such areas are favourable, because not all such zones contain petroleum. Nevertheless, where a favourable source facies exists, it underlies the main permeable facies in regressive sequences. Fig.6-1 indicates the stratigraphic setting.

Petroleum occurs commonly in transgressive sequences as well as in regressive sequences. Transgressive phases of sedimentary basin development tend to accumulate potential source rocks on

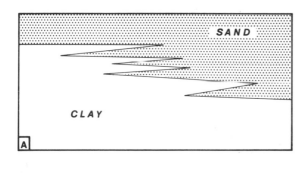

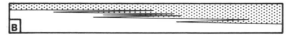

Fig.6-1. Diagrammatic stratigraphic cross-section through regressive sequence, indicating relationship between potential source rocks and potential reservoir rocks. A. vertical scale greatly exaggerated; B. more natural vertical scale. (Redrawn from Chapman, 1972, p.2185.)

top of the permeable facies. The accumulation of petroleum in dominantly transgressive sequences tends to be in stratigraphic traps, such as reefs (as in the Devonian of the Western Canada basin) or below unconformities. Anticlinal traps also occur, especially where the transgression follows a previous regression, or where the transgressions are merely episodes in a dominantly regressive development.

Hedberg's suggestion that high-wax oils are associated with freshwater or brackish environments and predominantly terrigenous vegetable organic matter, is an important clue to the origin of some oils (Hedberg, 1968). However, there does not appear to be an association between waxy oils and transgressive or regressive sequences, except in so far as carbonate reservoirs tend to be transgressive and to contain non-waxy oil.

There is some evidence that oil in transgressive sequences tends to be heavier than oil in regressive sequences (Curtis et al., 1958, p.291; Koesoemadinata, 1969) but much more data are required to confirm or deny this association.

The evidence therefore points to a source material that consists of fundamental organic compounds that are accumulated as clastics (either primary, or adsorbed to clay minerals) under anaerobic conditions on or just under the depositional surface, in a low-energy environment close to the permeable clastic (or organic) sediments accumulating near the marine margin of a physiographic basin. This is not to exclude the accumulation of organic matter in other environments or positions, of course; but a potential source rock must have a potential reservoir rock nearby if it is to yield an exploitable accumulation of petroleum. Some fine-grained carbonates may also be source rocks.

The study of Holocene sediments has shown that the hydrocarbons they contain are not directly comparable with those found in commercial accumulations. Deeper clays have been found to contain hydrocarbons that differ from those at the surface, and tend to approach those of petroleum accumulations with depth. There is therefore a diagenesis of the organic matter with depth during burial.

The diagenesis of the organic matter with burial is not fully understood. The principal factors are evidently temperature and pressure; but biochemical and catalytic influences may be present. The products of diagenesis fall within a wide range of liquid petroleums with various hydrocarbon mixtures, and a range of gaseous petroleums. Thus protopetroleum is converted to petroleum by burial, and expelled in one form or another from the source rock to the permeable rock that is, or leads to, the trap.

Coal and petroleum

It is natural that one should enquire whether the two great fossil fuels, coal and petroleum, have any significant geological relationship; and this enquiry has been going on for over 100 years. Coal results from the diagenesis of vegetable organic matter that accumulated in a favourable environment. Conditions on the actual surface of accumulation may have been reducing or oxidizing: but close below this surface reducing conditions prevailed. It consists largely of carbonized plant tissues, wood and bark, with spores (particularly the more durable spore coatings), leaf cuticles, waxes and resins. Coals form a series, with peat at one end and graphite at the other, and they are ranked according to their degree of alteration from lignites to anthracites. The *type* of coal groups coals of similar composition. Cannel coal, for example, is a coal rich in volatiles that burns easily, and commonly contains significant proportions of spore coatings. Heating of a "bituminous" coal results in the distillation of a gas that consists largely of hydrogen and methane, with numerous other components in small proportions (some being hydrocarbons). The coal-tar residue contains hydrocarbon oils (benzene, toluene, etc.) with other components.

Not surprisingly, early work on the association between coal and petroleum was carried out in Pennsylvania, U.S.A. — a coal mining area in which commercial oil production developed early. The early work culminated in White's "Carbon ratio theory" in which he related the occurrences of oil and gas to the percentage fixed carbon (see Glossary) in associated coals. He ranked petroleum, from low-ranking heavy oils to high-ranking light oils, and noted that oil occurred where the fixed carbon is less than 65%, mostly less than 60%; no commercial accumulation occurred when the percentage of fixed carbon is greater than about 70%; and gas occurred in the intervening zone (White, 1915). There was thus observed a ranking of oil with depth analogous to the ranking of coal with depth in many fields. This theory was considered to be widely applicable.

This line of thought, with the associated idea that petroleum was a distillation product of coal (a demonstrable process to some extent) went rather out of fashion as a marine origin for oil became a fashionable idea. But it has returned during the last two decades, with the increasing evidence that some petroleum accumulations are in non-marine sediments, and that some oils, particularly the waxy oils, have an important component of vegetable organic origin (Hedberg, 1968). The diagenesis of vegetable organic matter leading to petroleum accumulations seems well established now (Brooks and Smith, 1967, 1969). The large gas accumulations of northwest Europe (and under the North Sea) are considered by some to be the result of distillation of Upper Carboniferous (Pennsylvanian) coals (Stäuble and Milius, 1970).

Brooks (1970) considered that crude oil generation does not begin until the rank of the coal reaches 80% total carbon, dry mineral matter free; that oils are formed until the rank reaches about 85%; and light oils with gas, and dry gas, up to about 90% total carbon, dry mineral matter free. (60% fixed carbon is approximately equivalent to 83% total carbon dry mineral matter free; 65% to 86%; and 70% to 87% − but the relationship is not precise.)

While further discussion in this chapter relates to petroleum in sediments of marine and paralic environments, it should be remembered that the rank of coaly matter in sediments may be a valuable index in some areas. For the rest, we regard the diagenesis of plant organic matter in the sediments as a natural event in the generation of the petroleum of many accumulations. A causal relationship between coal *sensu stricto* and petroleum has not been demonstrated, but we may regard the processes of formation of both to be related by the physical environment during accumulation and burial.

Primary migration

Primary migration concerns the expulsion of petroleum from the source rock to the permeable rock. The process is certainly complex, because it is not yet fully understood in spite of its central concern to petroleum geologists. The only generalization that would receive general support is that primary migration from clay source rocks takes place during the compaction of the source rock. The obvious transporting medium is the interstitial liquid in the clay — but the mechanical problem of overcoming the capillary force of a two-phase liquid in which the liquid petroleum is finely disseminated through the very small pore spaces seems to exclude transport in a separate liquid phase. Let us examine the expulsion of liquid from a compacting clay again.

Athy's (1930a) clay compaction curve is commonly taken as representing the equilibrium density of clays with depth, because the data was derived from Palaeozoic clays (in northern Oklahoma) and the passage of time has probably allowed stress equilibrium between liquids and solids to be achieved. This curve, and similar ones derived by Hedberg (1926, 1936) and Dickinson (1953), represent the present distribution of clay densities with depth (note carefully that Athy used bulk *dry* densities, while some later authors have used bulk wet densities). Such curves have been *interpreted* as representing the compaction history of a clay during burial — more specifically, for Athy's curve, the *equilibrium* compaction density of a clay during burial. Since bulk density and porosity are related parameters of a rock (eq.3-1 and 3-1a), an empirical relationship between equilibrium porosity and depth can be obtained.

Rubey and Hubbert (1959, pp.175–177) did this for Athy's data, and on the assumption that Athy's curve represents the equilibrium state ($z = z_e$), their equation can be written as:

$$f = f_0 e^{-cz_e}$$

where f is the porosity of the clay in equilibrium at depth z, f_0 the initial porosity with a numerical value of 0.48 from Athy's data, c is a factor with a numerical value of $1.42 \cdot 10^{-3}$ per m ($4.33 \cdot 10^{-4}$ per ft.), and e is the base of the Napierian logarithms (but the

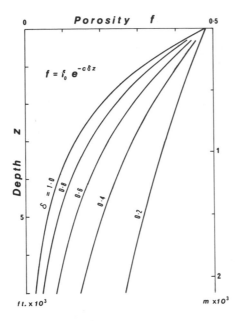

Fig.6-2. Porosity—depth relationship in clays for different values of δ. $\delta = 1$ corresponds to normal hydrostatic pressures; $\delta = 0$, to geostatic pressures.

subscript in z_e refers to the equilibrium depth). The general empirical equation relating porosity to depth and fluid pressure (through the parameter δ) is obtained by substituting eq.3-8a ($\delta = z_e/z$) into the equation above, obtaining:

$$f = f_0 e^{-c\delta z} \tag{6-1}$$

The porosity-depth relationship is plotted for various values of δ in Fig.6-2. (Note that on differentiating eq.6-1 with respect to z, $df/dz = -c\delta f$, we are led to the general deduction that the rate of loss of porosity with depth is proportional to both the porosity at depth z and the parameter δ in the rocks at that depth.)

Liquid expulsion from a compacting rock is related to the reduction of porosity (if one ignores the possibility of diagenesis in the mineral constituents) (Fig.6-3). The volume of liquid expelled is equal to the difference between the initial bulk volume of the rock and its compacted bulk volume. Alternatively, it may be regarded as the difference between the initial pore volume and the

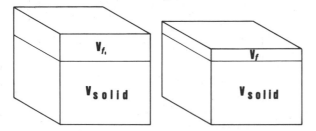

Fig.6-3. Compaction of unit initial bulk volume of clay. A measure of initial liquid is f_0. The corresponding measure of liquid remaining after compaction from porosity f_0 to porosity f is equal to the volume of solid multiplied by the void ratio.

pore volume present on compaction. Let us seek to relate fluid expulsion to compaction quantitatively.

If we consider unit initial bulk volume of clay, the initial porosity, f_0 is a measure of the initial liquid volume. The corresponding measure of solid volume is therefore $(1-f_0)$. On compaction, the *void ratio*, $f/(1-f)$, decreases. The proportion of liquid to solid decreases, but the volume of solids is considered to remain constant. Hence the measure of liquid remaining in the clay when it has compacted from an initial porosity f_0 to a porosity f is given by the expression $f(1-f_0)/(1-f)$. The expulsion of liquid during compaction is therefore proportional to:

$$q = f_0 - \frac{f}{1-f}(1-f_0) = \frac{f_0 - f}{1-f} \qquad (6\text{-}2)$$

where q is a measure of the volume of liquid expelled from unit initial volume of clay.

The expulsion of interstitial liquid begins on accumulation and continues until burial ceases and stress equilibrium is achieved. In Chapter 3 it was argued that the reversal of porosity, density, and equilibrium depth trends with depth in clays with abnormal interstitial liquid pressures in areas of gravity loading indicated that mean compaction had been retarded by the inhibited expulsion of liquid. Since the compaction of clay is regarded as essentially irreversible, this means that abnormally pressured clays have been abnormally pressured to some extent since burial to a shallow depth.

The compaction of a clay on loading by permeable rocks proceeds, as we have seen, from the outer surfaces towards the centre; and the loss of permeability in this compacting skin, a loss that increases down the fluid potential gradient, tends to seal the fluids in the clay. Since the pressure in the interstitial liquids has a limiting value equal to the geostatic pressure, it follows that in general a thick clay will have a smaller *mean* fluid potential gradient between its centre and an outer surface than a thin clay under the same instantaneous load. Hence a thick clay more readily acquires abnormal interstitial fluid pressures than a thin clay, and tends to retain them for a longer time. The consideration of compaction with abnormal interstitial liquid pressures is relevant because thicker clays are probably more important than thinner clays as source rocks — although it must be realized that only parts of a clay may be source clay.

It is not possible to be more specific about the effect of thickness quantitatively yet; but experience suggests that a clay that has an initial thickness of about 50 m (160 ft.) is probably sufficiently thick to suffer retarded compaction on rapid burial.

In order to examine the effect of fluid pressure on the compaction of a clay rock, let us accept that Athy's (1930a) clay compaction curve, and the functional relationships derived from his empirical data, represent the equilibrium compaction of a clay rock under a gravity load. On these assumptions, eq.6-2 can be evaluated for any depth z down to about 2,000 m (about 7,000 ft.) — the range of Athy's data — and for various values of the parameter δ, by substituting eq.6-1 into 6-2 obtaining:

$$q = \frac{f_0(1 - e^{-c\delta z})}{1 - f_0 e^{-c\delta z}} \tag{6-3}$$

There are some advantages in considering the ratio of liquid expelled from unit initial volume of clay to original initial interstitial liquid, i.e.:

$$\frac{q}{f_0} = \frac{1 - e^{-c\delta z}}{1 - f_0 e^{-c\delta z}} \tag{6-4}$$

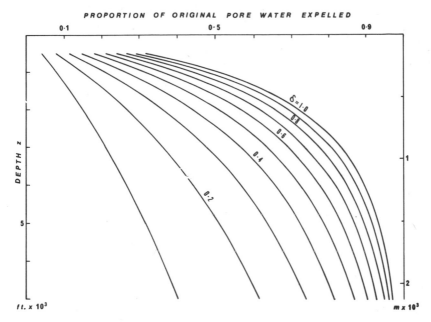

Fig.6-4. Proportion of original interstitial water expelled, and its relationship to depth and δ. (Redrawn from Chapman, 1972, p.2187.)

This ratio is plotted in Fig.6-4 for values of δ over the depth range of Athy's data. It shows that at any depth z, the higher the interstitial liquid pressure and the lower value of δ, the higher the proportion of initial liquid *retained* in the clay's pore space. In other words, a thin clay retains a small proportion of a small amount of original pore liquid, while a thick clay may retain a larger proportion of a larger amount of original pore liquid.

It is also of interest to assess the proportion of liquid expelled during burial to depth z to *liquid that would have been expelled had the clay been in stress equilibrium* ($\delta = 1$) at depth z, i.e.:

$$\frac{q}{q_e} = \frac{f_o(1 - e^{-c\delta z})/(1 - f_o e^{-c\delta z})}{f_o(1 - e^{-cz})/(1 - f_o e^{-cz})}$$

$$= \frac{(1 - e^{-c\delta z})(1 - f_o e^{-cz})}{(1 - e^{-cz})(1 - f_o e^{-c\delta z})} \tag{6-5}$$

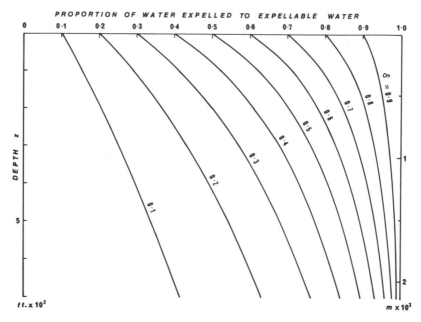

Fig.6-5. Ratio of water expelled to water that would have been expelled under equilibrium conditions, and its relationship to depth and δ. (Redrawn from Chapman 1972, p.2188.)

This relationship is plotted in Fig.6-5. The ratio takes the value of unity when δ = 1, that is, when liquid pressures are normal hydrostatic. It approaches zero as δ approaches zero when the liquid pressures approach the geostatic. It approaches the value of δ as z approaches zero — in other words, δ is only a *linear* measure of fluid expulsion at very shallow depth, and becomes increasingly non-linear with depth.

If Fig.6-5 is a reasonable approximation to reality (it must be remembered that it is based on the assumption that Athy's curve represents the equilibrium compaction with depth, and that there is no change in total volume of solids), a clay with a mean δ-value of 0.2 (λ = 0.9) at depth of 2,000 m (6,600 ft.) has expelled about 60% of its expellable liquids, but about 40% remains.

We are not as yet in a position to quantify the expulsion of interstitial liquid during burial because we have not been able to determine the patterns of interstitial liquid pressures in clays of

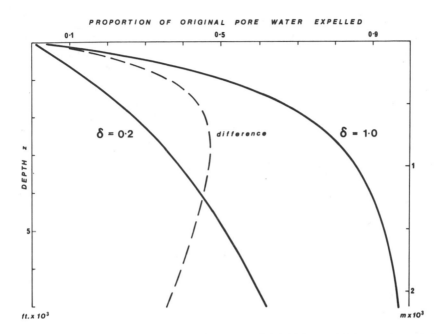

Fig.6-6. Comparison between proportions of initial interstitial water expelled from normally pressured ($\delta = 1$) and abnormally pressured ($\delta = 0.2$) clays during burial. (Redrawn from Chapman 1972, p.2188.)

different types, of different thicknesses, buried at various rates under differing loads. However, in order to gain some idea of the quantitative effect of retarded compaction — retarded liquid expulsion — on a clay during burial, let us consider unit initial volume of clay buried in such a way that the value of δ remains constant at 0.2. This does not seem unreasonable, since clays with this value occur within and well below the depth range considered here. Fig.6-6 compares the proportion of initial interstitial liquid expelled during burial to depth z under these conditions with that from a clay in which stress equilibrium is maintained ($\delta = 1$). Considering unit initial volumes, the difference between the amount of liquid expelled under the two conditions reaches a maximum at about 900 m (about 3,000 ft.), where it amounts to about 45% of the initial unit interstitial liquid volume. Below a depth of about 900 m, the difference decreases — largely because almost all the expellable liquid has been expelled from the clay in stress equilibrium. If we arbitrarily take the depths at which 50% of the initial interstitial liquid has been expelled, we can say that empirically most of the pore liquids have been expelled between depths of 300 and 1,500 m (1,000 and 5,000 ft.); if we take 75%, the depths become 700 m and deeper than 2,000 m (about 2,000 ft. and greater than 7,000 ft.). The correspondence of these depths with the empirical observation that most of the known accumulations of the world occur between depths of about 700 and 3,000 m (2,500 and 9,000 ft.) (see Weeks, 1958, p.22) supports the belief of long standing that the pore liquid is the transporting medium of petroleum during primary migration, and that compaction is the principal mechanism.

Empirical data on the depths of petroleum accumulation must be interpreted with caution. The evidence of some *young* accumulations in regressive sequences in growth structures is that the accumulations have never been much deeper, perhaps never deeper, than they are today, that subsidence has prevailed (as indicated by the overlying sequence of sediments) and that migration was short. Significant accumulations of this type occur above a depth of 1,500 m (about 5,000 ft.). This suggests in turn that the petroleum was formed at these depths and shallower, over a span of time during which the depth of the reservoir increased. This conclusion is in conflict (at least in part) with the findings of Philippi (1965) and Tissot et al. (1971) from geochemical studies, the latter concluding that the bulk of petroleum is formed at depths below 1,500 m. This conflict will not be resolved satisfactorily until the precise source of several young and shallow accumulations has been located.

Reverting more specifically to the primary migration of petroleum, the problem of *how* the petroleum migrates must now be faced. There appear to be three alternatives — as a separate phase, in solution, or (a compromise, perhaps) in colloidal solution. All three states are known to exist: as a separate phase in the accumulation, as a solution in groundwater, and as an emulsion in oil storage tanks.

Primary migration of petroleum from the source rock as a separate fluid phase in the pore water seems to be mechanically impossible unless the liquid petroleum accumulates as a slug that extends from the rock with high capillary pressure (fine grain) to the interface with rock of lower capillary pressure (coarser grain, higher permeability) (Hubbert, 1953, p.1979). Primary migration in solution is attractive because it is the state that requires least work. However, while it is known that most petroleums are soluble in water to some extent, and that different petroleums have different solubilities, some physical or chemical change is required to release the petroleum from solution. The problem is not so much whether primary migration can take place in solution – for petroleum occurs widely in solution in groundwater (Buckley et al., 1958) – but whether the process is quantitatively adequate to account for the accumulations.

Most of the changes that lead to the formation of petroleum are considered to occur within the source rock. There are two main reasons for this: first, clays are chemically more "active" than most reservoir rocks, and may contain other compounds and catalysts that could influence diagenesis; second, changes are required in the original organic matter for primary migration to take place.

Investigations into the diagenesis of organic matter into petroleum have indicated heat as the dominant influence. Geological evidence suggests that pressure may be important too. During burial, a thin clay is exposed to geothermal temperatures, and its fluids to normal (or near normal) hydrostatic pressures. A thick clay during burial is also exposed to geothermal temperatures, but its pore fluids are exposed to pressures much higher than normal hydrostatic. The geological evidence is strong that abnormal pressures in the source rock are essential if primary migration is to be postponed to depths at which petroleum and lateral or overlying traps can be formed.

Fig.6-7 shows a simplified temperature-pressure field that would apply to the pore liquids of clays during burial. Fig.6-6 (and 6-4) show that a clay compacting under equilibrium conditions retains 50% of its original pore liquids at about 300 m (1,000 ft.) of burial. The temperature in these liquids will be about 30°C (85°F), and the liquid pressure will be about 32 kg/cm² (460 psi). However, a clay with a mean value of δ of 0.2 retains 50% of its original pore liquids at about 1,500 m (nearly 5,000 ft.), where

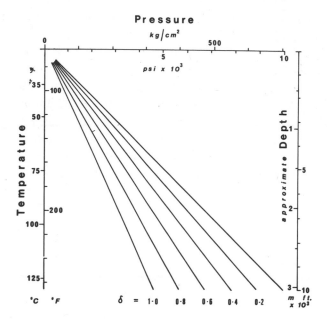

Fig.6-7. Simplified temperature-pressure field of pore liquids of clays during burial and compaction. For this figure, the geothermal gradient has been taken as 36°C/1,000 m (20°F/1,000 ft.), the normal hydrostatic gradient as 106 kg/cm² per 1,000 m (460 psi/1,000 ft.), and λ_e as 0.46. (Redrawn from Chapman 1972, p.2188.)

the temperature will be about 70°C (160°F) and the liquid pressure will be about 300 kg/cm² (4,300 psi). In the latter case, only about 15% of the original interstitial liquids will be expelled under the conditions of temperature and pressure in the clay in stress equilibrium.

Retarded mean compaction thus exposes more liquids to higher temperatures and much higher pressures for a longer time.

If protopetroleum is finely disseminated through a source rock, and if the components of this protopetroleum, or the products of its diagenesis, are soluble in water, the combined effects of higher temperatures and pressures and retarded mean fluid expulsion are capable of causing a larger proportion of the protopetroleum, or its derivatives, to be dissolved in the pore water. These components would be expelled progressively during burial, the pattern of expulsion and the nature of the petroleums expelled depending on the various factors already discussed.

During expulsion from a compacting clay, fluid moves essentially isothermally down a fluid potential gradient. The physical changes involved in this movement are dominantly pressure changes; and while the relative pressure change may be nearly constant at about one half (from abnormal to normal hydrostatic) on completion of expulsion, the absolute change increases with the depth of expulsion and could exceed 200 kg/cm^2 (3,000 psi). The qualitative effect of this reduction of pressure on gaseous components in solution would be to release a volume of gas from solution. The effect on liquid components is not clear. The release of gas from solution may affect the solubility of liquid hydrocarbons in water.

In general, the physical changes imposed upon the pore fluid during expulsion may have one of two effects: (1) if the water is sufficiently undersaturated with petroleum, the petroleum may be expelled in solution; or (2) if the saturation of any or all of the components is reached before expulsion, petroleum will be released from solution before expulsion from the clay.

In the first case, the petroleum is free to move in solution in the pore water in the hydrodynamic field present in the more permeable rock. If it is to be released from solution, some physical or chemical change must occur in, or on the way to, the trap.

In the second case, one conclusion is clear: if any petroleum is released from solution before expulsion, *the effective permeability to water will be reduced* in that zone, and fluid expulsion will be further retarded. Such release from solution will occur in a volume of rock in the compacting zone of the clay, and hence a slug will accumulate and may attain sufficient size for it to be expelled by capillary force — aided by the fluid potential gradient.* Cemented "cap-rock" reported near the top of abnormally pressured clays

---

* It should be noted that since the porosity of a clay decreases down the fluid potential gradient that exists during compaction, expulsion of petroleum as a separate phase is opposed by increasing capillary pressure as the porosity decreases.

suggests precipitation of salts from solution in the pore water during migration (see p.65).

There is little to be gained from further speculation on the precise nature of the processes because they involve disciplines with which most geologists are not familiar. Nevertheless, there is another pertinent geological factor. If the facies favourable for the accumulation and preservation of organic matter is not contiguous with the permeable facies, the primary migration of petroleum must involve passage through a non-source clay. Not enough is known about the facies of clays to know what possible effects this might have. It must be noted, however, that petroleum accumulates in lenticular sands that are entirely enveloped in clay. Temperature and pressure conditions in the sand are clearly essentially the same as those in the clay, so these cannot be the dominant influences on the phase change leading to *accumulation*. It appears sound to argue therefore that neither temperature nor pressure is necessarily important in the phase-changing process, which may therefore be catalytic.

Primary migration from dominantly transgressive source clays does not appear to be different from that from regressive source clays, except in the matter of timing. Significant compaction only occurs during significant burial, hence the compaction of a transgressive clay may take longer, and the downward component of primary migration is important. If the *rate* of change of temperature and pressure is important in the diagenesis of the organic matter, the composition of the petroleum generated and expelled from transgressive source clays may differ from those of regressive petroleums, but comparative studies have not yet been made on this basis (see p.124).

Secondary migration

Secondary migration concerns the movement of petroleum through permeable rocks until it can migrate no further and accumulates in a trap — or dissipates at the surface. Consideration of this stage of migration is confused by our ignorance of the primary migration processes. If the phase during primary migration is uncertain, the mechanism of secondary migration cannot properly be defined. Nevertheless, the circumstantial evidence is not so unsatisfactory.

When oil or gas is produced from a well, it flows through the reservoir rock down a fluid potential gradient. It is therefore indisputable that two-phase flow can take place in a permeable rock. However, as oil is withdrawn from a rock and water takes its place, it is found that not all the oil is removed. The residual oil, amounting to about 65% of the original oil in place in sandstone reservoirs (Bridgeman, 1969), is retained by capillary forces (mainly) and is not recoverable by flushing — at least in the time available to man. It therefore appears that secondary migration cannot take place as a separate phase unless there is more than some critical value of oil saturation. We have seen that phase changes and local accumulation are *more likely* to take place before primary migration is complete — but analogous physical or chemical changes within the permeable rock could take place during secondary migration.

As before, we are not really concerned whether secondary migration of some petroleums takes place in solution in the pore waters — it clearly does. What is not clear is whether the transport of liquid petroleum in aqueous solution is significant.

Whatever the phase of petroleum may be during secondary migration, its passage through the permeable rock is determined by gravity and the hydrodynamic field (which can also be ascribed to gravity, of course). We have seen that primary migration takes place during the compaction of the clay rocks, and that this compaction leads to the expulsion of large volumes of liquid with the consequent displacement of large volumes of liquid from the permeable rocks. Primary migration is largely vertical (see p.64); but secondary migration has an important lateral component (unless a single permeable lithology is present, in which case the likelihood of a trap is seriously reduced for lack of a seal). In an alternating sequence of clays and permeable facies, the downward fluid potential gradient at the base of each clay makes it a perfect barrier to upward fluid migration. Hence the patterns of secondary migration are the patterns of fluid potential gradients and of permeability. This is a geological matter.

The concept of a sedimentary basin, discussed in Chapter 1, involves several broader concepts. A physiographic basin is generally more extensive than the areas of *sedimentation,* and the areas of sedimentation more extensive than the areas of sediment accumulation. The distribution of these areas in space may change with the passage of time, and hence the facies associated with different sediments and different energy environments may change position relative to their positions at an earlier time. Such changes are necessary if reservoir traps are to be connected to source rocks by a permeable "carrier" bed. The essential difference between regressive and transgressive changes is that in the one, the reservoir migrates to the source whereas in the other the source migrates to the reservoir.

In dominantly regressive sequences, as we have seen, the loading of thick clays by the permeable facies creates mechanical instability that can lead to growth structures (potential traps) that are contemporaneous with fluid expulsion from the clays — and so, we assume, with primary migration of petroleum — and situated close to the source rocks. The paths of secondary migration in regressive sequences are therefore probably short. The apparent shortness of many secondary migration paths in regressive sequences suggests that the phase of petroleum is separate from the aqueous phase on expulsion from the source clay. The hydrodynamic field extends through the permeable facies to the surface near the margin of sediment accumulation, and petroleum in solution would pass through the growth anticlines and the growth synclines.

In dominantly transgressive sequences, the possible paths for secondary migration are more varied. When a clay is accumulating on a permeable clastic facies, such compaction that takes place under the gravity load of overlying sediments expels a proportion of its fluids downwards into the permeable facies. This will normally be a continuous permeable path to the surface at the margin in deposition. However, any irregularities in this surface — such as organic reefs, carbonate banks, or discontinuous sand bodies — may become the reservoir for petroleum expelled during deeper burial. To these, unequal subsidence may contribute a structural element.

Where transgressive clays accumulated on the surface of previously deformed sediments (some of which are porous and permeable) there may be an immediate potential reservoir subcropping against the source rock under the unconformity. Where a trap does not exist near the source facies, paths of lateral secondary migration may be long.

We see that there are several unsatisfactory aspects of our understanding of petroleum migration. In case these aspects have distracted us from our central purpose, let us seek to make a concise, positive statement on the migration of petroleum.

Petroleum migrates down fluid potential gradients. These are essentially vertical (upwards or downwards) during primary migration, but lateral during secondary migration that leads to accumulation (on account of the sealing of the permeable "carrier" bed). The length of the primary migration path is limited to the thickness of the clay unit as an approximate maximum. The length of the secondary migration path depends on the geology of the area, but is probably short in regressive permeable beds (being confined to the intertonguing zone of permeable/impermeable beds) and may be long in transgressive permeable beds.

Note on clay diagenesis and primary migration

The diagenesis of montmorillonite to illite has been proposed as a flushing mechanism for petroleum (Powers, 1967; Burst, 1969). The essence of this hypothesis is that the diagenesis reduces the mineral volume by the release of inter-layer water. This has not been considered in the main part of this chapter for two reasons: first, it is necessary to concentrate on essentials if the central processes are to be understood; and secondly, Powers does not regard the processes he proposes as operative above a depth of about 1,800 m (6,000 ft.), nor Burst between 800 and 2,500 m (2,600–8,500 ft.). Comparable depths were found by Perry and Hower (1970, p.171); and rather greater depths by Weaver and Beck (1971, p.18).

The problem is complex. Many clays at present being deposited are the *erosion* products of older clays: others are the *weathering* products of older rocks — mainly igneous. While the alteration of montmorillonite to illite seems entirely plausible and supported by X-ray analysis of clays from boreholes, and while such alteration would result in a reduction of solid volume and an increase in interstitial liquid volume, there may be a significant facies influence on the presence and proportions of discrete, detrital montmorillonite and illite.

In the Gulf of Paria, illitic clays are associated with the delta platform of the Orinoco river and waters of lower salinity (Van Andel and Postma, 1954). Montmorillonite is associated with a more saline environment (*op.cit.*, p.78). Illitic clays are also associated with areas of higher deposition rates (*op.cit.*, fig.75, p.159). If these associations are typical, a regressive sequence would consist of montmorillonitic clays underlying illitic clays underlying sand.

It may be, therefore, that there is an association of primary illite with regressive phases, montmorillonite with transgressive phases (that is, the ratio of montmorillonite to illite may be greater in transgressive clays). In a generally regressive sequence, such as the Tertiary of the Gulf Coast province of North America (to which the work referred to in the first paragraph applies), with a general increase of sand/shale ratio upwards, the shallower clays are likely to be transgressive. This *could* lead to a spurious association of primary illite with depth that affects the interpretation of the diagenesis of montmorillonite, but a real association between montmorillonite and source rocks (or illite and source rocks).

This short discussion is not intended to cast doubt on the processes proposed — they may well contribute to primary migration of petroleum — but rather to indicate that associations with depth require very careful examination.

Selected bibliography*

Athy, L.F., 1930a. Density, porosity, and compaction of sedimentary rocks. *Bull. Am. Ass. Petrol. Geol.*, 14:1—24.

---

* For a more complete bibliography, see Dott and Reynolds (1969).

Athy, L.F., 1930b. Compaction and oil migration. *Bull. Am. Ass. Petrol. Geol.*, 14:25—35.

Bridgeman, M., 1969. Recent advances and new thresholds in petroleum technology. (8th Cadman Memorial Lecture.) *J. Inst. Petrol.*, 55:131—140.

Brooks, B.T., 1948. Active-surface catalysts in formation of petroleum. *Bull. Am. Ass. Petrol. Geol.*, 32:2269—2286.

Brooks, J.D., 1970. The use of coals as indicators of the occurrence of oil and gas. *J. Aust. Petrol. Explor. Ass.*, 10:35—40.

Brooks, J.D. and Smith, J.W., 1967. The diagenesis of plant lipids during the formation of coal, petroleum and natural gas, I. Changes in the *n*-paraffin hydrocarbons. *Geochim. Cosmochim. Acta*, 31:2389—2397.

Brooks, J.D. and Smith, J.W., 1969. The diagenesis of plant lipids during the formation of coal, petroleum and natural gas, II. Coalification and the formation of oil and gas in the Gippsland basin. *Geochim. Cosmochim. Acta*, 33:1183—1194.

Buckley, S.E., Hocott, C.R. and Taggart, M.S., 1958. Distribution of dissolved hydrocarbons in subsurface waters. In: L.G. Weeks (Editor), *Habitat of Oil*. American Association of Petroleum Geologists, Tulsa, Okla., pp.850—882.

Burst, J.F., 1969. Diagenesis of Gulf Coast clayey sediments and its possible relation to petroleum migration. *Bull. Am. Ass. Petrol. Geol.*, 53:73—93.

Chapman, R.E., 1972. Primary migration of petroleum from clay source rocks. *Bull. Am. Ass. Petrol. Geol.*, 56:2185—2191.

Conybeare, C.E.B., 1970. Solubility and mobility of petroleum under hydrodynamic conditions, Surat basin, Queensland. *J. Geol. Soc. Aust.*, 16:667—681.

Curtis, B.F., Strickland, J.W. and Busby, R.C., 1958. Patterns of oil occurrence in the Powder River basin. In: L.G. Weeks (Editor), *Habitat of Oil*. American Association of Petroleum Geologists, Tulsa, Okla., pp.268—292.

Dickinson, G., 1953. Geological aspects of abnormal pressures in Gulf Coast Louisiana. *Bull. Am. Ass. Petrol. Geol.*, 37: 410—432.

Dott, R.H. and Reynolds, M.J. (Editors), 1969. Sourcebook for petroleum geology. *Am. Ass. Petrol. Geol., Mem.*, 5:471 pp.

Dufour, J., 1957. On regional migration and alteration of petroleum in South Sumatra. *Geol. Mijnb.*, (N.S.), 19:172—181.

Forsman, J.P. and Hunt, J.M., 1958. Insoluble organic matter (kerogen) in sedimentary rocks of marine origin. In: L.G. Weeks (Editor), *Habitat of Oil*. American Association of Petroleum Geologists, Tulsa, Okla., pp.747—778.

Gussow, W.C., 1955. Time of migration of oil and gas. *Bull. Am. Ass. Petrol. Geol.*, 39:547—573.

Hedberg, H.D., 1926. The effect of gravitational compaction on the structure of sedimentary rocks. *Bull. Am. Ass. Petrol. Geol.* 10: 1035—1072.

Hedberg, H.D., 1936. Gravitational compaction of clays and shales. *Am. J. Sci.*, 31 (5th ser.) :241—287.

Hedberg, H.D., 1964. Geologic aspects of origin of petroleum. *Bull. Am. Ass. Petrol. Geol.*, 48:1755—1803.

Hedberg, H.D., 1968. Significance of high-wax oils with respect to genesis of petroleum. *Bull. Am. Ass. Petrol. Geol.*, 52:736—750.

Holmquest, H.J., 1966. Stratigraphic analysis of sourcebed occurrences and reservoir oil gravities. *Bull. Am. Ass. Petrol. Geol.*, 50:1478—1486.

Hubbert, M.K., 1953. Entrapment of petroleum under hydrodynamic conditions. *Bull. Am. Ass. Petrol. Geol.*, 37:1954—2026.

Hunt, J.M., 1967. The origin of petroleum in carbonate rocks. In: G.V. Chilingar, H.J. Bissel and R.W. Fairbridge (Editors), *Carbonate Rocks, Developments in Sedimentology*, 9B. Elsevier, Amsterdam, pp.225—251.

Hunt, J.M. and Jamieson, G.W., 1958. Oil and organic matter in source rocks of petroleum. In: L.G. Weeks (Editor), *Habitat of Oil*. American Association of Petroleum Geologists, Tulsa, Okla., pp.735—746.

Kidwell, A.L. and Hunt, J.M., 1958. Migration of oil in Recent sediments of Pedernales, Venezuela. In: L.G. Weeks (Editor), *Habitat of Oil*. American Association of Petroleum Geologists, Tulsa, Okla., pp.790—817.

Koesoemadinata, R.P., 1969. Outline of geologic occurrence of oil in Tertiary basins of west Indonesia. *Bull. Am. Ass. Petrol. Geol.*, 53:2368—2376.

Landes, K.K., 1967. Eometamorphism, and oil and gas in time and space. *Bull. Am. Ass. Petrol. Geol.*, 51:828—841.

Magara, Kinji, 1968. Compaction and migration of fluids in Miocene mudstone, Nagaoka plain, Japan. *Bull. Am. Ass. Petrol. Geol.*, 52:2466—2501.

Meinschein, W.G., 1959. Origin of petroleum. *Bull. Am. Ass. Petrol. Geol.*, 43:925—943.

Perry, E. and Hower, J., 1970. Burial diagenesis in Gulf Coast pelitic sediments. *Clay Clay Minerals*, 18:165—177.

Philippi, G.T., 1965. On the depth, time and mechanism of petroleum generation. *Geochim. Cosmochim. Acta*, 29:1021—1049.

Powers, M.C., 1967. Fluid-release mechanisms in compacting marine mudrocks and their importance in oil exploration. *Bull. Am. Ass. Petrol. Geol.*, 51:1240—1254.

Roof, J.G. and Rutherford, W.M., 1958. Rate of migration of petroleum by proposed mechanisms. *Bull. Am. Ass. Petrol. Geol.*, 42:963—980.

Rubey, W.W. and Hubbert, M.K., 1959. Role of fluid pressure in mechanics of overthrust faulting, II. Overthrust belt in geosynclinal area of western Wyoming in light of fluid-pressure hypothesis. *Bull. Geol. Soc. Am.*, 70:167—206.

Smith, P.V., 1952. The occurrence of hydrocarbons in Recent sediments from the Gulf of Mexico. *Science*, 116:437—439.

Smith, P.V., 1954. Studies on origin of petroleum — occurrence of hydrocarbons in Recent sediments. *Bull. Am. Ass. Petrol. Geol.*, 38:377—404.

Stäuble, A.J. and Milius, G., 1970. Geology of Groningen gas field, Netherlands. In: M.T. Halbouty (Editor), *Geology of Giant Petroleum Fields. Am. Ass. Petrol. Geol., Mem.*, 14:359—369.

Stoffers, P. and Müller, G., 1972. Clay mineralogy of Black Sea sediments. *Sedimentology*, 18:113—121.

Tissot, B., Califet-Debyser, Y., Deroo, G. and Oudin, J.L., 1971. Origin and evolution of hydrocarbons in early Toarcian shales, Paris basin, France. *Bull. Am. Ass. Petrol. Geol.*, 55:2177—2193.

Van Andel, Tj. and Postma, H., 1954. Recent sediments of the Gulf of Paria. Reports of the Orinoco Shelf Expedition, v. 1. *Verhand. K. Ned. Akad. Wetensch., Afd. Natuurk., Eerste Reeks, Dl. XX*, 5:245 pp.

Von Engelhardt, W. and Gaida, K.H., 1963. Concentration changes of pore solutions during the compaction of clay sediments. *J. Sediment. Petrol.*, 33:919–930.

Weaver, C.E. and Beck, K.C., 1971. Clay water diagenesis during burial: how mud becomes gneiss. *Geol. Soc. Am., Spec. Pap.*, 134:96 pp.

Weeks, L.G. (Editor), 1958. *Habitat of Oil.* American Association of Petroleum Geologists, Tulsa, Okla., 1384 pp.

Welte, D.H., 1965. Relation between petroleum and source rock. *Bull. Am. Ass. Petrol. Geol.*, 49:2246–2268.

White, D., 1915. Some relations in origin between coal and petroleum. *Wash. Acad. Sci.*, 5:189–212.

Chapter 7. TOWARDS A SYNTHESIS

Summary

(1) The tendency for petroleum occurrences in regressive sequences to be in structural traps (anticlinal and fault traps) and for those in transgressive sequences to be in stratigraphic traps (particularly organic reefs) suggests that sedimentary basins are not initially folded as a whole, but rather that the regressive sequence is folded and faulted independently of (and preferentially to) the transgressive sequence.

(2) The association of normal faults (rather than reverse faults) with structural traps in regressive sequences indicates a component of horizontal tension, rather than compression. This suggests that the main deforming stress that causes contemporaneous anticlines in regressive sequences is vertical rather than horizontal, resulting from the sediments generated by a neighbouring orogeny rather than the orogenic forces themselves.

(3) A synthesis of petroleum geology in regressive sequences is therefore suggested, in which the deformation arises directly from internal causes in the sedimentary basin. The mechanical instability produced by regressive loading of clays leads to clay diapirism that is essentially contemporaneous with the expulsion of the bulk of the interstitial fluids from the clays.

(4) For the special case when these clays contain petroleum source rocks, the deformation creates structural traps down the fluid potential gradient that determines the path of migration; and these traps are initiated before the bulk of the petroleum has migrated, and may grow during migration.

(5) In transgressive sequences there is no inherent tendency for structural traps to form down the fluid potential gradient in the underlying permeable facies; but stratigraphic features may be present that will trap the petroleum.

Introduction

Our purpose in this chapter is to seek to unify the processes that have been discussed separately in earlier chapters — compaction, fluid migration, growth structures, diapirism — into a broad concept of sedimentary basin development that has general validity in geology, and specific validity in petroleum geology when part of the compacting clay is a petroleum source rock. While doing this, we must constantly be aware that the workings of nature are infinitely varied and that this is true also of the occurrences of petroleum. We must therefore be satisfied for the time being with generalizations that help understanding, rather than specific occurrences that contribute towards knowledge.

We shall consider first the deformation of sedimentary basins generally, and then pass to a review of a few selected areas that illustrate the main theme of petroleum in regressive sedimentary sequences. Finally, we shall consider the corollaries and extensions of this theme to the occurrence of petroleum in transgressive sequences.

Deformation of sedimentary basins

The view was expressed in Ch. 2 that geological ideas that were developed from surface geology in the 19th century have not been sufficiently re-appraised in the light of borehole data obtained during this century. In the matter of the deformation of sedimentary basins, there is a fundamental difference between what we are taught by the collective experience of surface geologists, and what we learn from the drilling of boreholes into the subsurface. We are taught that a sedimentary basin is typically deformed by horizontal tectonic forces after the sedimentary history of the basin is complete — or alternatively, that this deformation brings the sedimentary history to a close. We learn from boreholes that petroleum commonly exists in structures in sedimentary basins that are still actively receiving sediment, and have not yet been obviously deformed by horizontal tectonic forces.

Reports on the geology of many areas of the world commonly

postulate an orogenic folding phase after the accumulation of sediment. It seems axiomatic that this must be so, certainly if the sedimentary rocks are exposed at the surface. Yet the observed deformation of the sediments in sedimentary basins that are still receiving sediment (the younger basins, naturally) suggests that we must distinguish between orogenesis (mountain building) and other forms of diastrophism that do not form mountains.

Petroleum occurrences can be classified into two broad stratigraphic classes: those associated with dominantly transgressive sedimentary sequences, and those in dominantly regressive sequences. This would be a trivial classification were it not for the fact that when classified on this basis a further generalization can be made: petroleum of transgressive sequences tends to be in stratigraphic traps, while that in regressive sequences tends to be in structural traps. (Once again, it is emphasized that a tendency does not preclude exceptions — there are examples of structural accumulations of petroleum in transgressive sequences as well as stratigraphic accumulations of petroleum in regressive sequences.)

It is the purpose of natural science to examine such associations and to seek a rational explanation for them. It seems reasonable to assume that if folding involved a sedimentary basin as a whole, transgressive sequences would be as likely to contain petroleum in structural traps as regressive sequences. The discipline of science requires us to erect as many hypotheses as possible, and to examine each in the light of the evidence. While accepting that many sedimentary basins have had a long and complicated history, let us simplify the model and consider a young sedimentary basin with a single sedimentary cycle — a transgression followed by a regression. In the context of this topic, two broad hypotheses can be advanced, one involving horizontal deforming stresses and the other vertical.

The first hypothesis is that the sediments of sedimentary basins are deformed by regional horizontal compressive stress, and that the contrasts in materials between the basement framework and the sedimentary basin and between the different sediments within the sedimentary basin, lead to contrasts in deformation (i.e., differing response to stress). The more rigid basement inhibits folding in the lower transgressive sequence; but the upper, less

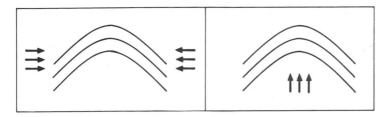

Fig.7-1. Alternative hypotheses of direction of deforming stresses in an anticline.

compacted regressive sequence has no such mechanical support, and so deforms more readily under stress. This broad hypothesis has been postulated by inference by many authors to account for the observation that structural trends commonly coincide closely with facies trends in sedimentary basins.

The second hypothesis is that sedimentary basins are deformed by vertical, essentially gravity processes. These have been discussed at some length in the previous chapters, and there is no need to summarize them here.

The mechanical interpretation of folds and faults in a qualitative sense in sedimentary basins is superficially simple, but complicated by the uncertainty that exists regarding the response of sedimentary rocks to stresses applied over great spans of time. The analysis of folding is often ambiguous (a simple fold may be regarded as the response either to horizontal compressive stress or to vertical compressive stress — Fig.7-1) but certain broad generalizations regarding faulting can be made. If one considers the principal stresses in a rock (along the vertical axis and two horizontal axes) these stresses are compressive below depths of a few metres in unconsolidated sediments (Hubbert, 1951). When the rock is in stress equilibrium, the stresses in all directions towards a point are equal (referred to as "hydrostatic" even though the rock material is being considered). But when the stresses in these directions are unequal, the rock tends to deform in a way that tends to restore equilibrium. If the time-rate of stress application is rapid enough, the rock will deform by fracture and faults will develop.

Reverse faults result when the direction of *maximum* compression is horizontal; and the direction of the fault (the strike of the fault surface) is normal to this direction. Normal faults result when the direction of *minimum* compression is horizontal (a condition colloquially referred to as "tension") and the strike of the fault is normal to this direction.

In general, therefore, areas of sedimentary basins with reverse faults are consistent with the first hypothesis, but inconsistent with the second: while those with normal faults are consistent with the second, but not with the first. In the context of petroleum occurrences, particularly those in Tertiary basins, normal faults are the common type (as the name suggests) with reverse faults far less common, and some of these (see later) are apparently causally associated with diapirism. The evidence of young sedimentary basins in general does not therefore lead to the rejection of either hypothesis (nor, of course, does it confirm them), but it does support the hypothesis that anticlines such as those associated with petroleum accumulations have been formed by *vertical* deforming stresses, which are diapiric in nature, in a stress field that has a horizontal component of tension.

What, then, is the nature of orogenesis and how does it affect sedimentary basins? Orogenesis is essentially the forming of mountains, and this is a diastrophic process that may include folding and faulting. Orogenic forces have been considered by many authors to be the direct cause of folding and faulting in neighbouring sedimentary basins that have not been (or not yet been) formed into mountains (see, for example, Schaub and Jackson, 1958, pp.1332 – 1335). But orogenesis cannot be regarded as generating horizontally compressive folds in adjacent sedimentary basins because the internal evidence of the sedimentary basins themselves, which we have just discussed, does not support the conclusion that the folding was formed by horizontal compressive stress.

We are thus led to the view that orogenesis is related to the initial folding within sedimentary basins largely by virtue of its influence on sediment supply – that the creation of mountains also creates sediment. When the energy of the environment is insufficient to disperse all the sediment supplied, a depositional regression results; and the accumulation of a depositionally regressive sequence of sediments leads to the autodiastrophism (folding and faulting from internal causes) observed in sedimentary basins.

Contemporaneous and subsequent diastrophism

We observe that the rocks involved in orogenesis are commonly rocks that had accumulated in a sedimentary basin. From this we deduce that orogeny is a process that can ultimately terminate a sedimentary basin's development (here we are in agreement with the orthodox conclusions derived from surface geology). The point must therefore be made that sedimentary basins commonly suffer two phases of diastrophism (or deformation). The first in time is the result of sediment accumulated from an adjacent orogeny: the second is the orogenesis of the basin sediments. In the Tertiary sedimentary basins in general, only deformation of the first kind has yet been suffered: in many older basins (but not all of them) orogenic deformation has also been suffered.

The timing of diastrophism in relation to the main period of fluid expulsion from clay source rocks is a matter of central concern to the petroleum geologist. Petroleum must, *a priori,* accumulate in a trap during the main period of fluid expulsion, or be lost. This requires that the trap be formed before the source clays are buried to depths greater than about 3,000 m (10,000 ft.) as a maximum (Fig.6-4, p.131), with 1,000 m (3,000 ft.) as a more realistic figure if the trap is to accumulate important quantities of petroleum. Folds and faults at such shallow depths are not uncommon today in areas that have not yet suffered orogenesis (such as many of those on the continental shelf).

We have seen that there is a logical link between the accumulation of a regressive sequence of sediments, its deformation into folds and faults, and the contemporaneous expulsion of the bulk of the fluids from the underlying clays. The significance of growth structures is therefore not so much that their development was contemporaneous with sediment accumulation (although this is essential for their recognition) but rather that their formation was contemporaneous with fluid expulsion. We can readily accept, therefore, that petroleum accumulation in regressive sequences is attributable to the initial diastrophism of a sedimentary basin; but

Fig.7-2. Petroleum accumulations against salt dome.

that subsequent orogenic events may modify the accumulations. It is therefore necessary to seek to clarify in our minds the significance of the geological evidence concerning the time of folding (or times of folding) and its role in petroleum accumulation. To do this, let us take an extreme example of entrapment.

Fig.7-2 shows schematically petroleum accumulations in sandstone reservoirs against a salt dome. The essential features of the trap are, first, the inclined reservoirs and secondly, their truncation up-dip by a relatively impermeable mass of salt. The sequence of events suggested by these relationships is: (1) sediment accumulation; (2) salt dome emplacement; and (3) petroleum migration and entrapment. Such a postulated sequence of events seems entirely logical — yet it is unsatisfactory. It is unsatisfactory because it requires the postponement of fluid migration until after salt emplacement. A more fundamental objection is that it represents a static view of a dynamic process.

The dynamic view suggests that sediment accumulation, petroleum generation and migration, and diapirism are broadly contemporaneous processes, and that the accumulation of petroleum largely preceded the salt emplacement, the petroleum accumulating initially in an anticline or dome that was created by the diapirism. These accumulations were then displaced to the flanks (some perhaps dispersed or partly dispersed) by the emplacement. If compaction was not complete, then these accumulations may have been added to by subsequent migration. Fig.7-3 clarifies this, for one must ask oneself the question, "What will happen to the overlying accumulation as salt emplacement proceeds?" The sequence of events is thus not easily listed, because each event tends

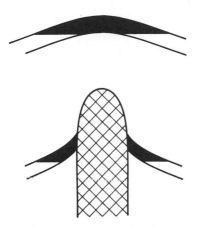

Fig.7-3. Petroleum accumulations above and against salt dome.

to occupy a span of time that overlaps the others. The time relationships of these events are shown schematically in Fig.7-4.

This example serves to indicate quite clearly that an initial trap can be modified by later events. By analogy, we may assume that orogenesis modifies the initial petroleum accumulations and that severe orogenesis will probably destroy them. In the process,

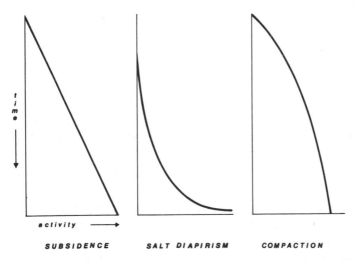

Fig.7-4. Schematic time relationships between subsidence, salt diapirism, and sediment compaction.

petroleum may be spilled from one trap to another (including from one type of trap to another, as from a stratigraphic trap to a structural trap). Orogenesis is not a geologically instantaneous event, and the initiation of a sedimentary basin in one area may be related to the beginning of orogenesis in an adjacent area.

Sedimentary basins and uniformitarianism

We must also consider the possibility that Tertiary sedimentary basins, in which the association between petroleum accumulations and structural traps in regressive sequences is most marked, are not typical of the preorogenic phase of older basins with similar lithological sequences. The lithology and mineralogy of the clays invites attention.

There is no evidence that the *mechanical* properties of clays have changed significantly with time. Athy's clay compaction curve was based on Palaeozoic clays: Dickinson's and Hedberg's curves for Tertiary clays are of similar shape, and could approximate Athy's with the passage of time (Hedberg, 1926, 1936; Athy, 1930; Dickinson, 1953). Dalgarno and Johnson (1968) describe diapiric structures in Late Precambrian sediments in the Flinders Ranges of South Australia. The diapiric sediments consist of a thick sequence of dolomitic mudstones, silts, shales, dolomites and limestones; and the apparent absence of evaporites was noted.

More significantly, Korn and Martin (1959) describe a convincing example of gravity sliding in the Naukluft Mountains of Southwest Africa, in which three successive regressive sequences of quartzites and limestones on shales have moved down a slope, producing isoclinal and recumbent folds, overthrusts and nappes. The age of these sediments is Late Precambrian (or possibly Cambrian). They also adduced evidence (*op.cit.*, p.1070) that some of the folding at least was contemporaneous with sediment accumulation.

The evidence that the proportions of clay minerals (principally montmorillonite and illite) in shales today show changes with the age of the shale (Weaver, 1967) cannot be taken as evidence of differences of original composition unless the alternative of post-depostional changes can be ruled out. Even if this should be so, it would not necessarily imply significant differences in the mechanical behaviour of the clay rocks.* The theoretical approaches of Bredehoeft and Hanshaw (1968) and Smith (1971) to the generation and maintenance of abnormal interstitial fluid pressures suggest low permeability or hydraulic conductivity as the principal parameter.

Accepting that the chemical and physical properties of petroleum have remained essentially constant over the last $0.6 \cdot 10^9$ years, and that the processes of expulsion of fluids from compacting clays have remained essentially constant over the last 10^9 years at least, it seems reasonable to apply the principle of uniformitarianisn, and expect that the accumulation of regressive sequences involving thick clay sequences led to initial diastrophism analogous to that observed in the Tertiary basins today.

Initial diastrophism in Southeast Asia

Petroleum occurs in dominantly regressive sequences in many parts of the world, and some of them are major producing areas: for example, California (Santa Barbara Channel region), the United States' Gulf Coast, Trinidad, Nigeria, and many areas of Southeast Asia. They have several features in common: growth structures, underlying clays with abnormal interstitial fluid pressures, and petroleum accumulations mainly in structural traps, with multiple sand reservoirs and a tendency for the oils to be lighter with increasing reservoir depth. The regressive sequences mentioned above are of Tertiary age.

Examples are taken from Southeast Asia for discussion because

---

* This is a good example of the difficulties of associations. There is a school of thought that attributes abnormal interstitial fluid pressures to clays with important montmorillonite constituents. Montmorillonitic clays are associated with Mesozoic and Cenozoic sediments (see Weaver, 1967). Abnormal interstitial fluid pressures are also associated with Mesozoic and Cenozoic sediments. However, the absence of significantly abnormal interstitial fluid pressures in Palaeozoic clays may be due merely to the passage of time, during which leakage has reduced the pressures. The *causal* relationship is not easily determined.

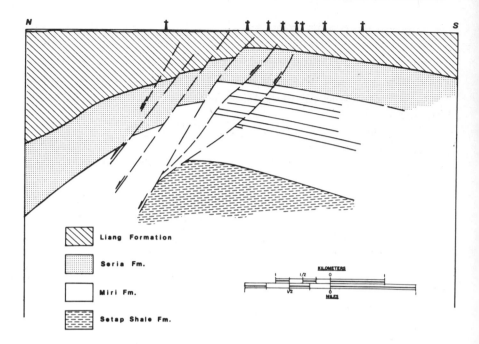

Fig.7-5. Cross-section across Seria field, Brunei. (After Schaub and Jackson, 1958, p.1333, fig.3.)

they can be set in a sequence that illustrates the development of initial diastrophism.

In West Irian (W. New Guinea) in the early 1950's field geologists used to say that the geology of the young Tertiary basins was the geology of anticlines without synclines. The pattern of folding is not a wave-like sequence of anticlines and synclines, but rather of narrow, relatively steep anticlines separated by broad, gentle synclines. This pattern is also a feature of the Tertiary basins of Borneo; and such anticlines, usually faulted, are the sites of important petroleum accumulations in Brunei (Seria field), Sarawak (Miri field), and several fields in Kalimantan. (Figs.7-5, 7-6, 7-7).

Gesa anticline, Waropen Coast, W. Irian

In the North Coast basin of W. Irian near the Mamberamo river,

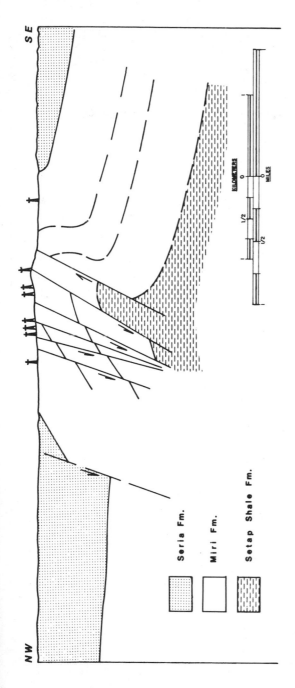

Fig.7-6. Cross-section across Miri field, Sarawak. (After Schaub and Jackson, 1958, p.1332, fig.2.)

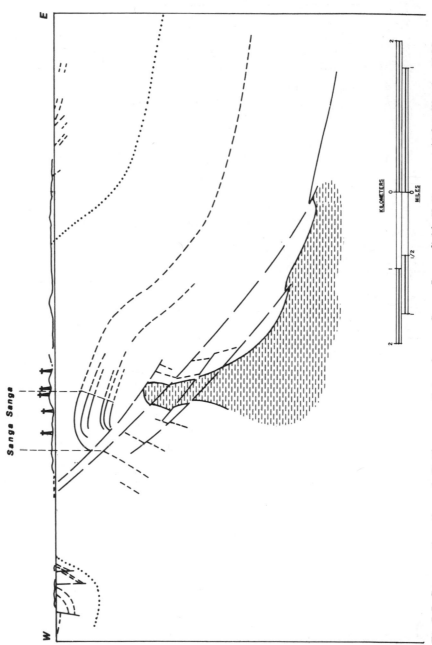

Fig.7-7. Cross-section through Balikpapan oil trend, over Sanga Sanga field, Kalimantan. (After Weeda, 1958, p.1345, fig.5.)

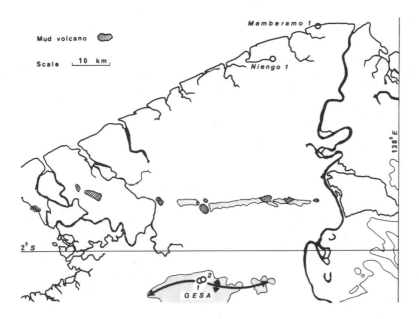

Fig.7-8. Map of part of the Mamberamo delta, West Irian. Mud-volcanoes shown with diagonal lines. Relevant Plio–Pleistocene outcrop, stippled. (After Visser and Hermes, 1962, enclosure 1–III.)

a line of mud-volcanoes occurs in the swampy plains of the Mamberamo delta (Fig.7-8). This line is about 35 km (22 Miles) long, and forms part of a general line about 100 km long (60 miles). The area has been described by Visser and Hermes (1962). Some of the mud volcanoes are on a narrow ridge, with outcrops of young Tertiary (Plio–Pleistocene) sandy and argillaceous sediments. Warm salt water and some methane is extruded with the mud. Further south, inland, there are some anticlines in which Plio–Pleistocene paralic sands with lignite beds and subordinate clays are exposed. One of these anticlines, the Gesa anticline, is a very gentle elongated dome, with the axis roughly parallel to the line of mud volcanoes. Into this anticline two boreholes were drilled between 1956 and 1958, both of which encountered abnormal interstitial fluid pressures at depths of about 1,300 m (4,300 ft.) in the predominantly clayey sediments (marine) that underlie the more sandy lithologies. The ensuing drilling difficulties prevented their reaching their target, and no significant accumulation of petroleum was found.

The extent of the abnormality is not clear because the data given by Visser and Hermes (1962, fig.V-17, p.230) cannot be taken at face value, and require careful analysis (after the correction of the pressure scale! An entertaining hour can be spent on this diagram; it illustrates well the difficulty of drawing valid conclusions from raw data). It seems quite certain that down to the depths penetrated the fluid pressure never exceeded the geostatic in spite of the excessive mud-weights used. It is inconceivable that the side-track to Gesa 1 (Gesa 1A) penetrated rocks with significantly higher pore pressures than those encountered in Gesa 1. Hence the troubles in Gesa 1A are to be attributed more to excessive mud weight and consequent loss of mud (as mentioned by Visser and Hermes on p.228). The problems of Gesa 2 (500 m from Gesa 1) are likely to be analogous, with spuriously high fluid pressures indicated by the mud. A value of λ of about 0.75 ($\delta = 0.54$) is indicated at a depth of about 1,800 m (5,900 ft.) in Gesa 1.

The Gesa anticline has therefore strong indications of a diapiric origin, both from its proximity to mud volcanism and the presence of abnormally pressured clays at shallow depth. (The low-speed refractor reported at 1,500 m could be abnormally pressured clays, the velocity of elastic waves being less in rocks with high porosity.) It is clearly at a very early stage of development, and this may account for the lack of significant petroleum accumulations. *Gas was reported in the clays only* (cf. p.137).

Since Visser and Hermes mention that the present writer suggested in 1954 that gravity sliding was the cause of these structures (*op. cit.*, p.171), it is appropriate to record here that the data obtained from drilling suggest that this hypothesis was wrong—at least in part. This matter will be reconsidered when the evidence of other areas has been introduced.

Seria field, Brunei (Fig.7-5)

In the North Coast basin of Borneo an extensive and thick argillaceous rock unit, the Setap Shale Formation, accumulated during part of the Oligocene and Miocene. This formation is associated with mud volcanism and diapirism in many areas (Schaub and Jackson, 1958; Liechti et al., 1960). In the Seria Field, the Setap Shale Formation is overlain by more sandy formations, the Miri Formation and the Seria Formation, forming a regressive sequence from neritic to paralic sediments. Schaub and Jackson (1958) suggest that Seria is possibly diapiric, and there is no difficulty in accepting this because they mention also growth faults in the Seria field, and abnormal interstitial fluid pressures exist in the Setap Shale Formation at depth.

Miri field, Sarawak (Fig.7-6)

Down the coast of Borneo to the southwest from Seria field lies the Miri field, which was discovered in 1910 (Schaub and Jackson, 1958). This accumulation is in an anticline in which the Setap Shale Formation is overlain by a similar regressive sequence to that in the Seria field. Again, Schaub and Jackson suggest a possible diapiric origin for this structure; and again, we have no difficulty in accepting this for the same reasons as those for accepting a diapiric origin for the Seria field. The section through the Miri field shows that the structure is steeper than the Seria field, and the shale core is prominent in a fault block bounded on one side by a reverse fault. (This reverse fault seems clearly caused by the shale core, for the net throw across the block is small). If it is accepted that this structure is also diapiric, it is clearly in a more advanced stage of development than the Seria anticline.

Sanga Sanga field, Kalimantan (Fig.7-7)

A stratigraphic section through the oil basin of East Borneo is shown in Fig.7-9. The Sanga Sanga field is situated on the Balikpapan trend, and is seen to be in a regressive sequence with marine shales overlain by a paralic permeable facies. We may agree with Weeda (1958) that this anticline has a diapiric influence. The stage of development is perhaps a little more advanced than that of the Miri field, and small thrust faults have been interpreted that

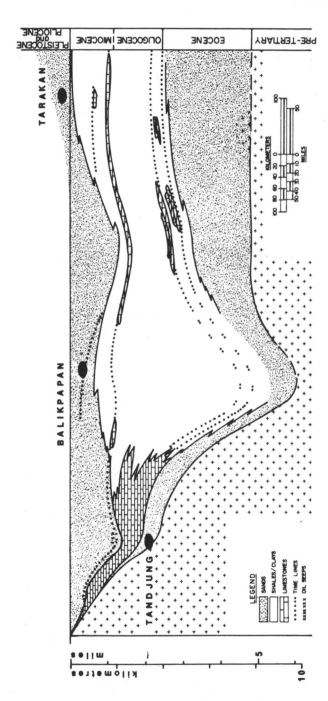

Fig. 7-9. Hypothetical stratigraphic section through Kalimantan (E. Borneo). (After Weeda, 1958, pp.1342–1343, fig.3.)

displace the shale core as well as the younger permeable facies. These are on the west flank with overthrusting towards the west.

These four structures — Gesa, Seria, Miri and Sanga Sanga — appear to illustrate a sequence in the diapiric diastrophism that affects regressive sequences of sediments in which there is a significant thickness of clays (shales). It was earlier mentioned that the present writer was wrong in suggesting in 1954 that gravity sliding was the cause of structures such as the Gesa anticline in West Irian. We may return to that topic and see that the parameter required for gravitational sliding according to the fluid-pressure hypothesis of Rubey and Hubbert (1959) — i.e., high values of λ — is included amongst those that favour clay diapirism — i.e., high values of λ with consequent low mechanical strength, relatively high porosity, and eventually relatively low bulk density. Indeed, one may speculate that there is a link between the two processes. The earliest diastrophism is diapiric; and this is characteristically in the form of narrow, steep anticlinal trends separated by wide, gentle synclines. If a regional dip is present at the interface between the permeable and the relatively impermeable facies (or induced later, but before the dissipation of the abnormal pore pressures) sliding and overthrusting may take place. The size of the thrust sheets would then be determined by the spacing of the diapiric trends, which may be regarded as the dominant wave-length of diapirism (see Biot and Odé, 1965). Mud volcanoes may be indicative of incipient sliding. It is unsafe to argue that this has already begun in the Miri and Sanga Sanga anticlines, with the formation of reverse faults and thrusts, because orogenesis may also have begun here.

Similar relationships to those in Borneo are to be found in south Sumatra, where important petroleum accumulations occur in structural traps in regressive sands that overlie a thick shale. The stratigraphic relationships are shown in Fig.7-10, and are seen to be analogous to the oil basin of East Borneo (Kalimantan) in that a complete sedimentary cycle representing transgression followed by regression is known (Wennekers, 1958; Koesoemadinata, 1969). It is significant that the petroleum occurrences in the regressive sequence are not directly superimposed on those in the

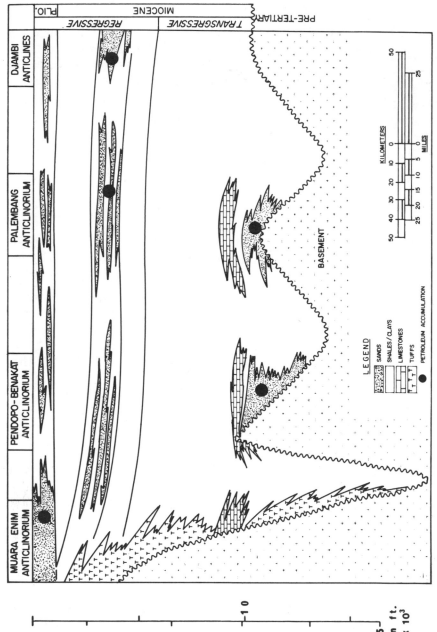

Fig. 7-10. Simplified section across the South Sumatra basin. It is understood that petroleum has now been found in transgressive sequences near "Djambi anticlines". (After Wennekers, 1958, p.1356, fig.7.)

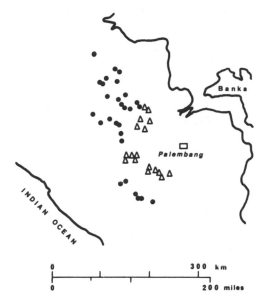

Fig.7-11. Distribution of petroleum occurrences in South Sumatra basin. Triangles, in transgressive sequences; black dots, in regressive sequences. (After Koesoemadinata, 1969, p.2374, fig.4.)

transgressive sequence in the sense that production is not obtained from both sequences in one field. As Fig.7-11 shows, the "regressive" accumulations lie generally west of the "transgressive" accumulations.

Transgressive sequences

It is natural that we should now enquire into the occurrences of petroleum in transgressive sequences, for these are important habitats of petroleum that differ from regressive sequences in two important respects. First, a transgressive episode tends to accumulate potential source rocks on top of potential reservoir rocks. Secondly, there is no inherent instability in a transgressive sequence that tends to form structural traps during the migration (downward, then lateral) of fluid.

Petroleum occurs in important quantities in transgressive sequences in organic reef reservoirs of Upper Devonian age in western Canada (Grayston et al., 1964; Committee on Slave Point and Beaverhill Lake Formations, and Belyea, 1964) of Cretaceous age in Mexico (Viniegra O. and Castillo-Tejero, 1970), and of Paleocene age in Libya (Terry and Williams, 1969). These are stratigraphic traps in which closure is due to the morphology of the reefs, not to folding.

Examples of petroleum in clay/sand sequences are to be found in the Tertiary of the Maracaibo basin in the Bolívar Coastal field (Miller et al., 1958); the Lower Cretaceous Viking Sand and Athabasca oil sand of western Canada (Rudkin, 1964); the Cretaceous Dakota Sandstone of the Denver basin (McGinnis, 1958), the San Juan basin (Wengerd, 1958), and other areas of North America; and in Tertiary basins of Indonesia (Weeda, 1958; Wennekers, 1958; Koesoemadinata, 1969). Many of these accumulations are in stratigraphic traps or structural traps with a strong stratigraphic influence.

Organic reefs of western Canada

The Western Canada basin extends from the Arctic Islands down through the Northwest Territories and Alberta to the central part of the North American continent (Fig.1-3). Within this basin a remarkable series of organic reefs grew during a dominantly transgressive phase in Middle and Late Devonian time. Many of the reef complexes became petroleum reservoirs, and some of them are prolific. But a significant feature of these areas (noted by many writers) is that no obvious structural control has been detected either on the reef growth itself, or on their subsequent role as petroleum reservoirs. The dips are very low. These Devonian reefs are important to economic geology not only for their petroleum but also for their base metal mineralization near the surface at Pine Point, Northwest Territories (see Jackson and Beales, 1967; Jackson and Folinsbee, 1969). Our interest here is the nature of the processes leading to accumulation of petroleum in some reefs but not in others, for this may suggest the nature of accumulations in transgressive sequences.

It seems most unlikely that the rich organic matter of the reefs themselves is petroleum source material, or even that the petroleum source rocks are necessarily close to the reefs. The reasons for this statement are that not all reefs in an area contain petroleum in spite of apparent similarities of form and ecology; and reefs tend to be surrounded by well-aerated water that is favourable for their living organisms but inimicable to the preservation of organic matter after death. Petroleum in the Devonian reefs of western Canada is associated with reefs that grew on a carbonate base or platform that was permeable, at least in part. A relatively long secondary migration path is indicated through permeable carrier beds, the petroleum originating in deeper-water, fine-grained sediments that probably accumulated in euxinic conditions away from the reefs.

A depositional transgression tends to accumulate potential source rocks on top of potential reservoir rocks. If follows that the normal migration path for part of the fluids expelled by compaction is downwards into the permeable facies, then laterally under the influence of the hydrodynamic field present in those rocks. This will normally be towards the surface in the direction of the littoral zone (where fluid can escape to the surface), and the bulk of the fluid will tend to follow the better permeability paths down this fluid potential gradient. The large gathering area afforded by the interface between the transgressive clay and the underlying permeable rock unit may compensate for the smaller proportion of the total interstitial fluids that is in the zone of downward fluid potential gradient.

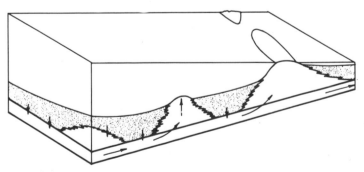

Fig.7-12. Block diagram illustrating fluid migration paths in transgressive sequence with reefs.

The secondary migration paths in the permeable unit will be influenced by permeability/porosity paths and by subtle changes in the shape of the rock unit, so that the petroleum will tend to migrate along various paths towards the areas of lowest fluid potential that are accessible. These are probably unpredictable, and change as diagenesis of carbonate carrier beds proceeds. As regards the reefs themselves, these may be "chimneys" for the escape of fluid until effectively sealed by relatively impermeable material. Different reef structures may become dealed at different times. Once sealed, petroleum will only accumulate if a path of low fluid potential lead into it. Fig.7-12 shows schematically some of the variations on this theme.

Transgressive sands of South Sumatra (Wennekers, 1958; Koesoe-madinata, 1969)

In the South Sumatra basin, Tertiary sediment accumulation records a simple sedimentary cycle that began with an Early Tertiary (Oligocene) depositional transgression over a basement of pre-Tertiary rocks that are largely metaporphic and igneous. This was followed by a depositional regression that began during the Miocene and is perhaps continuing today. This cycle is shown in Fig.7-10.

The transgressive sequence contains terrestrial and paralic sands and conglomerates that are well developed over the basement "highs". These sands and conglomerates are diachronous, and contemporaneous clays are a lateral facies. The transgression led to a migration of facies so that littoral and neritic clays and lime-stones overlie the basal unit. These in their turn are overlain by a thick argillaceous unit (Telisa Shale).

The source of the petroleum in general terms is clearly the Telisa Shale superimposed on or adjacent to the reservoir rocks, but this unit is unlikely to be a petroleum source rock everywhere. The pattern of fluid migration in the transgressive sequence is also clearly downward across the clay/sand interfaces, then laterally through the permeable rocks to the traps. The traps are anticlinal in form, with a strong stratigraphic influence on the distribution of reservoir rock. The age of the folding was considered by Wennekers (1958) to be Plio–Pleistocene, long after the initiation of the transgressive accumulations.

The time of migration of petroleum into the underlying reservoirs would begin as soon as the source rock was buried deep enough for petroleum to be generated, and accumulation would begin with the sealing of the trap and continue until the completion of accumulation of the Telisa Shale *and* to some extent at least, during the accumulation of the regressive Palembang sands. This is a teasing problem of some interest.

The Telisa Shale accumulated to a thickness of 1,500–2,000 m (5,000–6,500 ft.) over the reservoirs during the Miocene before loading by the regressive sands. This accumulation took less than $20 \cdot 10^6$ years. So the minimum indicated rate of accumulation including compaction is of the order of 0.1 mm per year. Such a rate is comparable with that of the Tertiary of the U.S. Gulf Coast $(0.1–0.2 \text{ mm yr}^{-1})$.

Empirical and theoretical data suggest that the compaction of a clay accumulating at such a rate is such that stress equilibrium is not maintained, and abnormal fluid pressures are generated. Magara (1968) describes downward migration from a Miocene mudstone into underlying permeable volcanic and pyroclastic rocks in some fields in Japan, and demonstrates that a downward fluid potential gradient still exists today at the base of the mudstone, which is at depths between 1,000 and 2,500 m (3,000–8,000 ft.). Smith (1971) constructed a mathematical model of clay compaction in which 3,000 m of clay accumulated at the same rate of 0.1 mm yr^{-1} (but with other parameters that may not be applicable to the Telisa Shale) and abnormal interstitial fluid pressures were indicated below 1,000 m.

Whatever the quantitative solution to this problem may be, it is clear that the process of downward migration of fluids through a transgressive sequence is protracted, and continues during regressive loading as the clays compact towards a new equilibrium. Secondary migration paths may be long, for there is no inherent tendency for traps to form close to the source unless basement relief localizes both source and permeable facies. In either case, there is a strong stratigraphic influence on trap formation.

We are thus led towards a general synthesis of petroleum geology with respect to clay source rocks.

Synthesis

(1) At any one time, coarser permeable sediments tend to be deposited near the marine margins of physiographic basins, and finer grained sediments —clays, marls, and silts — tend to be transported further from the land. In the finer grained sediments, organic matter is preserved and included in the sediment to form a potential source facies, if the environment of deposition is anaerobic or the organic matter is buried rapidly to an anaerobic environment. In areas of subsidence or rising baselevel, these sediments tend to accumulate, preserving in the sedimentary basin the pattern of facies in the physiographic basin and the changes of that pattern with time.

(2) During burial the sediments and their contained fluids are exposed to increasing temperatures and pressures. Increasing pressures in the solid framework of the sediment tends to compact it; increasing pressures and temperatures lead to other diagenetic changes, particularly in the organic matter. Compaction of the sediment expels interstitial fluids, but the time-rate of compaction depends on the hydraulic conductivity of the sediment as well as the load and the rate of loading (depth of burial and rate of burial).

(3) Clays compact from the bottom towards the top until loaded by permeable sediments, when compaction from the top towards the bottom also begins to take place. The loss of permeability through compaction in the outer layers of a clay unit tends to seal the interstitial fluids in the clay. Water-soluble products of diagenesis dissolve in the interstitial water, the composition of these products depending largely on the stage of diagenesis reached.

(4) The precise nature of primary migration from a clay source rock is still not well understood. The retarded mean compaction that accompanies abnormal interstitial fluid pressures exposes more fluids to higher temperatures and much higher pressures for

a longer time, thus facilitating the solution of water-soluble products of the diagenesis of organic matter. If the physical changes along the fluid potential gradient are such that petroleum is released from solution within the clay, this petroleum must accumulate in the clay until a globule of sufficient dimensions is attained that can be expelled by capillary force aided by the fluid potential gradient. It is probable that the catalytic properties of some clay minerals play an important role.

(5) During transgressive phases, potential source rocks accumulate (with fine-grained non-source rocks) on top of potential reservoir rocks, and a downward fluid potential gradient is induced in the lower part of the clay unit. The injection of fluid into the underlying permeable sediments induces a fluid potential gradient that will normally be lateral towards the nearer marine margins of the physiographic basin, which will usually be also towards the nearer margins of the sedimentary basin. Interstitial fluid pressures in the underlying permeable unit are abnormal if the hydraulic conductivity of the unit as a whole is insufficient for the dispersal of the fluids.

(6) Any petroleum that is in this fluid as a separate phase tends to accumulate in areas of minimum fluid potential, e.g., in reefs and banks, and in diachronous permeable units over basement irregularities, once they have been sealed. Where the underlying permeable facies is in the subcrop (beneath an unconformity) petroleum accumulates in the permeable subcrop in areas of minimum fluid potential, which may be determined by folds or faults in the subcrop, facies changes in the subcrop, or by the configuration of the surface of unconformity.

(7) During regressive phases, potential source rocks tend accumulate (with fine-grained non-source rocks) below potential reservoir rocks, and the upward fluid potential gradient is increased both by the load and by the compaction of the upper layers of the clay. The interstitial fluid pressures, always abnormal to some extent during compaction, increase in such a way that the ratio of fluid pressure to overburden pressure (λ) increases. The extent of this increase depends largely on the rate of loading — the rate of burial. Regressive loading can affect downward expulsion of fluids

in the transgressive sequence to the extent that compaction under the new equilibrium is achieved.

(8) The mechanical properties of porous, fluid-filled rocks are affected by the interstitial fluid pressure in such a way that the higher the value of λ, the less competent is the rock. In clays, porosity is function of both depth and fluid pressure: clays with abnormal fluid pressures retain higher porosity that corresponds to a shallower depth of burial, and correspondingly low bulk density, as well as low equivalent viscosity (incompetence).

(9) The combination of low equivalent viscosity, naturally unequal loading by the overlying permeable sequence, and low bulk density relative to the overlying permeable sequence leads to mechanical instability that in turn leads to the deformation of the sedimentary sequence by diapiric processes. The anticlines and faults so formed are contemporaneous and penecontemporaneous with sedimentation and sediment accumulation, and strictly contemporaneous with the expulsion of the bulk of the interstitial fluids.

(10) Petroleum expelled upwards with the water as a separate phase tends to accumulate in areas of minimum fluid potential, commonly in anticlines and faults formed by diapiric processes contemporaneously with the expulsion of the bulk of the fluids. Accumulation is favoured in the lower and distal portions of the permeable regressive sequence, where interfingering clay units can act both as cap rocks and source rocks.

(11) Other geological events and situations that, fortuitously or not, duplicate the essential requirements of trap formation before or during the main period of fluid expulsion, may also lead to petroleum accumulation. Such accumulations may be in permeable volcanic rocks, or in structures formed by contemporaneous regional tectonic events (such as orogenesis).

(12) Orogenesis contributes to the development of adjacent sedimentary basins at least in its influence on sediment supply, leading to the final depositional regressive phase. Orogenesis may later affect the sedimentary basin as a whole, modifying (perhaps relocating) and later destroying petroleum that accumulated in pre-orogenic traps.

Selected bibliography

Athy, L.F., 1930. Density, porosity, and compaction of sedimentary rocks. *Bull. Am. Ass. Petrol. Geol.*, 14:1—24.

Barss, D.L., Copland, A.B. and Ritchie, W.D., 1970. Geology of Middle Devonian reefs, Rainbow area, Alberta, Canada. In: M.T. Halbouty (Editor), *Geology of Giant Petroleum Fields. Am. Ass. Petrol. Geol., Mem.,* 14:19—49.

Biot, M.A. and Odé, H., 1965. Theory of gravity instability with variable overburden and compaction. *Geophysics*, 30:213—227.

Bredehoeft, J.D. and Hanshaw, B.B., 1968. On the maintenance of anomalous fluid pressures I. Thick sedimentary sequences. *Bull. Geol. Soc.Am.*, 79:1097—1106.

Chapman, R.E., 1972. Petroleum and geology: a synthesis. *J. Aust. Petrol. Explor. Ass.*, 12 (1): 36—38.

Committee on Slave Point and Beaverhill Lake Formations, and Belyea, Helen R., 1964. Upper Devonian. In: R.G. McCrossan and R.P. Glaister (Editors), *Geological History of Western Canada.* Alberta Society of Petroleum Geologists, Calgary, Alta., pp.60—88.

Dalgarno, C.R. and Johnson, J.E., 1968. Diapiric structure and Late Precambrian—Early Cambrian sedimentation in Flinders Ranges, South Australia. In: J. Braunstein and G.D. O'Brien (Editors), *Diapirism and Diapirs. Am. Ass. Petrol. Geol., Mem.* 8:301—314.

Dickinson, G., 1953. Geological aspects of abnormal reservoir pressures in Gulf Coast Louisiana. *Bull. Am. Ass. Petrol. Geol.*, 37:410—432.

Grayston, L.D., Sherwin, D.F. and Allen, J.F., 1964. Middle Devonian. In: R.G. McCrossan and R.P. Glaister (Editors), *Geological History of Western Canada.* Alberta Society of Petroleum Geologists, Calgary, Alta., pp.49—59.

Hedberg, H.D., 1926. The effect of gravitational compaction on the structure of sedimentary rocks. *Bull. Am. Ass. Petrol. Geol.*, 10:1035—1072.

Hedberg, H.D. 1936. Gravitational compaction of clays and shales. *Am. J. Sci.*, 31 (5th ser.): 241—287.

Hedberg, H.D. 1964. Geological aspects of origin of petroleum. *Bull. Am. Ass. Petrol. Geol.*, 48:1755—1803.

Hubbert, M.K., 1951. Mechanical basis for certain familiar geologic structures. *Bull. Geol. Soc.Am.*, 62:355—372.

Hubbert, M.K., 1953. Entrapment of petroleum under hydrodynamic conditions. *Bull. Am. Ass. Petrol. Geol.*, 37:1954—2026.

Jackson, S.A. and Beales, F.W., 1967. An aspect of sedimentary basin evolution: the concentration of Mississippi Valley-type ores during late stages of diagenesis. *Bull. Can. Petrol. Geol.*, 15:383—433.

Jackson, S.A. and Folinsbee, R.E., 1969. The Pine Point lead-zinc deposits, N.W.T., Canada. Introduction and paleocology of the Presqu'ile reef. *Econ. Geol.*, 64:711—717.

Koesoemadinata, R.P., 1969. Outline of geologic occurrence of oil in Tertiary basins of west Indonesia. *Bull. Am. Ass. Petrol. Geol.*, 53:2368—2376.

Korn, H. and Martin, H., 1959. Gravity tectonics in the Naukluft Mountains of South West Africa. *Bull. Geol. Soc. Am.*, 70:1047—1078.

Liechti, P., Roe, F.W. and Haile, N.S., 1960. The geology of Sarawak, Brunei and the western part of North Borneo. *Bull. Geol. Surv. Dept. Br. Terr. Borneo*, 3:360 pp.

Magara, Kinji, 1968. Compaction and migration of fluids in Miocene mudstone, Nagaoka Plain, Japan. *Bull. Am. Ass. Petrol. Geol.*, 52:2466—2501.

McGinnis, C.J., 1958. Habitat of oil in the Denver basin. In: L.G. Weeks (Editor), *Habitat of oil*. American Association of Petroleum Geologists, Tulsa, Okla., pp.328—343.

Miller, J.B., Edwards, K.L., Wolcott, P.P., Anisgard, H.W., Martin, R. and Anderegg, H., 1958. Habitat of oil in the Maracaibo basin, Venezuela. In: L.G. Weeks (Editor), *Habitat of Oil*. American Association of Petroleum Geologists, Tulsa, Okla., pp.601—640.

Rubey, W.W. and Hubbert, M.K., 1959. Role of fluid pressure in mechanics of overtrust faulting, II. Overthrust belt in geosynclinal area of western Wyoming in light of fluid-pressure hypothesis. *Bull. Geol. Soc. Am.*, 70:167—206.

Rudkin, R.A., 1964. Lower Cretaceous. In: R.G. McCrossan and R.P. Glaister (Editors), *Geological History of Western Canada*. Alberta Society of Petroleum Geologists, Calgary, Alta., pp.156—168.

Schaub, H.P. and Jackson, A., 1958. The northwestern oil basin of Borneo. In: L.G. Weeks (Editor), *Habitat of Oil*. American Association of Petroleum Geologists, Tulsa, pp.1330—1336.

Smith, J.E., 1971. The dynamics of shale compaction and evolution of pore-fluid pressures. *J. Int.Ass. Math. Geol.*, 3:239—263.

Terry, C.E. and Williams, J.J., 1969. The Idris "A" bioherm and oilfield, Sirte basin, Libya — its commercial development, regional Palaeocene geologic setting and stratigraphy. In: P. Hepple (Editor), *The Exploration for Petroleum in Europe and North Africa*. Institute of Petroleum, London, pp.31—48.

Van Bemmelen, R.W., 1954. *Mountain Building*. Nijhoff, The Hague, 177 pp.

Viniegra O., F. and Castillo-Tejero, C., 1970. Golden Lane fields, Veracruz Mexico. In: M.T. Halbouty (Editor), *Geology of Giant Petroleum Fields*. *Am. Ass. Petrol. Geol., Mem.*, 14:309—325.

Visser, W.A. and Hermes, J.J., 1962. Geological results of the exploration for oil in Netherlands New Guinea. *Verh. K. Ned. Geol.-Mijnb. Genootsch., (Geol. Ser.)*, 20:1—265.

Weaver, C.E., 1967. Potassium, illite and the ocean. *Geochim. Cosmochim. Acta*, 31:2181—2196.

Weeda, J., 1958. Oil basin of East Borneo. In: L.G. Weeks (Editor), *Habitat of Oil*. American Association of Petroleum Geologists, Tulsa, Okla., pp.1337—1346.

Wengerd, S.A., 1958 Origin and habitat of Oil in the San Juan basin of New Mexico and Colorado. In: L.G. Weeks (Editor), *Habitat of Oil*. American Association of Petroleum Geologists, Tulsa, Okla., pp.366—394.

Wennekers, J.H.L., 1958. South Sumatra basinal area. In: L.G. Weeks (Editor), *Habitat of Oil*. American Association of Petroleum Geologists, Tulsa, Okla., pp.1347—1358.

Chapter 8. DRILLING HOLES IN THE GROUND

Cable tool drilling

The young oil industry did not have to invent drilling; it simply adopted and adapted the equipment and techniques of the water-well drillers. The petroleum industry owes even more than that to the water-well drillers, because it was the accidental occurrence of oil and gas in water and brine wells that encouraged the early attempts at drilling specifically for oil. Oil had been found in Pennsylvania in a borehole drilled for salt 40 years before Drake's famous well of 1859.

Holes were drilled in the ground by the cable tool, or percussion, method. The essential mechanism is shown in Fig.8-1. The bottom of the hole is struck by a bit suspended on a cable. The cyclic motion at the surface is converted to vertical reciprocal motion, and the repeated blows cut and break the rock. By feeding the cable from the drum by means of the brake, the hole is deepened; and the drum can be connected to the motor for pulling the bit for dressing.

To drill a straight and round hole, it is essential that the bit rotates. This is accomplished by the lay of the rope, and a rope socket connection to the tools that allows the rope to rotate freely when slack. When lifting the tools off bottom, the weight stretches the rope, imparting a torque through the lay. This turns the bit slightly. On impact with the bottom of the hole, the rope is momentarily slack, and twists back to its natural lay removing the torque. Lifting again imparts another slight rotation to the bit, so that on impact it is not quite in the same position as before — and so on. Modern ropes are of flexible steel wire with a left hand lay, which imparts a clockwise rotation to the bit when viewed from above. A dulled bit is sharpened by heating it in a fire, dressing it by hammering, then re-tempering it.

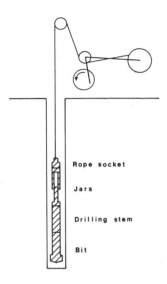

Rope socket

Jars

Drilling stem

Bit

Fig.8-1. Cable tool mechanism and drilling assembly.

The straightness of a borehole is also important, mainly because crooked holes lead to drilling difficulties. Straightness is achieved with cable tools by drilling with a "tight" line. If the bit is hung about 5 cm (2 or 3 inches) off bottom before setting the rig in motion, the bit will begin to strike the bottom because of stretch in the rope and because of movement of the crown block against a spring in a slide. The rope is thus in tension when the bit strikes. The cumulative effect of this is to drill a more vertical and straighter hole than one would with a slack rope.

The rock fragments, or *cuttings*, broken off by the bit tend to accumulate at the bottom of the hole, and eventually impede drilling and wear the shoulders of the bit (making it undergauge). They are removed by bailing. The bailer is simply a length of pipe, open at the top, but with a valve at the bottom that allows entry from below (Fig.8-2). After pulling the bit, the bailer is run on the sand line. It is then raised and lowered in a pumping action for a few strokes. The turbulence below the bailer on the upstroke tends to suspend cuttings in the water or mud, which pass into the bailer on the downstroke. These cuttings are the fragments of the rock that have been drilled since the last bailing, contaminated to

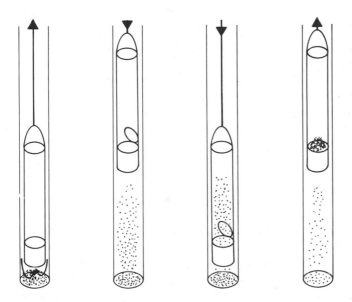

Fig.8-2. Bailer operation.

some extent by cuttings that were not bailed previously and by
cavings from higher up in the hole, dislodged by the rope or by
driving the casing. When they are viewed against drilling performance and the "feel" of the rope, a very complete and accurate
log of the rock types drilled, and their depths, can be drawn up.

The role of fluid in the borehole is also important. It provides
suspension for the cuttings, both during drilling and bailing, and it
cools the bit. In most parts of the world, any hole drilled in the
ground will be found to contain some water within about 10 m
(30 ft.) of the surface. If there is no groundwater, then water must
be put in the hole for it cannot be drilled far without.

It was part of the traditional knowledge of cable tool drilling
that if the hole contained mud rather than water, drilling performance and bailing were improved because of improved suspension
of the cuttings in the mud. Often the sedimentary rocks drilled
contained sufficient clay to turn the groundwater in the hole into
mud. If not, then clay could be added with advantage.

The *static water level* is always well known to cable tool drillers,
and this level is watched and noted. The new bit can be heard

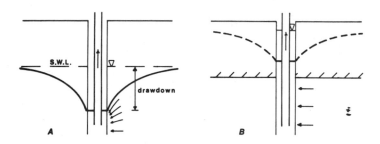

Fig.8-3. Drawdown in producing water wells. A. unconfined aquifer; B. confined aquifer. *S.W.L.* = static water level. The drawdown forms a *cone of depression*.

splashing into the water when running in, and the water level can be felt on the sand line with the bailer. If the hole is straight and vertical, daylight (or sunlight from a mirror) is reflected back from the surface of the water. Indeed, this is a standard check on straightness and verticality. Any change in the static water level during drilling is significant, for a sudden rise or fall indicates that an aquifer has been penetrated that has different hydraulic properties from those already drilled. If normal bailing results in a lowering of the level in the borehole, then clearly the rocks penetrated so far have little capacity to yield water. Rates up to about 1 l/sec (800 gallons/h) can be achieved with a bailer at shallow depth. The *drawdown* (Fig.8-3) is thus a measure of the permeability of the rocks to water. (If the shape of the drawdown curve can be determined by drilling "witness" wells, quantitative hydraulic parameters of the aquifer can also be determined.)

In hard rocks the bit drills a hole only marginally larger than the bit, and the margin can be so slight that a bit pulled undergauge may have been drilling a hole too small to take a full-gauge dressed bit. However, in soft rocks the hole drilled is larger — sometimes substantially larger — than the bit, due to the surge of mud past the bit at each stroke.

The hole must be protected from cavings, for these can cause the bit to stick (a stuck bit may be freed by an upward blow through the jars). This protection is given by lining the hole with steel pipe (casing). At the surface, a few joints of large diameter conductor pipe will normally be cemented in the hole through the soil layer. Below this, when drilling in soft rock, it is often possible to drive a string of casing with an O.D. (outside diameter) less than the hole, and an I.D. greater than the bit. This provides almost continuous protection while drilling in soft rock. Once the casing "freezes" the hole has to be drilled ahead without this protection — but the freezing usually indicates that the borehole has reached more competent rocks. As each string of casing becomes necessary and is run, so the hole diameter has to be reduced. In general, the deeper the planned depth of the hole, the larger the diameter of the bit used to start the hole.

This method of casing a hole is satisfactory for water wells in general, but it does lead to some waste when artesian water is struck. Since only the surface conductor pipe is usually cemented (unless artesian water is expected) artesian water, when confined by well-head installations, can pass outside the casing and enter porous and permeable formations of lower hydraulic head, because there is no seal between casing and the wall of the borehole. Clearly these were unsatisfactory features of cable tool drilling, when used for drilling for petroleum.

While the water-well drillers' techniques could be borrowed by the petroleum industry with little or no modification, there was another disadvantage that was both wasteful and dangerous. That is, the hole during drilling was necessarily open to the atmosphere. When water, oil, or gas was struck, there was nothing to stop it flowing out at the surface other than gravity. Water, of course, only flowed at the surface if an artesian aquifer was struck. Oil would flow slowly at the surface even under normal hydrostatic conditions unless the column of oil in the borehole balanced the column of water in the formations outside the borehole. One trip with the bailer could swab oil into the hole. Gas coming out of solution in the oil because of the reduction in pressure could accelerate the flow, reducing the mean density of the oil in the borehole. Gas without oil, unless contained by a column of mud, would tend to pass through the mud and, by expansion of the bubbles, tend to empty the hole of liquids. "Gushers" may have been the delight of drillers, but they were wasteful both of natural resources and of reservoir energy.

Cable tool rigs are still used extensively in the world for water drilling; but for petroleum they have been replaced by the rotary method. The cable tool rig remained competitive in some areas, notably Pennsylvania (where it all started) until the 1950's.

Rotary drilling

With the introduction of rotary drilling early this century, much of the terminology and jargon of cable tool drilling — such as crown block, drilling line, sand line, cuttings, fishing, striking oil or gas — were passed on, and many of the principles were consciously or unconsciously adopted. While the overall performance of rotary drilling exceeded that of cable tool, the advantages were not in every respect. The quality of direct geological data tended to diminish, and the petroleum geologist tended to lose touch with the rocks themselves. These losses were to be compensated for to an important extent by the introduction and development of electrical logging.

The process of rotary drilling is too well known to need much description here. The drilling string is made up of an assembly of a bit, drill collars (sometimes with reamers or stabilizers), and then drill pipe to the surface. Into the drill pipe below the drill floor is screwed the kelly — a pipe of square or hexagonal section — by which the rotary motion is applied to the string from the rotary table. Mud is circulated from the suction tank through the pumps to the swivel on top of the kelly; from there down the inside of the drill pipe to the bit; then up the annulus to the shale-shaker at the surface, and so back to the suction tank after passing through settling tanks in which much of the solids settle out.

At the bottom of the hole, the mud serves various purposes: it cools the bit, it assists the drilling process not only by removing the cuttings and keeping the bit clean, but also by actively scouring the bottom of the hole by virtue of nozzles in the bit that accelerate the mud into jets. The hydraulic energy of mud accelerated to a velocity of 100 m/sec or more makes a significant contribution to the penetration rate and general bit performance.

The drilling mud has another essential function. Its density ("weight" in the jargon) can be adjusted so that the pressure it exerts at the bottom of the hole is greater than that exerted by the formation fluids. It thus excludes formation fluids from the bore-hole.

While these factors represent great gains in the drilling and engineering aspects of the petroleum industry, they do not benefit the geologist in his study of the rocks penetrated by the drill. Cuttings there are, but they have been so abused by the time they reach the surface that they may be almost useless. When a more substantial sample of the subsurface rock is required, cores are obtained either by conventional coring, or by taking samples from the wall of the hole. Conventional coring is done with a special bit and core-barrel. The bit drills an annulus, leaving a core of rock to pass up into the core-barrel. When the length of the core-barrel (less a little) has been drilled, the core is broken off by fast rotation of the bit. The broken-off core should then be retained in the barrel by spring retainers. The core assembly is pulled slowly and carefully. Each *stand* of pipe (3 × 30 ft. − 10 m − *joints* of drill pipe) is unscrewed not by spinning the string in the hole with the rotary table as normal, but by unscrewing the stand above the slips. The expense of a core in terms of rig-time alone requires justification for the core sample; and its expense demands careful treatment of it. The core is extracted from the barrel not by hanging it over the core boxes and hammering, but by taking the barrel off the drill floor and extracting it with a hydraulic pump in a horizontal position. Government regulations may require a fixed or minimum coring programme.

The penetration rate is of general interest. The action of the bit on the rock at the bottom of the hole is a matter of mechanical engineering, rock mechanics and geological engineering. In the final analysis, what matters is not so much the length of hole drilled per bit, or the rate of drilling per bit, but the overall performance of the operation with its associated down-time for round trips, reaming an under-gauge hole, and other delays. From the geologists' point of view, optimization of the penetration rate, which is a parameter in the overall economy, is concerned largely with the optimization of the destruction of the rock and the removal of the cuttings.

The main parameters of the penetration rate are: (1) bit tooth geometry; (2) weight on bit; (3) rotation rate; (4) hydraulic energy and properties of the mud in circulation; (5) fluid potential gradient across the bottom of the borehole; (6) the "drillability" or the competence of the rock at the bottom of the borehole under the stresses existing in it and imposed upon it.

If the first four are kept constant, the penetration rate reflects changes in the last two factors. We shall return to the geological use of this in the next chapter.

The elimination of formation fluids from the borehole is one of the essential features of rotary drilling; but it also denies the geologist the insight he used to receive from the variations in the static water table. He is no longer aware of the hydraulic properties of permeable formations, nor of their capacity to yield water. Formation fluids only enter the borehole if they are at a pressure sufficiently high to displace the mud column. Although the petroleum geologist is no longer in touch, as it were, with the static water table, the geology of interstitial fluid pressures in the subsurface is one of his major concerns.

Fluid inflow into the borehole, or loss of mud to the formations is detected by observing the level in the suction tank. Modern rigs record this level automatically from a float, and an alarm bell is rung on the rig floor if the level reaches pre-set limits. The physical protection against a blowout (which may be defined as an uncontrolled flow of fluid through the borehole) is provided by the casing and the surface equipment, consisting of blowout preventers (abbreviated BOPs). The BOP stack includes one that closes the open hole (BOP with blind rams), one that closes around the drill pipe (pipe rams), and one that combines these needs with an expandible rubber compound (Hydril).

The casing in a borehole drilled by rotary has a dual purpose; the first is protection against caving (as with cable tool holes) and the second is for the isolation of fluids by sealing the casing to the wall of the borehole.

The first string of casing is the *conductor* (Fig.8-4), which is a large diameter pipe that may be driven into the surface. The purpose of this casing is to conduct the bit into the hole from below the rotary table, to prevent the unconsolidated surface

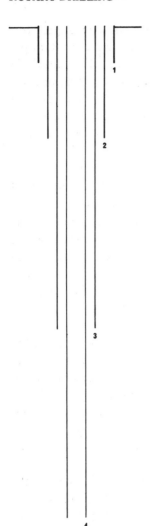

Fig.8-4. The various casing strings in borehole drilled for petroleum (schematic). *1* = conductor; *2* = surface string; *3* = protective string; *4* = production or oil string.

materials from collapsing into the hole, and to return the mud through the shaleshaker to the tanks.

The *surface* casing is cemented into a drilled hole, and also serves several functions. It is chiefly a protection against the caving of the relatively unconsolidated sediments at shallow depth, but also serves the important function of preventing the contamination of fresh-water aquifers by the drilling mud. The depth at which this casing is set, or landed, varies with local conditions but is usually at least 100 m (300 ft.) and may be set at about 10% of the planned total depth. Its diameter depends on the depth scheduled for the well, and the size of the anticipated production string (also called the oil string).

The *protective* casing is the casing on which the safety of the drilling operations will depend. It is therefore set in competent rocks, but not so deep that any risk is run before it is set. It may be necessary to run and cement two protective strings before the oil or production string is run. In areas where abnormal pressures occur at depth, it will be common to set the first at a relatively shallow depth, followed by the second at the first sign of abnormal pressures (which will usually be a drilling "break", when the penetration rate increases perceptibly over an interval). Protective casing is usually cemented to the surface. This may involve dual, or multiple, stage cementing in which the lower part is cemented as usual by displacing cement from the casing to the annulus, and the upper part is cemented through a sleeve in the casing that is opened by a plug pumped down inside the casing. The geologist should note that while this procedure reduces the pressure necessary to displace the cement, it does not reduce the hydrostatic pressure due to the column of liquid cement in the annulus, which may approach the geostatic or overburden pressure.

The production string serves the dual purpose of isolating the reservoir or reservoirs to be produced from other reservoirs (petroleum or water), and of providing easy access for the tubing, packers, etc., that will be necessary during its producing life. The sealing function is of paramount importance. As with the uncemented casing in a cable tool borehole that enters an artesian aquifer, so petroleum reservoirs of different hydraulic properties can communicate with each other behind the casing if it is not sealed. The production string is not necessarily cemented to the surface, but to a level comfortably within the protective casing. The reservoirs will be produced through perforations in the casing made by bullets or shaped charges fired from a gun lowered into the hole on a cable.

Geological considerations enter into the casing programmes of all wells. Such considerations are particularly important in exploratory holes drilled in areas without experience for guidance. The protective string must be set well into consolidated sediments, preferably landed with the shoe in an impermeable bed, such as a clay. Boreholes are logged before running each string of casing (except the surface string, usually), and the precise depth for the casing shoe is chosen after examination of the log. Geological considerations are not the only ones. Drilling engineering aspects, such as the amount of open hole (uncased) that it is considered safe to carry, are also important. And in many areas, Government regulations determine the depths of strings other than the production string.

Depth measurements are made from the level of the rotary table, the height of which above the surface of the ground and the survey datum level is determined. All depths for geological use are converted to depths below datum. On completion of the well, the elevation of the rotary table (or derrick floor — D.F.) is recorded with reference to the top of a casing flange, so that depth measurements in service and work-over operations can be related to the driller's depths, recorded in the drilling reports.

Deviated or directional drilling

The efficient development of a petroleum reservoir sometimes requires drainage points that are vertically beneath sites that are either impossible to drill from or unpractical due to expense. Such points are reached by drilling boreholes that are intentionally deviated from the vertical below a practical drilling site (Fig.8-5). These skills, which have grown with experience since the 1930's, are now such that it is normal practice to develop off-shore fields by drilling 10 or more wells from a single platform. The attainable precision of deviated drilling is illustrated by its other important application, the control of a well that has blown out and destroyed the rig or platform, or required the rig to be removed. A

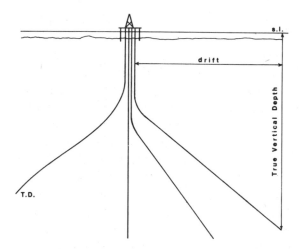

Fig.8-5. Deviated wells drilled from a marine platform. *T.D.* = total depth (measured along the borehole from the rotary table or derrick floor).

deviated hole is then drilled from a safe position, to penetrate the troublesome formation as close to the original well as possible. Water, mud, and cement is then pumped from the one to the other.

The principles of deviated drilling are best understood by comparison with those of drilling vertical holes. To drill a vertical hole, the number of drill collars made up in the assembly is such that their weight in mud is greater than the weight to be put on the bit. Thus, when drilling normally, the lower part of the drill collar assembly is in compression, for which the collars are designed, while the upper part and the drill pipe are in tension.

The neutral point is within the drill collar assembly, and it moves down when the weight on the bit is reduced, and up when it is increased. A crooked hole is straightened by reducing the weight on the bit, gravity then helping as with the taut line in cable tool drilling.

A deviated hole is started vertically, for oil drilling rigs are not designed to do otherwise, to the "kick-off" point. The bit is then pulled, and a whipstock run. The whipstock is essentially a wedge that forces the bit to deviate about 2½° from the line of the hole. This initial deflection is oriented in the desired direction. (In areas of soft sediments, the whipstock has been replaced by a bit with one eccentric nozzle, which blasts a hole slightly to one side, giving the same effect.)

The whipstock is now pulled and an ordinary drilling bit is run on a short assembly, or even on drill pipe without drill collars. Applying a light weight, the assembly bends, and the hole is deviated beyond the 2½° of initial deflection. The rate of deviation, or build-up, is controlled by controlling the weight on the bit, and so controlling the bending. The assembly is gradually lengthened to the normal length by the addition of drill collars, (one of which will be on non-magnetic monel metal, for the deviation surveys) and, at intervals between the collars, stabilizers or reamers are inserted to hold the assembly centrally in the hole. The angle of deviation is then controlled by the stabilizer spacing at the bottom of the assembly, the length of the short drill collar inserted between the lowest stabilizer and the bit (sometimes called a "stinger"), and the weight on the bit. The course is controlled to some extent by the speed of rotation; but may also be controlled if necessary by a primary deflection tool − the whipstock or the bit with an eccentric nozzle.

Deviated drilling complicates the geologists' work by the distortion of logs (compared with those of vertical holes) and by requiring the correction of depths measured along the borehole to true vertical depths. In the geological planning of a deviated borehole, the execution of the plan must be born in mind. The tolerances of position − the "tunnel" within which the borehole should be confined − should be as large as is compatible with the objectives of the borehole. Course corrections are expensive, and an unnecessarily restricted deviated hole will take longer to drill and cost more than a less restricted one.

The measurement of deviation in a vertical hole is not normally a matter that concerns the geologist greatly during drilling. The course of the well will be known with sufficient precision on completion from directional survey data acquired during drilling and logging (from the dipmeter, for instance). But in a deviated hole, the positions at different depths along the borehole vary considerably, and may vary considerably from those planned. Ultimately, the positions of significant parts of the borehole must be known as precisely as the data allows. The "navigation" of a deviated hole is accomplished by directional measurements made at intervals, the interval depending on the past performance, but usually before pulling each bit. The survey device is lowered inside the drill pipe on a wire line to a non-magnetic drill collar ("monel") in the assembly. The deviation is measured on a combination pendulum and compass that is photographed. The path of the borehole is estimated from these readings.

It is important for the petroleum geologist to be familiar with the drilling operations from which his basic data is acquired; and to learn the jargon of those who drill them. He must understand the problems of acquiring his data, for he must make his own assessment of the value of the information he seeks and the risks involved in getting it. To run a bulky logging device, such as the dipmeter, in a deep hole involves risks of losing it. This risk is small and readily accepted in most geological contexts. But if the bottom 500 m of a 4,000-m hole is shale, then there may be a valid argument for running this tool not from bottom, but from two or three hundred metres off bottom. The basis of such an argument would be that the cost and the risk would not be rewarded by the value of the information obtained over the bottom part.

Selected bibliography

Brantly, J.E., 1961. *Rotary Drilling Handbook* (6th. ed.). Palmer, New York, N.Y., 825 pp.

Craft, B.C., Holden, W.R. and Graves, E.D., 1962. *Well Design: Drilling and Production.* Prentice-Hall, Engle Wood Cliffs, N.J., 571 pp.

Moore, P.L. and Cole, F.W., 1965. *Drilling Operations Manual.* Petroleum Publishing Co., Tulsa, Okla., (various pagings).

Staff of British Petroleum Co. Ltd., 1970. *Our Industry Petroleum.* British Petroleum Co. Ltd., London, 528 pp.

Staff of Royal Dutch/Shell Group, 1966. *The Petroleum Handbook* (5th ed.). Shell International Petroleum Co. Ltd., London, 318 pp.

Chapter 9. THE LOGGING OF BOREHOLES

Summary

(1) Wire-line logging devices provide borehole logs that are essential documents for the description and interpretation of the subsurface geology of petroleum acuumulations. They are used both qualitatively and quantitatively. They are run in the hole after drilling a section of the hole, before running casing. While drilling, a plot of penetration rate versus depth gives a valuable indication of the rock units penetrated, and it is commonly more reliable than the cutting samples obtained.

(2) The basic log is an electrical log that records resistivity and spontaneous potential (S.P.) against depth.

The resistivity of a porous rock is a function of its porosity, the pore-space geometry, the resistivity of the interstitial fluids (salinity of the groundwater) and their temperature.

The S.P. log distinguishes clays (shales) from other lithologies. The deflections opposite lithologies other than clays (shales) are due to natural electrical currents circulating around the intersection of the borehole with a lithological boundary. These currents are partly due to the contrast in salinity between the mud and the formation fluids; partly to clay or shale acting as a semi-permeable membrane; and, to a small extent, to the movement of fluid from the borehole to the formation.

(3) The dipmeter is an electrical device that measures the dip of strata in the borehole. It is used principally for the determination of structural attitude, but is being used increasingly as an aid to the elucidation of the environment of deposition of sequences of sediments.

(4) Radioactivity logs record either the spontaneous or induced radioactivity of rocks in the borehole. They are used for determining lithology, porosity, fluid content, and bulk density of the

rocks. The gamma ray log, which records natural emissions of gamma rays, can be run in cased holes.

(5) The sonic log provides a record of the velocity of sound through the rocks adjacent to the borehole. It has geophysical uses; but it is also valuable for the determination of porosity and the estimation of interstitial fluid pressures in clays and shales.

General

The desire and need to know the succession of rock-types penetrated by a borehole dates from the early days of drilling; and as the geological basis for drilling increased, so did the need for accurate and informative borehole logs. The primary need was probably for geological information from which the shape of the structure could be determined; but with increasing knowledge of the technological problems of petroleum production, the parallel need for physical data on the rocks also grew. It became necessary not only to know at what depths the various rock types were encountered, but also to know the nature of the rock, its porosity and permeability, its temperature, the nature of the contained fluids (known in this context as "formation fluids") and the depths of any fluid contacts or interfaces.

The process of drilling holes in the ground consists necessarily of breaking the rock and removing the cuttings from the borehole. When drilling by cable tool, the cuttings are bailed from the bottom of the hole at intervals, and these cuttings are reliable samples of the rock penetrated since the last bailing. Contamination is largely confined to caving from higher parts of the hole (from driving casing, or from the lash of the cable), and the only loss is a tendency for clays to form mud with the water in the borehole. Fluid samples are also obtained when bailing; but these tend to be contaminated. Once oil or gas was encountered, this was usually quite obvious because it flowed into the borehole, and sometimes at the surface until it could be controlled. The compilation of all these data was incorporated into the driller's log.

The introduction of rotary drilling significantly altered the nature of the problem of logging the borehole. The mud column confined the fluids within the formations, and samples of these could only be obtained (intentionally or unintentionally) by producing them into the borehole.

The rotary drilling process is so destructive of the cuttings that it has become much more difficult to determine the nature of the rock from which they came. As holes are drilled deeper, and ways are found of improving drilling performance, so the destructive forces applied to the cuttings increase. The time taken by the cuttings in transit to the surface increases as the depth of the borehole increases, so the sample taken at the shale-shaker refers not to the present depth of drilling, but some shallower depth. From the time the cutting is broken by the bit tooth and blasted by mud that has been accelerated through nozzles in the bit, to the time it comes onto the shale-shaker, it has been thoroughly abused. It has been accelerated up the annulus between the drill collars and the wall of the hole; decelerated at the top of the drill collars, accelerated past each tool joint at about 10 m (30 ft.) intervals, all in a spiral motion, and no doubt hammered from time to time by the drill pipe. Clay fractions become part of the mud. The larger rock fragments travel more slowly than the smaller, the round more slowly than the angular, the denser more slowly than the less dense. The cuttings collected at the shale-shaker of a deep borehole can hardly be thought of as reliable samples of the rock; and there are occasions when the well-site geologist should not be required to follow tradition and examine and describe all samples, because the reward cannot recompense the labour.

The sample must be taken, however, because it may contain fossils, and these form an important part of the geological record of the borehole. It must be remembered, though, that if Nature has been very selective in the matter of which organisms are preserved as fossils, the drilling process is further selective in destroying all but the micro-fossils, and even then perhaps in destroying some of the larger, or more delicate, forms. The biostratigraphic record of a borehole also suffers from uncertainties.

An essential aid to the logging of boreholes is to have installed (and properly functioning!) a penetration-rate recorder that enables one to make a plot of penetration-rate versus depth. If the normal operational drilling parameters are kept constant (that is, weight on bit, rate of rotation, hydraulic energy and properties of the mud) the rate of penetration is a function of bit wear, fluid potential gradient across the bottom of the hole, and the mechanical properties of the rock being drilled. In practice, when drilling normally pressured rocks, the rate of penetration varies significantly with different lithologies, and only towards the end of a bit's run does the dulling of the bit mask these changes. If a plot is kept of "minutes to drill 1 m (or x ft.)" versus depth, the resulting "penetration log" will commonly be found to correlate closely with the "spontaneous potential" log when it has been run. The penetration rate log is therefore an indispensable part of the drilling record, and is a valuable aid to making sense of the cuttings.

Contamination of the mud is also an important part of the drilling record. Part of the fluid content of the rock drilled is retained in the cutting or in the mud. *Gas-cutting*, dilution with formation water, and any other significant changes in mud properties must be recorded, and these changes compared with the penetration rate log and, eventually, the electrical logs. Modern rigs run a continuous sampling of the mud returns for hydrocarbons.

There is always a need to know as fully as possible the sequence of rocks, their properties and their fluids, as they are drilled. This need can be urgent when drilling towards a sequence with abnormal interstitial fluid pressures, or when wishing to land casing at a particular stratigraphic position, or below a particular reservoir. The nature of the record is necessarily incomplete while drilling is in progress because so much of the evidence is destroyed.

Coring is generally too slow, and so too expensive, for general use. At the best, a core will provide a few metres of fairly reliable information; but there is a danger here of regarding it as more reliable than it really is. The core has been cut by drilling around it, broken off by spinning the pipe, removed from the subsurface conditions of temperature and pressure to the surface, and extracted from the core barrel. Parameters such as porosity and permeability can be measured with great precision, and this precision beguiles us into accepting them as valid *in situ*. Nevertheless, they are very valuable samples to the geologists, for they indicate the lithology and environment of the sediments cored, and provide a valuable check on porosity and permeability data obtained by other means.

Electrical logging of boreholes was developed in the late 1920's by the French engineer, Schlumberger, and the techniques have grown with the demands until it is now an essential service using a wide range of sophisticated tools for subsurface logging and interpretation.

Techniques have developed so fast in the last two decades that no attempt will be made here to discuss the details of the tools available. These details, and the description of interpretive methods, can be obtained from the companies performing this service. The petroleum geologist — indeed, any geologist today — must acquire a knowledge of the principles of borehole logging with wire-line devices if he is to read his logs intelligently.

The principles of electrical logging

The basic log used by the petroleum geologist consists of a recording of the resistivity of the rocks and the spontaneous potential in the borehole, versus depth (Fig.9-1). This log is obtained in a single run in the borehole. The device is contained in a *sonde* which is lowered down the hole on a cable within which electric cables pass. The common electrode arrangements are shown in Fig.9-2. Most logs are run from the bottom of the hole to the top, for this direction, with a taut cable, gives more positive depth control on the log, which is measured from the cable movement at the surface. (Temperature logs are run while running in.) The readings from the sonde are converted into a signal at the surface that is recorded on photographic film that is wound past the signal at a speed scaled to the speed of the sonde in the borehole.

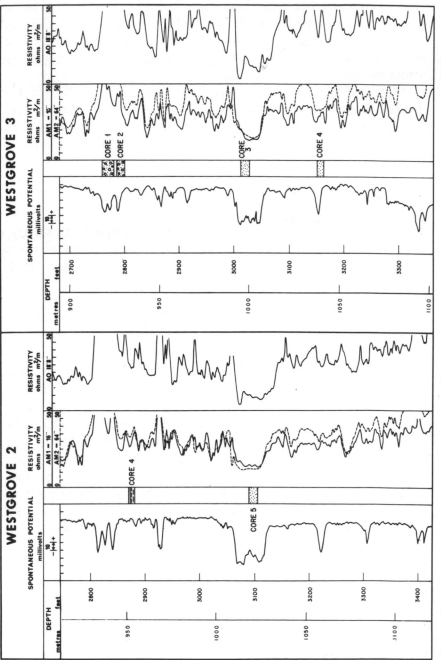

Fig. 9-1. Electrical logs of part of two Westgrove wells, Queensland, Australia. The left-hand resistivity curves are short and long normal; the right-hand curves the inverse. Electrode arrangements as in Fig. 9-2, but the nomenclature for the inverse

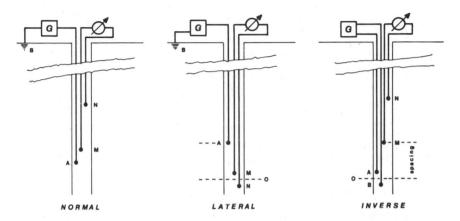

Fig.9-2. Electrode arrangements of normal, lateral, and inverse resistivity devices. G = generator; A and B are current electrodes; M and N are measuring electrodes. The inverse device is equivalent to the lateral, for interchanging the electrode functions does not alter the measurement. The inverse arrangement allows duplication of electrodes in the sonde for running short normal, long normal, and inverse simultaneously. (Courtesy of Schlumberger Seaco Inc., Sydney.)

Resistivity

Nearly all the common rock-forming minerals are non-conductors of electricity. Dry porous rocks are non-conductors because the fluid in the pore spaces (air) is also a non-conductor. In the ground, however, porous rocks contain a fluid: that fluid is usually water, and the water is usually saline. Saline water, an electrolyte, conducts electricity by the movement of charged ions that result from the dissociation of salts in solution in water.

The conductivity, or capacity of groundwater to conduct electricity, is proportional to the number of ions, each of which can conduct a specific amount of electrical charge. Groundwater contains many different ions. The common ones are Na^+, Ca^{2+}, Mg^{2+} (cations); Cl^-, SO_4^{2-}, CO_3^{2-} and HCO_3^- (anions). Each of these ions has a different conducting capacity, so a valuable simplification is to consider a NaCl solution or an *equivalent* NaCl solution. In general, the more saline the solution, the more conductive and less resistant it is.

The resistivity of a material is a measure of the difficulty with which an electric current flows through the material. It is the inverse of conductivity. Some electrical logging devices measure conductivity, but most measure resistivity.

The unit of *resisitivity* in electrical logging is the *resistance* of a cube of the material with sides of 1 m, that is, the *Ohm metre* (Ωm, sometimes written Ohm m^2/m, Ohm-metre, or Ohmm). Resistance is proportional to length, inversely proportional to the area in a plane normal to the current direction (length).

Consider a cube of non-conducting material, 1 m $\times$ 1 m $\times$ 1 m. The resistivity of this cube is infinite. If a straight hole of 1 cm^2 cross-sectional area is drilled through the cube normal to the two faces between which the current will be passed, and this hole is filled with water of resistivity (R_w) 1 Ωm, the *resistance* of this water in the hole will be:

$$\frac{R_w \times length}{area} = \frac{1 \times 1}{0.0001} = 10,000 \ \Omega$$

and the *resistivity* of the cube will be 10,000 Ωm. If a second hole of the same size is drilled parallel to the first, and both holes are filled with water of resistivity $R_w = 1 \ \Omega$m, the resistivity of the cube will be 5,000 Ωm. Increasing the number of holes will decrease the resisitivity of the cube. If there are 2,000 such holes, the resistivity of the cube will be 5 Ωm, and the "porosity" will be 20%. The resistivity of the cube is thus inversely proportional to the "porosity" when R_w is constant.

If the holes are now filled with water of a different resistivity, the resulting resistivity of the cube will be different. Other things being equal, the higher the resistivity of the water, the higher the resistivity of the cube.

In nature, the pore passages of porous rocks are neither straight nor of constant diameter. Nor are they all connected; but we are concerned only with *effective* porosity, because fluid entirely enclosed by a non-conductor takes no part in the flow of electricity. The path of the current through waterfilled pores is tortuous and therefore longer. A metre cube of rock with a porosity of 20%, the pores being filled with water of 1 Ωm resistivity, would have a resistivity greater than 5 Ωm.

There is a further variable to be considered apart. from porosity and the resistivity of the interstitial water. The conductivity of water is a function of its temperature, which in turn is a function of its depth in the context of sub-surface electrolytes. The higher the temperature, the lower the resistivity.

A fundamental parameter in electrical log interpretation which may conveniently be considered at this point, is the ratio of the resistivity of a porous rock filled with an electrolyte, and the resistivity of the electrolyte. This is called the *formation resistivity factor* (*F*) and was defined by Archie (1942) as:

$$R_o = F R_w \qquad\qquad (9\text{-}1)$$

where R_o is the resistivity of a rock saturated with water of resistivity R_w. Empirical data showed that the formation resistivity factor (sometimes abbreviated to formation factor) is a measure of porosity; but its significance is perhaps clearer when considered in the following manner.

Following Wyllie (1963), the formation resistivity factor can be re-expressed as the ratio of the *resistance* of a metre cube of water-filled rock (r_o) to the resistivity of the water:

$$F = r_o/R_w \ .$$

The resistance of a metre cube of porous rock filled with an electrolyte is:

$$r_o = \frac{R_w \times \text{length of pore passages}}{\text{area of pore passages}}$$

The length of the pore passages for the movement of ions is greater than 1 m, say (1 + Δ) m. The proportionate cross-sectional area of the pore passages in a plane normal to the direction of the current is numerically equal to the mean porosity, with a statistical variation about the mean in different planes. So the resistance of the cube of electrolyte-filled rock may be written:

$$r_o = \frac{R_w \times (1 + \Delta)}{f}$$

where f is, as before, the porosity ($0 \leqslant f < 1$).

Hence:

$$\frac{r_o}{R_w} = \frac{1+\Delta}{f} = F$$

Since $r_o = R_o$ in a metre cube, the formation factor is seen to be inversely proportional to porosity, and proportional to a factor that relates to the pore geometry. *It is independent of the salinity or the resistivity of the pore fluid.* In other words, if a porous rock is found to have a formation factor of 5 (as in the example of the drilled cube) any change in the resistivity of the fluid in the same specimen will not change the value of $F = 5$ for this specimen. It does not mean that all rocks with 20% porosity will have a formation factor of 5, because the geometrical factor $(1 + \Delta)$ will vary from one rock-type to another.

Archie suggested the following relationship (now known as "Archie's formula"):

$$F = R_o/R_w = f^{-m} \qquad\qquad\qquad (9\text{-}2)$$

where m is commonly, though perhaps not very accurately, known as the *cementation factor.* The value of m depends on the rock type, and varies from about 1.3 for clean unconsolidated sand to about 2.1 for hard sandstone. ($m = 1$ in the case of the drilled cube, with straight non-constricted pores.)

Satisfactory approximations to the formation factor are:

$$F = 0.81 f^{-2} \qquad \text{for sand} \qquad\qquad (9\text{-}2a)$$

$$F = f^{-2} \qquad\quad \text{for hard sandstone} \qquad (9\text{-}2b)$$

$$F = 0.62 f^{-2.15} \qquad \text{the "Humble formula"} \qquad (9\text{-}2c)$$

In short, if the value of F can be measured by saturating a rock sample with an electrolyte of known resistivity, the resistivity of that rock saturated with a fluid of another resistivity can be calculated if the resistivity of that fluid is known. Alternatively, knowing or estimating F and the resistivity of the rock, the resistivity (and hence the salinity) of the pore fluids can be calculated or estimated. An estimate of F leads to an estimate of porosity.

So far, we have considered only clean porous rock saturated with an electrolyte. These relationships do not hold for "dirty" sands, that is, sands with an appreciable clay content, because a wet clay material contributes to the conductivity of a rock. The evaluation of dirty sands presents problems that are best referred to a specialist petrophysicist.

Contamination of the formation fluid by petroleum is very much the petroleum geologist's business. Oil and gas are both non-conductors of electricity. Petroleum in a porous and permeable rock does not replace all the water that was originally present in the pore spaces. Most rock-forming minerals are water-wet, and retain a film of water over the surfaces of the grains (Fig.9-3). Capillary forces cause this film to vary in thickness, the petroleum occupying only the central part of the pores. The effect is thus one of reduced porosity, and a rock with interstitial petroleum has a higher resistivity than the same rock with interstitial brine.

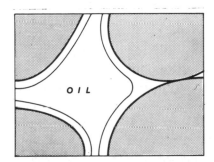

Fig.9-3. Oil and water in pore space of water-wet rock.

The resistivity of a petroleum-bearing rock is not only a function of R and R_w, but also of the interstitial water saturation, S_w. S_w is the proportion of *pore* volume occupied by water ($0 < S_w \leq 1$). The oil saturation is similarly the proportion of pore volume occupied by oil. Experimentally it has been found that:

$$S_w \approx (R_o/R_t)^{1/n} \qquad (9\text{-}3)$$

where R_t is the true resistivity of the rock containing some petroleum, and n is a saturation exponent with a value of the order of 2. Substituting eq.9-1 into eq.9-3, we get:

$$S_w \approx (FR_w/R_t)^{1/2} \qquad\qquad\qquad\qquad (9\text{-}4)$$

from which we can write:

$$R_t \approx FR_w/S_w^2 \qquad\qquad\qquad\qquad (9\text{-}4a)$$

From this it can be seen that the true resistivity of a petroleum-bearing rock is only relatively higher than that of the same rock saturated with water. The true resistivity may be quantitatively quite low when the formation factor is low (high porosity) and the resistivity of the interstitial water is low (high salinity or high temperature). As a *guide* to possible production, the ratio R_t/R_o, the resistivity index, may be useful. The smaller the value of the resistivity index, the higher the expected proportion of water produced (water cut) with the petroleum.

The determination of R_t is one of the main goals of electrical logging. It is not simple. Its determination is in the realm of the specialist petrophysicist.

The contamination of formation fluids by drilling fluids is both a help and a hindrance: in any case, it is unavoidable. Drilling mud in the borehole is given a higher pressure gradient than that in the formation fluids, hence at any given depth, there is a fluid potential gradient outwards from the borehole into the rocks. The resulting flow of fluid is insignificant into the relatively impermeable lithologies, such as clays, silts, marls, and some evaporites, during the time interval between drilling through them and logging them. But it is significant into the more permeable beds, such as sands, sandstones, limestones and dolomites.

The wall of the borehole in a permeable bed acts as a filter to the mud, with the result that a *filter cake* (also called a *mud cake*) forms on the wall of the borehole. Through this filter cake, mud filtrate passes to the pore spaces of the permeable rock. This contamination ranges from nearly 100% in water-bearing sands in the immediate vicinity of the borehole (virtually complete flushing of the original fluids) to nil at some distance from it. In oil-bearing sands flushing is not complete, and residual oil remains in the pore spaces. The proximal zone is known as the "flushed zone" (and

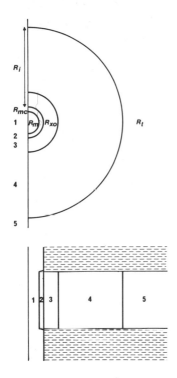

Fig.9-4. Invasion of permeable water-bearing bed by mud filtrate (plan and section). *1* = borehole filled with mud; *2* = mud cake; *3* = flushed zone; *3 + 4* = invaded zone; *5* = uncontaminated zone. Invasion of a petroleum-bearing permeable bed differs mainly in that there is a tendency for gravity segregation. (Courtesy of Schlumberger Seaco Inc., Sydney.)

parameters relating to it are given the suffix "xo", as in R_{xo}), and the contaminated zone beyond this and including the flushed zone is known as the "invaded zone" (suffix "i"). (Fig.9-4).

The dimensions of these zones are not only variable from bed to bed, but they are also likely to be variable at different levels within a single bed. In representing them commonly as circular in plan, one makes this assumption from ignorance of its true geometry. There is also a dimension of *time* involved in the invasion of the rock unit by mud filtrate.

In spite of these difficulties, it will be clear that within the flushed zone there will be a fluid the resistivity of which can be measured. If the temperature of the filtrate in the rock is known, then the formation factor can be obtained, in theory, by applying eq.9-4a, thus:

$$R_{xo} = FR_{mf}/S_{xo}^2 \qquad\qquad (9\text{-}4b)$$

where R_{mf} is the resistivity of the mud filtrate at the temperature of the flushed zone, R_{xo} and S_{xo} the resistivity and water saturation respectively of the flushed zone. In a water sand, $S_{xo} = 1$. It must be remembered, however, that R_{xo} is measured in the zone most affected mechanically by the drilling, hence the value of the formation factor in the flushed zone may not be representative of the bed as a whole.

The electrical resistivity logging devices are designed taking these fundamental principles into account. In general, the greater the electrode spacing (always recorded on the heading to the log) the greater the lateral "depth" of investigation. But current passed between electrodes passes partly through the mud in the borehole, partly through the flushed and invaded zones, and a part — usually only a small part — through the uninvaded, uncontaminated rock. Qualitative inferences from the resistivity readings of different devices over the same rock unit are important in the geological use of electrical logs. They are best learnt from practice, not from books.

Spontaneous potential (S.P.) log

The S.P. log is run concurrently with one or more resistivity devices and is an important part of the basic log used by the petroleum geologist, or the geologist working on any area in which borehole logs are available. It records the potential difference between a fixed electrode at the surface and a movable electrode in the borehole. The unit of measurement is the millivolt (mV). The base line for the measurement is not a line on the scale of the log, but the line recorded opposite shales. It is known as the *shale base line* or *shale line*. Deflections from this are measured to the left of this line (negative) or to the right (positive). The deflections result from natural electric currents in the borehole that are caused by electromotive forces of electrochemical and electroinetic origins. The position of the base line is arbitrary with respect to the scale, and is normally placed in a position that allows the deflections (observed by the operator when running in) to fall conveniently within the scale area.

An *electrochemical potential* (E_c or E_{ch})' results from the introduction of a conductive borehole fluid (the drilling mud) across porous rocks with fluids of a conductivity different from that of the fluid in the borehole and its filtrate. This potential, which contributes most (if not all) of the deflection on the log, consists of two components in a sequence of alternating lithologies with clays (shales).

Consider a porous, permeable bed between two thick, porous, but relatively impermeable, clays in a borehole (Fig.9-5). Let us assume that the electrolytes — the formation water, the mud and its filtrate — are NaCl solutions, and that the mud and its filtrate are less saline than the formation water. The composition of clays and shales is extremely complicated and variable; but they may be considered as composed of grains in which there are layers of Al, Si, and O atoms with some layers of water that are bound to the lattice (not interstitial) by residual charges due to the substitution of one positive atom in a clay mineral by another of lower valency (e.g., Mg^{2+} replacing Al^{3+}). O^- tends to occur on the outer margins of the layers, with the result that clays are more permeable to Na^+ ions than Cl^- ions. Na^+ tends to pass through the clay from the more saline solution (assumed for discussion to be the formation water) to the less saline solution in the borehole, and

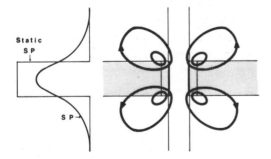

Fig.9-5. S.P. diagram. (Courtesy of Schlumberger Seaco Inc., Sydney.)

this is the direction of the electrical current (+). This is known as the *membrane potential.*

Within the permeable bed, however, invasion of mud filtrate gives rise to contrasting salinities in the pore spaces, across the interface between the mud filtrate and the formation water. Cl^- ions are more mobile than Na^+ ions, so there is a net flow of Cl^- from the more saline formation water to the less saline mud filtrate, with a resulting current flow in the opposite direction. This is known as the *liquid junction potential.*

These two components give rise to an electric current circulating around the interface between the clay and the permeable unit near the borehole, and the potential of this current is measured. The intensity of the electrochemical potential is greatest at the level of the interface in the borehole. If the static S.P. could be measured, that is, the S.P. that is not reduced by the resistance encountered by the current flow through the rocks and fluids, it would be rectilinear and mark the change of lithology at the borehole precisely. Nevertheless, the slope of the S.P. as recorded is proportional to the electromotive force in the borehole, and the lithological boundary is indicated by the *inflection point* of the curve. This may well not coincide with the mean value of the deflection. The S.P. log is therefore of fundamental geological value in locating the rock units penetrated by the borehole.

When the salinity of the mud and its filtrate is greater than that of the formation water, the direction of the currents is reversed, and the deflection opposite the permeable bed will be positive with respect to that opposite the shale. Fresh-water aquifers, commonly in the higher part of the borehole, are so revealed (see Fig.10-1). Holes drilled with sea water or a mud based on sea water also lead to S.P. reversal over at least the upper part of the log. And where the salinity of the mud and its filtrate are equal to that of the formation water, no deflection of the S.P. occurs.

The total electromotive force corresponding to the electrochemical potential can be expressed:

$$E_{ch} = -K \log \frac{a_w}{a_{mf}} \tag{9-5}$$

where a_w and a_{mf} are the chemical activities of the formation water and the mud filtrate, and K is a coefficient proportional to the absolute temperature. However, if the concentrations of the two NaCl solutions are less than about 80,000 p.p.m., their chemical activities are approximately inversely proportional to their resitivities, so that eq.9-5 can be approximated by:

$$E_{ch} \approx -K \log \frac{R_{mf}}{R_w} \tag{9-5a}$$

Of these parameters E_{ch} can be estimated, and R_{mf} measured.

The electrokinetic (or streaming)potential (E_k) in a borehole is considered by some to be very small, and by others to be non-existent from a practical point of view. This potential is attributable to the flow of mud filtrate across the mud cake into the permeable rock unit. It is often large, but approximately equal to that opposite the shales. The contribution of E_k is the difference between the e.m.f. across the mud cake and that into the shale (for few shales are so impermeable that no flow takes place into them). There is no argument that whatever its value, E_k makes at most a small contribution to the total deflection of the S.P.

In theory, many parameters influence the shape and amplitude of the deflection of the S.P. opposite the more permeable beds. They include the thickness and R_t of the permeable bed, and the resistivity of the adjacent beds; the resistivity of the mud and its filtrate; the resistivity of the invaded zone and its diameter; and the diameter of the borehole. It is not strictly a permeability log, because a small fraction of a millidarcy (mD) is sufficient for an e.m.f. to be generated. Nevertheless, it is an invaluable log from which clays can be distinguished from more permeable lithologies, fresh formation water can be distinguished from brine (reversed S.P. and high resistivity). Quantitative analysis leads to the determination of formation water salinities without the need of a sample at the surface. It is the log from which lithological boundary depths are recorded, and from which the thicknesses of rock units are obtained.

Resistivity devices

The *microlog* is a resistivity device of some direct importance to geologists. It consists of three electrodes with very short spacing (1 inch and 2 inches) that are held to the wall of the hole in a spring-loaded pad. The depth of investigation is thus confined to the immediate vicinity of the borehole. Opposite impermeable beds, the resistivities measured by the two spacings are essentially the same, and their curves are more or less superimposed on the log. Opposite permeable beds, where a mud cake has formed, the shorter spacing measures the resistivity of the mud cake (mostly) while the longer spacing measures that of the mud cake and of some of the flushed zone beyond. These resistivities are usually different, and the curves show a separation on the log. The spring-loaded arm that holds the pad to the wall of the hole serves also as a caliper, and the hole diameter is also recorded on the log. The caliper log shows those sections of the hole that have been washed out to a larger diameter (usually shales or clays) and the separation of the curves indicates qualitatively the permeable sequences of the sediments penetrated by the borehole. Quantitative analysis leads to estimates of the formation factor and the porosity through eq.9-4b with the reservations made in that discussion.

The *dipmeter* is a resistivity device (usually) that is not intended primarily to measure the properties of the rocks penetrated, but the dip of the beds and laminations. Three oriented electrodes at 120° radially in a plane normal to the sonde axis permit the computation of the dip of a bed relative to the axis of the borehole when that bed can be recognized on the traces of all three electrodes. Some dipmeters with 4 electrodes at 90° are in use. An oriented pendulum records the inclination of the borehole and the direction of that inclination, so that the dip relative to the borehole can be corrected to an absolute measurement of the direction and amount of the dip of the bed. The dipmeter, apart from its basic structural use, is valuable for the detection of faults, and for the recognition of some environments of deposition that have characteristic laminations (such as cross bedding) that can be detected by the dipmeter. The refinement of this tool over the last 15 years has greatly improved its value to the geologist, and further refinement will no doubt further improve its value.

The *radioactivity* logs record natural or induced radiation from the rocks. Of these, we single out the gamma ray log, as this records the natural emission of gamma rays into the borehole. It primarily distinguished clays from other lithologies on account of the higher gamma radiation from clay minerals. It is not as precise as the S.P.; but it has the merit not only of being obtainable through casing, and in holes drilled with sea water or highly saline muds, but also of indicating clayey sands, and variable carbonate lithologies that are not clearly indicated on the S.P.

Finally, the *temperature log*. There is a growing interest in the temperature gradient in petroleum areas, but this is *not* the log to use. The temperature log is run primarily in boreholes to determine the top of cement behind casing. The process of cement hardening is exothermic, and appreciable temperature changes can be detected in a borehole about 10 hours after cementing the casing. The drilling process seriously disturbs the temperature equilibrium in the subsurface adjacent to a borehole: reliable temperature measurement for geological use should be obtained from the reservoir engineer. Provisional bottom hole temperatures can be estimated from those recorded during a logging programme and taken from the log headings in the sequence in which they are run.

Fluid pressures from wire-line logs

One of the most pressing operational problems of drilling during the last two decades has been that of obtaining warning of abnormal interstitial fluid pressures in the sequence to be penetrated by the borehole. This problem was solved to an important extent by the development of drilling techniques that accentuated the drilling "break" — the sudden and often dramatic increase in the penetration rate observed when drilling into an abnormally pressured sequence. The search for *warning* signs in electrical and other logs has not been so successful; but this is largely because logs can only be run in a hole that has already been drilled, and so they are unlikely to reveal what was not revealed during drilling.

Study of the problem of detecting abnormal interstitial fluid pressures in boreholes by means of electrical and other logs has been successful, and if these are of limited value for operational warning, they are of great value to the geologist. Qualitatively, the methods to be described here may be regarded as reliable: quantitatively, there is room for improvement. Improvement can be confidently expected because the history of subsurface techniques in boreholes has shown a general trend towards measuring indirectly *in situ* what earlier could only be measured directly – usually on a sample brought to the surface.

Success in this direction is not without interest for the geologist. Interstitial fluid pressures as we have seen, are pertinent geological data. Time considerations limit the acquisition of direct measurements to reservoirs and potential reservoirs. Thus the pressure distribution in many sequences must be obtained indirectly, if it is to be obtained at all. If the methods are quantitatively still rather crude, the data obtained are better than no data at all. Relative accuracy should reveal the main fluid potential gradients in the sediments of an area, and so reveal the main patterns of fluid migration.

In the geological context, the acquisition of pressure data is cumulatively and collectively valuable, and in the operational context this information may be almost as valuable as a direct warning would be, leading to better borehole design.

Promising tools for interstitial pressure analysis are: resistivity logs, particularly the short normal; the induction log (conductivity); the sonic log; and the formation density log. Qualitative and quantitative analysis (whichever tool is used) is based on the comparison of *clay* rocks penetrated by the borehole and the inter-relationships between their depths. their porosities, and their interstitial fluid pressures. Chapters 3 and 6 provide the basis for this section.

The porosity of a clay rock is a function both of its depth and its interstitial fluid pressure. And porosity is a parameter of a rock that affects not only its bulk density and its resistivity (as we have seen), but also the velocity of sound through it. In general, the higher the porosity the lower the resistivity, the lower the bulk density, and the slower the velocity of sound through it. Hence, if these parameters can be determined for a clay that is in stress equilibrium, with normal hydrostatic interstitial fluid pressures, the degree of compaction of other clay units can be assessed (qualitatively or quantitatively) by comparison.

Shale resistivity

Qualitatively, it has been observed that the resistivity of "shales" tends to increase with depth, but that it tends to decrease in the upper transition zone of abnormal pressures. Below the base of the transition zone the shale resistivity tends to increase again with depth (Fig.9-6). A purely empirical approach has been to seek to construct a plot of the ratio of normal shale resistivity to abnormal shale resistivity against the observed ratio of fluid pressure to depth (e.g., Hottman and Johnson, 1965). The construction of such an empirical curve can only be done if some per-

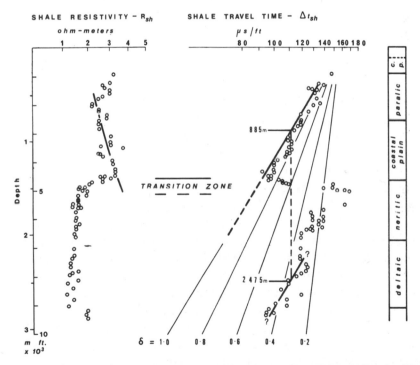

Fig.9-6. Plot of shale resistivity and shale travel time against depth. (Data from a well in Borneo, by courtesy of Bataafse Internationale Petroleum Maatschappij N.V., The Hague.)

meable rock units have been tested and their interstitial fluid pressures measured. The assumption is then made that abnormally pressured permeable beds reflect the pressure in the adjacent shales. This method has led to some satisfactory results within areas for which the empirical data has been obtained.

Theoretical treatment of shale resistivities is not yet satisfactory, for there are many variables. Wet clay is not a non-conductor of electricity, as is the solid matrix of a quartz sand (for example). Furthermore, comparison of shale resistivities must take temperatures and interstitial fluid salinities into account.

Similar considerations apply to the use of the induction log.

The value of the shale resistivity (or conductivity) method for detecting abnormal interstitial fluid pressures appears to be limited at present to the warning given if a reduction of shale resistivity is observed near the bottom of an intermediate log that is run before the planned total depth of the borehole has been reached.

Sonic log

The speed of sound through sedimentary rocks is a parameter of geophysical and geological interest. It depends partly on the nature of the solid matrix and partly on the porosity. Sound travels faster through solids than through liquids. The sonic log, which measures the speed of sound in the wall of the borehole, is therefore commonly available.

The sonde consists of a sound signal generator and three or more detectors (Fig.9-7), and the resulting log is a plot of sound pulse travel time (in μs/ft. or per metre) versus depth. If the travel time in shale (obtained by correlation with the S.P.) is plotted on a logarithmic scale against a linear depth scale, an approximately linear trend is obtained over normally compacted shales (Fig.9-6), with the shale travel time (Δt_{sh}) decreasing with depth. This relationship results from a logarithmic reduction of shale porosity with depth, an approximately linear relationship between sonic velocity and porosity, and approximately constant matrix velocity (velocity is not sensitive to liquid composition).

In the upper transition zone of an abnormally pressured sequence, the increasing porosity with increasing depth results in a

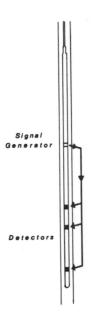

Fig.9-7. Sonic log device. (Courtesy of Schlumberger Seaco Inc., Sydney.)

reduction of sonic velocity (increase in Δt_{sh}); and at the bottom of the transition zone, this trend commonly reverts to one roughly parallel to, but laterally displaced from, that in the normally pressured sequence.

The porosity, and hence the fluid pressure, can be estimated directly from the sonic log in conjunction with the neutron and/or formation density logs (the procedures for which can be obtained from the companies providing the services). Knowing the porosity and the depth, the value of δ $(= z_e/z = (1-\lambda)/(1-\lambda_e))$ can be computed from the relationship:

$$\delta = \frac{\log (f_o/f)}{cz \log e} \tag{9-6}$$

(derived from eq. 6-1, p.128), or other empirical relationship of local validity.

Alternatively, an estimate of δ can be obtained from the plot of Δt_{sh} versus depth (z) by the procedure indicated in Fig.9-6. If it can be assumed that clays with the same value of Δt_{sh} have the same porosity, and hence are at the same degree of compaction, the equilibrium depth (z_e) of a clay now at depth z is indicated by the depth at which the value of Δt_{sh} at depth z coincides with the normal trend. Since $z_e/z = \delta$, the pressure at depth z can be estimated. (Note carefully that this method cannot be used with resistivity data because there is another depth-dependent variable, temperature, that affects the value of the shale resistivity).

From both a theoretical and a practical viewpoint, the normal trend line of Δt_{sh} vs. z should be drawn not through the mean trend, but rather through points of low to minimum Δt_{sh}. Thin clays, and the upper and lower parts of thick clays reach stress equilibrium before the middle parts of thick clays; these points should be the basis of the normal trend line. Such a procedure also tends to underestimate δ, if anything, and so to err on the side of caution. Lacking good arguments to the contrary, the abnormal trend may be taken as the mean trend, but it is not necessarily linear. Gross underestimation of δ is as dangerous as gross overestimation, for anticipation of pressures much higher than reality can lead to problems of its own (as in the Gesa anticline, p.160).

The example shown in Fig.9-6 indicates a value of $\delta = 0.36$ (dividing $z_e = 885$ m by $z = 2,475$ m) at a depth of 2,475 m (8,120 ft.), for an estimated pressure of 455 kg/cm^2 (6,500 psi). The maximum interstitial pressure indicated when drilling at that depth was 475 kg/cm^2 (6,750 psi). This result is closer, perhaps, than one has a right to expect: but it does indicate a fair degree of reliability. Note also that there seems to be a tendency towards abnormality in the interstitial fluids at a depth of about 1,100 m (3,700 ft.).

It is a simple matter, using the relationship $\delta = z_e/z$, to draw on the plot of Δt_{sh} vs. depth the lines of equal δ-value, on the assumption that the baseline corresponds to $\delta = 1$. When this is done on Fig.9-6, it reveals the general pattern of interstitial fluid pressures (through the parameter δ, which is now considered as a function of λ and λ_e) and two features are noted. First, the Δt_{sh} readings at the base of the transition zone are suspiciously large (low velocity). The mudweight used (s.g. 1.76) corresponds to a δ-value of about 0.42; and while *shale* δ-values in excess of this may cause no problems because of lack of permeability, such large values of Δt_{sh} seem unlikely and probably represent Δt in the mud in the borehole. The electrical (and caliper) logs and the drilling reports would indicate whether the sonic log is giving reasonable indication of the interstitial fluid pressures, by comparing mudweights used across permeable beds with the δ-value indicated for adjacent shales. It must also be recognized that there may be a flaw in the arguments used. Secondly, there are strong indications, both from the Δt_{sh} trend and the shale resistivities, that the value of δ is increasing with depth towards the bottom of the hole. (Note that trends parallel to the line $\delta = 1$ indicate hydrostatic equilibrium in the interstitial fluids: those more steep indicate an upward fluid potential gradient, while those less steep indicate a downward fluid potential gradient.) This may indicate that normally pressured permeable rocks lie deeper, and any review undertaken of the geology of the area should consider the petroleum potential of such a permeable sequence, *and* the geological significance of the implied continuity of its pore spaces to the surface. This is a transgressive sequence, and stratigraphic traps should be looked for towards the marine margin of the physiographic basin at that time.

Present assessment would be that the Sonic Log is the most reliable log from which to derive interstitial fluid pressures.

Formation density log (Fig.9-8)

This log is based in part on the principle that when a rock is bombarded with gamma rays, the energy lost through collisions with electrons is proportional to the number of electrons, and hence the bulk density of the rock. Bulk density is related to porosity through eq.3-1 (p.50):

$$\rho_{bw} = f\rho_w + (1-f)\rho_g$$

(where ρ_w in *permeable* rocks is that of the mud filtrate, in the present context). Thus if one has an estimate of a clay's bulk density, grain density, and interstitial fluid density, an estimate of the interstitial fluid pressure can be obtained from eq.9-6.

Alternatively, a graphical estimate of the value of z_e can be

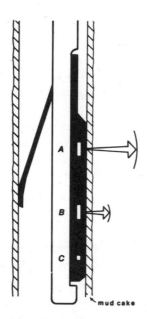

Fig.9-8. Formation density logging device (Schlumberger F.D.C.). A = long spacing detector; B = short spacing detector; C = source. (Courtesy of Schlumberger Seaco Inc., Sydney.)

obtained in a manner analogous to that used with the sonic log data.

Present assessment of this tool for estimating interstitial fluid pressures is that it tends to be rather unreliable. Clays tend to be washed out in boreholes, and the variable hole diameter makes interpretation of this log over clay sections rather unreliable. (Its value over non-clay sections is considerable.)

Selected bibliography*

Archie, G.E., 1942. The electrical resistivity log as an aid in determining some reservoir characteristics. *Trans. Am. Inst. Min. Metal. Eng.*, 146:54–62.
Archie, G.E., 1950. Introduction to petrophysics of reservoir rocks. *Bull. Am. Ass. Petrol. Geol.*, 34:943–961.

----

* Consult also the handbooks issued by companies performing wire-line logging services.

Barsukov, O.A., Blinova, N.M., Vybornykh, S.F., Gulin, Yu.A., Dakhnov, V.N., Larionov, V.V. and Kholin, A.I., 1965. *Radioactive Investigations of Oil and Gas Wells.* (Translated from Russian by J.O.H. Muhlhaus, edited by N. Rast.) Pergamon, Oxford, 299 pp.

Boatman, W.A., 1967. Measuring and using shale density to aid in drilling wells in high-pressure areas. *J. Petrol. Technol.,* 19:1423–1429.

Hottman, C.E. and Johnson, R.K., 1965. Estimation of formation pressures from log-derived shale properties. *J. Petrol. Technol.,* 17:717–722.

Griffin, D.G. and Bazer, D.A., 1969. A comparison of methods for calculating pore pressures and fracture gradients from shale density measurements using the computer. *J. Petrol. Technol.,* 21:1463–1474.

Lynch, E.J., 1962. *Formation Evaluation.* Harper and Row, New York, N.Y., 422 pp.

MacGregor, J.R., 1965. Quantitative determination of reservoir pressures from conductivity log. *Bull. Am. Ass. Petrol. Geol.,* 49:1502–1511.

Moore, C.A., 1963. *Handbook of Subsurface Geology.* Harper and Row, New York, N.Y., 235 pp.

Winsauer, W.O., Shearin, H.M., Masson, P.H. and Williams, M., 1952. Resistivity of brine-saturated sands in relation to pore geometry. *Bull. Am. Ass. Petrol. Geol.,* 36:253–277.

Wyllie, M.R.J., 1963. *The Fundamentals of Well Log Interpretation* (3rd ed.). Academic Press, New York, N.Y., 238 pp.

Wyllie, M.R.J. and Gregory, A.R., 1953. Formation Factors of unconsolidated porous media: influence of particle shape and effect of cementation. *Trans. Am. Inst. Min. Metal. Eng.,* 198:103–110.

Wyllie, M.R.J., Gregory, A.R. and Gardner, G.H.F., 1958. An experimental investigation of factors affecting elastic wave velocities in porous media. *Geophysics,* 23:459–493.

Chapter 10. CORRELATION AND COMPILATION

Summary

(1) The correlation of rock units and the compilation of geological data are directed towards the construction of a deterministic model of the geology of an area.

(2) Correlation has two aspects: the recognition of individual rock units and the recognition of contemporaneous sequences. Rock unit interfaces must not be thought of as isochronous time surfaces over a sedimentary basin, but they may be so regarded over the area of a petroleum accumulation.

(3) Compilation is essentially a graphic summary of various aspects of the geology of an area. There are many components: stratum and fault contour maps and sections to illustrate the structure; isopach and cumulative isopach maps to illustrate the development of thickness in the sedimentary basin; facies maps to illustrate the development of facies in the physiographic basin over the sedimentary basin; and stratigraphic cross-sections to illustrate the interrelationships of the rock units.

(4) The geology of petroleum requires for its understanding an emphasis on the relationship between structure and the thicknesses of the rock units involved, so that contemporaneous deformation can be detected; the relationship between thickness of rock and time units and facies, so that the development of the sedimentary and physiographic basins may be related; the direction and magnitude of fluid potential gradients, so that possible petroleum migration paths may be assessed; and the geology of an area in its regional context, so that the role of all the influences may be assessed.

Introduction

The geology of sedimentary basins can only be fully understood when the relative positions of the different rock units have been established, and these placed within a time framework. The establishment of the relative positions of rock units is largely a matter of lithostratigraphy; the construction of the time framework, largely a matter of biostratigraphy. Both aspects overlap to some extent, because concepts of facies influence both. The object of correlation and compilation is the construction of a deterministic model of the geology of an area from which the results of future boreholes can be predicted.

Correlation consists of establishing the lateral continuity and vertical sequence of rock units in a lithostratigraphic context; and in a biostratigraphic context, it seeks to relate synchronous sequences. Regionally, it is almost axiomatic that rock unit interfaces are only approximate time planes even along the depositional strike. Locally, on the scale of most petroleum fields, lithological

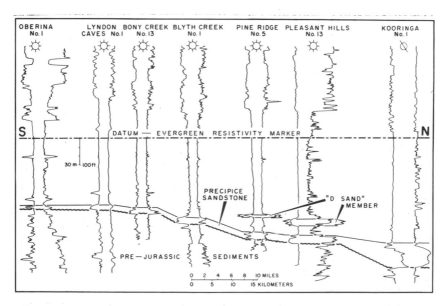

Fig.10-1. Electrical log correlation through central Queensland (Australia) gas wells. Note fresh water in Precipice Sandstone in Kooringa No.1. (Courtesy of Mines Administration Pty. Ltd., Brisbane, Queensland.)

boundaries may be regarded as approximately parallel to the time planes, for this assumption is probably more accurate than the faunal sampling errors in boreholes.

Most petroleum accumulations occur in alternating sequences of sediments, such as sand/clay or carbonate/clay. because of the requirement of permeable reservoirs and "impermeable" seals to them. A moment's reflection will confirm that such rock units must be diachronous to some degree, for to postulate isochronous units implies alternation of total environment. This is clearly un-real. Hence, when we make the lithological correlations evident in Fig.10-1, we accept them as time lines only over short distances. Within a larger area — say, greater than 20 by 20 km — there may be area in which clay accumulation was more or less continuous, areas in which sand accumulation (for example) was more or less continuous, and areas in which the pattern of clay and sand ac-cumulation changed with time. This inter-relationship is shown in a *stratigraphic cross-section* (such as in Fig.7-9, p.162). It is thus clear that the pre-requisite for an understanding of the geology of an area is the correct correlation of rock units and time units between the data points in the area.

Résumé of subsurface geologic methods

Correlation of rock units

Electrical logs are so commonly used for the correlation of rock units in the subsurface, and their qualitative interpretation in terms of lithologies has become so natural, that it is easy to forget that their correlation is not on the same basis as correlation be-tween rock units at the surface. Surface rock-unit correlation is based on lithology, mineral composition, colour, texture, and so on: subsurface correlation is based qualitatively on porosity, per-meability, and interstitial water salinity — and it is influenced by the electrical properties of the mud in the borehole. In subsurface correlation, the emphasis is on the vertical variations in the elec-trical properties of the rocks and their contained fluids; and, in general, the greater the variability within boreholes and the greater the correspondence of this variability between boreholes, the greater the confidence in the correlation. Over intervals with little or no correlation indicated on the electrical log, other logs (such as the gamma ray or other radioactivity log, the sonic log, or different resistivity devices) may help.

The basic geological document of an area is therefore the *correlation chart*, in which the correlation of rock units between the electrical logs of each borehole is shown. This correlation is based on *markers*; but the sedimentary sequence may be subdivided into rock-stratigraphic units (formation, member, tongue, lens) following the Code of Stratigraphic Nomenclature (see Krumbein and Sloss, 1963, appendix, p.621). The correlation chart should be an objective document, as far as possible; and the first working copy should contain only factual data, with no restitution of sequences cut out by faults, or missing due to unconformities or stratigraphic hiatus, because these are subjective matters of interpretation.

The interpretation of the correlation chart begins with the recognition of faults, hiatus, and normal stratigraphic thickening and thinning of units. This is simply stated, but not so simply put into practice. It is a phase of interpretation that requires the utmost care, for any error must necessarily lead to an erroneous interpretation of the geology of the area. (A more detailed approach to this phase is discussed in Chapter 11.) When these problems have been resolved to the extent that the data permit, structural cross-sections are drawn.

Cross-sections

Cross-sections should be drawn with their vertical scales equal to their horizontal scales (unless this defeats the object of the document, which is to indicate the structural features graphically in a form easily assimilated). As many cross-sections as possible should be drawn, both parallel to the structural trend and across it. Dipmeter readings (corrected for the line of the section) and the fluid contents and contacts are inserted. Boreholes that are close to the line of the section may be projected onto it along strike, but the section must show clearly which boreholes have been projected.

From these cross-sections, the apparently unfaulted parts of the sequence are drawn in, and the fault intersections with boreholes are related to each other. While the throws of faults may provide some indication of a fault's identity, it must be remembered that the throw of a particular fault may change both with depth and position along the strike of the fault.

Structural contour maps

The next stage is the construction of provisional stratum and fault contour maps on selected strata and all the faults revealed by the correlation chart and charts derived from it. This work is continued until the structural contour maps are consistent with the structural cross-sections.

The contour interval must be chosen with care. On the one hand, too great an interval may result in inadequate representation of the structure; while, on the other hand, too small an interval may lead to a spurious impression of precision and a crowded map. All boreholes drift to some extent, so that the position of the datum points of a contour map are not, in general, accurate enough for the detection of fine detail.

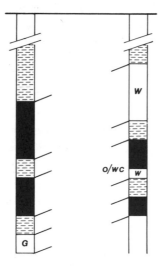

Fig.10-2. Anomalous fluid contents of porous rocks. G = gas; W = water; black = oil.

The fluid content of permeable rock units has an important role to play in the interpretation of the structure of a petroleum accumulation. Any inconsistencies in fluid content (Fig.10-2), such as gas in a rock unit at a greater depth than the same rock unit in another borehole that contains water, must be resolved in the interpretation. Likewise, production data are also pertinent, for production from reservoirs in the same rock unit but different fault blocks may be significantly different.

Isopach maps

Before finalizing the structural contour maps and cross-sections, isopach maps and sections of the intervals contoured should be drawn. The ultimate objective of the isopach maps and sections is to describe the thickness variations of the rock units, both from a geological point of view and from the more direct operational viewpoint of determining reservoir volumes. The preliminary objective, though, is to refine the structural contour maps and sections — and even the correlation chart, for inconsistencies of correlation are sometimes revealed. The isopach map also provides data for a better estimate of the throw of faults, and growth faults should be included in the map. Finally, there is a mutual "feedback" between these isopach maps and the stratum contour maps on the surfaces bounding the isopach intervals, for the thickness of the sequence at any point is the difference between the two bounding contours.

The choice of contour interval is also important, and may be numerically very small. The thickness of units can be measured with considerable precision in vertical boreholes (corrected if necessary for dip), and the exact position of the datum points is not usually critical since the rate of change of thickness over an area is usually small.

Production maps

The stratum contour maps may now be refined, and production maps produced for each reservoir, for operational use. Production maps show an outline of the structure of the reservoir mapped and a summary of each well that penetrates that reservoir. Each well that produces from the reservoir, or has produced from it, has against it (usually in coded form) data such as the total depth, casing depths, perforations, and initial and present production characteristics (with dates). The purpose of the map is to indicate the drainage pattern, and the patterns of water encroachment or gas expansion.

Cumulative isopach maps

Once the operational requirements have been met, further maps of geological interest should be drawn. High on the list of priorities are cumulative isopach maps and sections. Cumulative isopach maps are a series of isopach maps that begins with the lowest

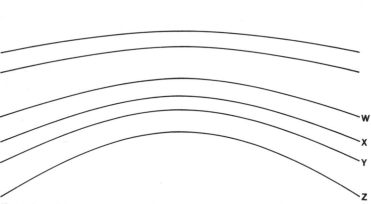

Fig. 10-3. Diagrammatic section across growth anticline.

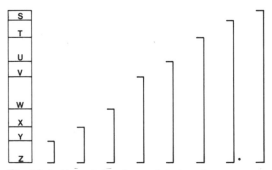

Fig. 10-4. Cumulative isopach intervals.

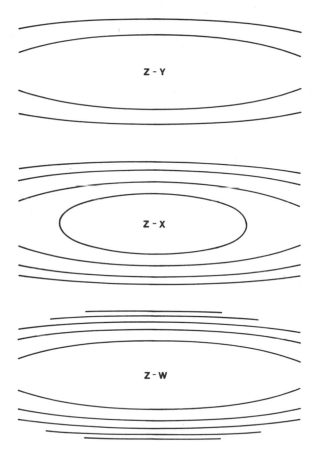

Fig.10-5. Cumulative isopach maps.

interval and adds a higher interval for each map, as shown in Fig.10-3, 10-4 and 10-5. Comparison of these maps, and of the sections drawn through them, will reveal the pattern of thickness changes with time, and thus reveal any influence of contemporaneous structural growth on the thicknesses of the sequences accumulated. Contour intervals should be the same on each map, if practicable, so that changes are more readily appreciated.

Facies maps

Facies maps are also of interest as they throw light on the geology of an area and the petroleum occurrences within it. Successive facies maps show the changes of the physiographic environments in the area with the passage of time.

The basic facies map for petroleum geology shows the areal distribution of a quantitative parameter relating potential reservoir rocks (sands, limestones, etc.) to potential cap rocks and source rocks (clays, shales, marls, evaporites). The parameter is usually either a ratio, such as the sand/shale ratio (thickness of sand in a specified stratigraphic interval divided by the thickness of clays, shales, etc. in that interval); or a percentage, such as the percentage of sand in a specified stratigraphic interval.

Facies maps may reveal significant associations with petroleum occurrences or production characteristics, and so materially assist in the geological contribution to the development of an area. Youngquist (1958) describes a good example of sand/shale ratio maps showing a significant relationship to petroleum occurrence.

For a more extensive discussion of facies maps, see Krumbein and Sloss (1963), Chapter 12; and for an extensive treatment of subsurface geologic methods, see Moore (1963).

This resumé of the compilation of geological data indicates that many of the stages are complementary, and must be done together. The cross-sections can be refined from the stratum contours: the stratum contours from the isopach maps. To treat them as separate operations in isolation from the others is to incur the risk of error. Nevertheless, in the early stages of the development of a petroleum field, the operational requirements must take priority over the geological requirements of a longer-term nature, and there may be no time for refinement. Drilling sites must be selected to a time schedule determined by factors that are not controlled by the geologist; and he must choose these on the data available to him in the time available to him.

In the longer-term view, however, the principles of petroleum geology discussed in the previous chapters require us to highlight certain aspects of the compilation of data. The main points are: (1) the relationship between rock-unit thicknesses and structure, so that contemporaneous deformation of the sediments may be revealed; (2) the relationship between thicknesses and facies of stratigraphic units (including the parameters of porosity and permeability); (3) interstitial fluid pressures in the contexts of stratigraphy and structure; and (4) the geology of an area in its regional context.

(1) *Contemporaneous deformation* is revealed by the drawing of isopach maps and cumulative isopach maps. The interpretation of these, however, requires the assumption that the surface of sediment accumulation was horizontal. This assumption is easier to make than to justify. Hydrographic work on the continental shelves (the environment of deposition of the greater bulk of the sediments preserved in sedimentary basins) indicates that the topography is not flat. But the sea floor is the surface of the sediments, or the outcrop of rock, not the surface of sediment accumulation. If we can regard baselevel in an area as parallel to (if not coincident with) the surface of sediment *accumulation.* Then this may be regarded generally as a plane surface that is nearly horizontal. In detail, however, the baselevel is not constant with respect to sealevel, for its position is determined by two opposing influences — the energy available to move sediment, and the resistance of that sediment to movement. In general, the baselevel of sand accumulation is higher than that of clay accumulation. Other obvious reservations relate to environments in which the energy of the water is variable, such as in littoral and inner neritic areas near prominent coastline irregularities or islands, submarine channels and canyons, and areas of organic reef growth. With these reservations, the assumption of a horizontal surface of sediment accumulation not only appears reasonable, but also leads to satisfactory results in many areas. The isopach map of a rock unit may therefore be regarded as stratum contours on the lower marker with the upper marker as datum level. This is the net relationship today, the original deformation having been modified by compaction. Variations in thickness of the rock unit are thus attributed to variations in net subsidence (i.e., net accumulation).*

---

* See footnote on next page.

Fig.10-5 shows such an isopach map, with marker Z at the base, marker Y at the top. If the interval is now enlarged, keeping the base on marker Z as before, but taking the top as marker X, the resulting isopach map may be regarded as a stratum contour map on marker Z when marker X was accumulating. (The difference between these two indicates the difference in net subsidence during the time interval represented by the sequence $Y-X$: that is, the isopach map of the interval $Y-X$.) Cumulative isopach maps of this nature reveal the development and position of contemporaneous deformation. It is repeated that they must be viewed as indicating differences in net subsidence, not in terms of uplift unless there are convincing arguments to support such a view.

Likewise, the development of growth faults, if contemporaneous with the growth anticline, will affect sedimentary thicknesses over an area; and in these areas, the isopach maps are material evidence for the position of the growth faults, and the growth faults will be shown on the isopach maps.

The treatment of hiatus in isopach maps is not a matter for dogmatism. The writer's view is that an isopach map properly represents net accumulated thickness of sediment, as modified by compaction, and that a hiatus is merely a specific area of non-accumulation and should not therefore be restored. Rather, an attempt should be made to map the hiatus itself. If the contours on an adjacent marker that underlies the hiatus are subtracted from those on an adjacent overlying marker (in each case choosing the nearest marker that is never missing on account of the hiatus) lines of "equal inferred non-accumulation" can be drawn. (Fault cut-outs may be restored, of course, but beware of arguing in circles by first determining the throw of the fault from the isopachs.)

Isopach maps on individual reservoirs are of both theoretical and practical importance. The theoretical interest centres around

---

* An interesting example of an alternative view, that sedimentary thickness is proportional to water depth, will be found in Hobson (1971). The result is much the same as if baselevel had been taken as datum. There are two reasons for this: first, baselevel is usually regarded as a horizontal plane, and is therefore parallel to sea-level; secondly, the maps of inferred differences of water depth are merely isopach maps that have been numerically processed. The postulate seems to require that growth faults developed a scarp, with the downthrown side in deeper water.

the growth against the time-scale represented by the accumulation of the permeable, relatively incompactible, rock unit. The practical interest, of course, centres around the determination of gross reservoir volumes, but isopach and cumulative isopach maps may also help resolve ambiguities in structural interpretation.

(2) *The relationship between thickness and facies* of a stratigraphic unit is particularly important because facies is attributable to the physiographic basin while thickness is attributable to the sedimentary basin. (It must constantly be remembered that isopachs can rarely be interpreted in terms of *physiographic* basin development. The thinning of a rock or time-stratigraphic unit will usually be largely or entirely independent of the development of the physiographic basin, the margin of which may have lain far beyond the margin of the sedimentary basin at that time.) Where the unit isopached is a time-stratigraphic unit, isopachs are a measure of the time-rate of sediment accumulation (or subsidence relative to baselevel) while the facies indicates the influence of the physiographic basin on sedimentation in the area of the sedimentary basin during that time. Hence the combination of the two leads to a better understanding of the history of the physiographic basin in relation to the sedimentary basin. When the stratigraphic unit isopached is a rock unit, the rewards of combining facies and thickness are usually less. Interpretation is usually limited to the development of the sedimentary basin with respect to a single facies or association of facies.

The interrelationship is assessed by superimposing on an isopach map a quantitative parameter that reflects the facies of the rocks in the sequence isopached. There are numerous facies parameters in use; but the significant ones in petroleum geology are usually those relating potential reservoir rock to potential source and cap rocks — such as the "sand/shale" ratio or the "carbonate/shale" ratio.

The choice of the parameter requires some thought, and probably experimentation: the result must be meaningful. Not all facies maps use a ratio or a percentage as the parameter; but when used in conjunction with an isopach map, care must be exercised to ensure that the one does not duplicate the other. For instance, a "sand/shale" ratio or sand percentage map will show constant values over an area of constant convergence; a sand thickness map would merely reflect the isopachs.

Relating facies to thickness in a stratigraphic unit may be, in effect, relating depth of water to thickness of sediment accumulation. A common observation is that, on a regional scale, the shallower-water sediments accumulate to greater thickness than the deeper-water sediments. Within the area of a normal petroleum field, there may be no significant relationship — but that is the matter to be determined.

Within an oil or gas field, the interrelationship between reservoir thickness, porosity and permeability is of direct interest. It not only provides the basis for a volumetric estimate of the reservoir, but also suggests the conditions of accumulation. The slower rate of accumulation in the relatively thin areas may well lead to better grain sorting, less clay content, better permeability and perhaps better porosity. The time-rate of accumulation may significantly affect the facies in this context.

Finally, there is the problem of the significance of "zero" lines — the line of zero thickness, zero sand/shale ratio and so on. As was mentioned in Chapter 1, the line of zero thickness of a stratigraphic unit does not necessarily indicate the margins of distribution of the sediment, nor necessarily the margins of temporary accumulation. It is merely the margin of effective accumulation. Likewise, the line of zero "sand/shale" ratio, for example, delimits sand occurrence in the unit; but it is not safe to infer that it marks the limit of sand distribution at that time. There are many variations on this theme, and each case must be thought out in the light of the evidence.

(3) *The interstitial fluid pressure* in a reservoir is of central concern to the reservoir engineer. It is not without interest to the geologist. There are two aspects to be considered — regional and local. Taking the latter first, the production of petroleum from reservoirs in a field results in a reduction of the reservoir pressure unless the *water-drive* is sufficiently strong to maintain it. This reduction of pressure will not usually be such that normal hydrostatic equilibrium will be maintained over the area. Hence, reservoirs juxtaposed across a fault may develop a pressure differential, during production, across that fault. If this pressure differential

breaks the resistance of the fault, fluids will pass through the fault from the reservoir with the higher fluid potential to the other. If the reservoir with the higher potential is wet (and not produced) the risk of contamination of a juxtaposed petroleum reservoir is considerable.

Reduction of reservoir pressures also enhances compaction, and this has led to measurable subsidence at the surface over some petroleum fields with the passage of time (see Mayuga, 1970, for example). The subsidence is due to compaction; and the compaction is probably due mainly to the elastic deformation of the grains of the reservoir rock as a result of the reduction in interstitial fluid pressure (eq.3-4); but it is partly due to the further compaction of clays due to the increased fluid potential gradient between them and the depleted permeable rocks. Pressure maintenace programmes in producing fields have almost eliminated surface subsidence over petroleum fields, and in some areas the surface in areas of subsidence has been raised slightly by water injection into the depleted reservoirs.

On the regional scale, we are interested in the interstitial fluid pressures in both permeable and "impermeable" rocks, and their stratigraphic context. The main goals are the determination of fluid potential gradients, the anticipation of pressures that might cause drilling difficulties, and the understanding of the autodiastrophic processes (the processes resulting from internal instability rather than those due to external forces). The pressure itself is not a suitable parameter to map because it is largely depth dependent. Useful derived parameters are the hydrostatic head, λ (the ratio of fluid pressure to geostatic pressure), and δ (the ratio $(1-\lambda)/(1-\lambda_e)$). The choice is governed by the use to which the map will be put. The latter two, δ or λ, are best for stratum contour maps as they can readily be converted to a mud-weight. The hydrostatic head, from which a contour map of the piezometric (or potentiometric) surface can be drawn, is probably better for regional maps to illustrate the fluid potential gradients. It will be remembered that the direction of fluid migration is down a fluid potential gradient.

If the hydrostatic head is calculated from

$$h' = (p/\gamma_w) - z \tag{9-1}$$

where p is the pressure, γ_w the specific weight of the water in units consistent with z, the depth; h' is the height of the piezometric surface at that point above (+) or below (−) the level $z = 0$ (see Glossary Fig.G-3, p.275). After relating the levels $z = 0$ to a datum level, the piezometric surface can be contoured, and the fluid potential gradients are normal to the contours, with a tendency for fluid to flow down the surface. The closer the contour spacing, the greater the fluid potential gradient. (See Frederick, 1967, for an example of this.)

Much remains to be learnt about the geological significance of lateral variations in interstitial fluid pressures, and the relationship of such variations to variations in the overburden lithologies and petroleum occurences.

(4) *The geology of an area in its regional context* cannot be properly understood unless the sedimentary sequences can be divided into reliable time-stratigraphic units. For this, the cooperation of palaeontologists is required.

The principles involved are simply stated. The division and subdivision of the sedimentary sequence into time-stratigraphic units provides the basis for the interpretation of the development of the physiographic basin on the one hand, and the sedimentary basin on the other. The development of facies in successive time-units, as we have said before, indicates the changes of the physiographic basin with time; while the development of thickness of time-units indicates the development of the sedimentary basin during that time. Putting the principles into practice is not so simple. The data density normally varies considerably over a sedimentary basin; most of the data are acquired from boreholes, and the fossils contributing to the basic data are those that survive the drilling process.

The main problem is that of distinguishing facies faunas from faunas that are good time indices. While this is the task of the palaentologist, the geologist must not accept the conclusions of the palaeontologist uncritically. As a general rule it can be said that biostratigraphic units that coincide with lithostratigraphic units are almost certainly not significant as time indices. The passage of time is independent of the lithologies accumulating in a sedimentary basin, hence biostratigraphic units with time significance are broadly independent of rock-stratigraphic units.

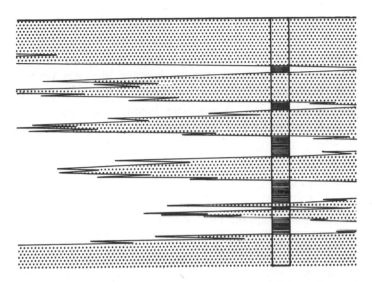

Fig.10-6. An alternating sequence in an area is usually part of a regional intertonguing sequence.

There are many examples in the literature of confusion between rock-stratigraphic and time-stratigraphic units, and it cannot be overemphasized that the basic rock-stratigraphic unit is the formation, which is a mappable unit that has no time connotation whatsoever. It is defined on the basis of lithology or lithologies; and may not be defined on the basis of its fossil content. The formations that accumulated in a sedimentary basin, when considered in a regional context, must be assumed to be diachronous, and regional time-planes must be established if the patterns of facies migration are to be elucidated.

Faunal evidence must be supplemented where possible by physical evidence. Alternations of similar lithologies on a local scale commonly form part of an intertonguing relationship on a regional scale (Fig.10-6). As an approximation, time planes are considered to be symmetrical to the surfaces of the tongues. Isopachs on a particular shale bed or group of beds may indicate a tendency to thicken in a particular direction, and sands to thin in the same direction. Sand/shale ratios may therefore be used and local patterns of facies migration assessed. The thickening itself may not be diagnostic because it reflects the development of the sedimentary basin.

Regional geological methods are best studied from the reading of case histories. Good examples of regional analysis are to be found in *Habitat of Oil* (Weeks, 1958), from which are recommended for first reading Layer's paper on Alberta, Wengerd on the San Juan basin, Galley on the Permian basin of Texas and New Mexico, Miller et al. on the Maracaibo basin, Dunnington on northern Iraq, and Falcon on southwestern Iran.

Selected bibliography

Dunnington, H.V., 1958. Generation, migration, accumulation, and dissipation of oil in northern Iraq. In: L.G. Weeks (Editor), *Habitat of Oil*. American Association of Petroleum Geologists, Tulsa, Okla., pp.1194–1251. (See also Weeks, 1958, pp.38–42.)

Falcon, N.L., 1958. Position of oil fields of southwest Iran with respect to relevant sedimentary basins. In: L.G. Weeks (Editor), *Habitat of Oil*. American Association of Petroleum Geologists, Tulsa, Okla., pp.1279–1293.

Frederick, W.S., 1967. Planning a must in abnormally pressured areas. *World Oil*, 164 (No.4, March): 73–77.

Galley, J.E., 1958. Oil and geology in the Permian basin of Texas and New Mexico. In: L.G. Weeks (Editor), *Habitat of Oil*. American Association of Petroleum Geologists, Tulsa, Okla., pp.395–446.

Hobson, G.D., 1971. Thickness variations in Roblecito Shale of Mercedes area, Guárico, Venezuela. *Bull. Am. Ass. Petrol. Geol.*, 55:2141–2160.

Krumbein, W.C. and Sloss, L.L., 1963. *Stratigraphy and Sedimentation* (2nd ed.). Freeman, San Francisco, Calif., 660 pp.

Layer, D.B., 1958. Characteristics of major oil and gas accumulations in the Alberta basin. In: L.G. Weeks (Editor), *Habitat of Oil*. American Association of Petroleum Geologists, Tulsa, Okla., pp.113–128.

Mayuga, M.N., 1970. Geology and development of California's giant — Wilmington oil field. In: M.T. Halbouty (Editor),*Geology of Giant Petroleum Fields. Am. Ass. Petrol. Geol., Mem.*, 14:158–184.

Miller, J.B., Edwards, K.L., Wolcott, P.P., Anisgard, H.W., Martin, R. and Anderegg, H., 1958. Habitat of oil in the Maracaibo basin, Venezuela. In: L.G. Weeks (Editor), *Habitat of Oil*. American Association of Petroleum Geologists, Tulsa, Okla., pp.601–640.

Moore, C.A., 1963. *Handbook of Subsurface Geology*. Harper and Row, New York, N.Y., 235 pp.

Weeks. L.G., (Editor), 1958. *Habitat of Oil*. American Association of Petroleum Geologists, Tulsa, Okla., 1384 pp.

Wengerd, S.A., 1958. Origin and habitat of oil in the San Juan basin of New Mexico and Colorado. In: L.G. Weeks (Editor), *Habitat of Oil*. American Association of Petroleum Geologists, Tulsa, Okla., pp.366–394.

Youngquist, W., 1958. Controls of oil occurrence in La Brea-Pariñas field, northern coastal Peru. In: L.G. Weeks (Editor), *Habitat of Oil*. American Association of Petroleum Geologists, Tulsa, Okla., pp.696–720.

Chapter 11. FAULTS AND STRATIGRAPHIC HIATUS

Summary

(1) A sedimentary sequence is rarely, if ever, complete in the sense that the time span represented by the whole sequence is continuously represented by sediment. Breaks in the sequence (*hiatus* in general) range from *diastems* to *disconformities.*

(2) Where there is contemporaneous diatrophism, the hiatus may be over limited areas. Hiatus may be associated with growth anticlines and growth faults. It is essential to distinguish hiatus from faults in boreholes if the geology is to be correctly interpreted.

(3) In general, a hiatus may be regarded as a "negative" rock unit, and its stratigraphic position remains approximately constant over its area. Gaps in the sedimentary sequence in boreholes due to faults have no inherent tendency towards stratigraphic constancy. The basis for their recognition lies on this contrast.

(4) Stratigraphic hiatus may be intimately associated with growth faults, for non-accumulation of sediment differs only in degree from reduced accumulation of sediment.

(*Note:* This chapter assumes a knowledge of elementary statistics. The reader is encouraged to acquire this knowledge — if he has not already done so — from one of the works listed in the selected bibliography at the end of this chapter).

Introduction

In Chapter 1, the concept of a sedimentary basin was discussed at some length, and we saw that some of Barrell's work is important for an understanding of sediment accumulation in the dimension of time. Explicit in Barrell's concept of sediment accumulation are numerous breaks in the sedimentary record, ranging from diastems (Barrell 1917, p.794) to disconformities.

It is not difficult to accept the evidence that the record of the sedimentary rocks is a very incomplete record of time, and that most sedimentary sequences contain diastems that are individually hard to recognize and yet collectively may represent a larger proportion of time than the rocks in the sequence. At the other end of the scale there are disconformities that, locally, may pass undisputed. We are concerned here with the significant part of the range of hiatus, in which recognizable rock units or recognizable parts of rock units are absent.

Diatrophism that is contemporaneous with sediment accumulation, leading to growth faults and growth anticlines, affects the rate of sediment accumulation, impeding sediment retention in those areas that are subsiding more slowly. This effect may be quite local. The difference between impeded retention and no retention at all is only one of degree.

It is apparent that the very nature of the diastrophism that is associated with regressive phases of the development of sedimentary basins implies the possible — even probable — coexistence of faults and stratigraphic hiatus in areas where early accumulation of petroleum is likely. In a borehole, however, it is rarely possible to distinguish a "gap" in the sequence caused by a fault from one caused by a stratigraphic hiatus. Yet it is, of course, essential to make this distinction if the geology is to be correctly interpreted. The problem is illustrated in Fig.11-1.

Faults and hiatus

A curious contrast appears to exist between surface and subsurface geology in the matter of disconformities and hiatus in general. Neritic sediments in outcrop commonly exhibit these features; yet published subsurface interpretations rarely include them. Part of the problem lies with recognition, part with significance. The immense complexity of faulting commonly shown in maps and sections of salt domes is plausible. Yet the nature of diapirism suggests that stratigraphic hiatus could occur in the overlying

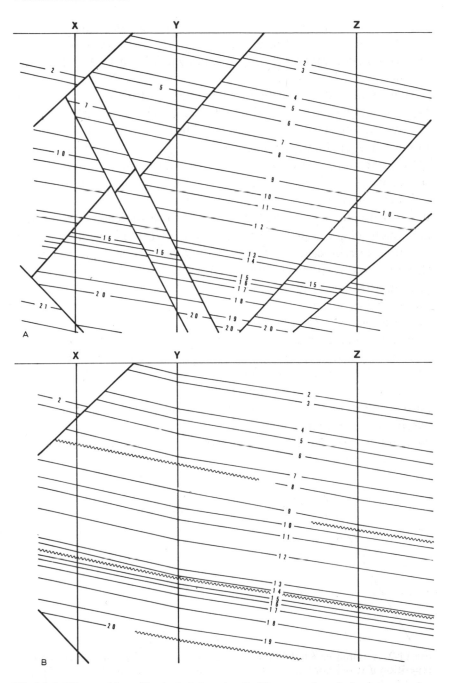

Fig. 11-1. The problem illustrated (see text). The same borehole data may be interpreted in terms of faults only (A) or faults with stratigraphic hiatus (B).

sedimentary sequence as a result of impeded subsidence. Is it possible that misinterpretation of gaps in boreholes has led to spurious structural complexity in some cases? Fig.11-1A illustrates this point.

A normal fault is a plane or surface of fracture across which the beds are displaced, so that the sequence above the fault is dropped relative to the sequence below the fault. The fault surface commonly dips at angles between 40° and 70°; it may be curved in plan, in section, or in both; it may bifurcate, die out horizontally or vertically, and be displaced by other faults. The thickness of sediment may be greater on the downthrown side than on the upthrown side, so that the throw of the fault increases with depth; and such changes may vary laterally. (Note in passing that a deviated borehole that passes through a normal fault from upthrown to downthrown block shows a *repetition* of beds; one passing through a reverse fault from downthrown to upthrown block shows a *gap* — Fig.11-2.) Finally, a fault may terminate upwards against a stratigraphic hiatus.

A stratigraphic hiatus of any sort is a stratigraphic unit analogous to a rock unit. It is, as it were, a negative rock unit. The surface of a hiatus is generally concordant with the adjacent rock units, but strict concordance is not an essential feature and rock units underlying a hiatus may be less concordant than those overlying it. A hiatus may represent a synchronous time interval over much of its area, or it may be diachronous. When quantified

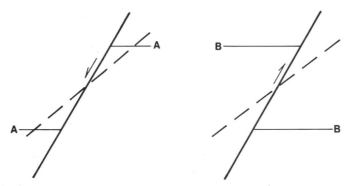

Fig.11-2. A borehole (dashed line) that penetrates a fault from below shows a repetition if it is a normal fault ($A-A$), a gap if it is a reverse fault ($B-B$).

by reference to the thickness of rocks measurable elsewhere that represents the hiatus, this value of the hiatus may vary. The true value of a hiatus should be in time units, but this cannot as yet be measured. A stratigraphic hiatus may bifurcate by virtue of lateral discontinuity of the sequence between two hiatus.

The ambiguity of a gap in the sequence of rocks encountered in a borehole results from the fact that the area (or volume) of rock in the diameter of a borehole is too small to distinguish the essential geometry of the gap with certainty. However, the nature of the two possible causes of a gap suggests points of difference. Positive points of difference are:

(1) A stratigraphic hiatus has inherent stratigraphic constancy, comparable to that of a rock unit: a fault may intersect a borehole in any stratigraphic position for it is independent of the strati-graphic sequence.

(2) A marker horizon cannot occur both above and below one and the same hiatus: it can occur both above and below fault gaps that occur in similar stratigraphic positions.

(3) The displacement of fluid contacts, or anomalies of fluid content (water compositions or petroleum compositions), and the repetition of part of the sequence, may be taken as evidence of faulting.

Negative points of difference are:

(4) The dipmeter may detect and measure the inclination of a fault surface, but the absence of a fault indication is not proof of a hiatus.

(5) Fault contours that agree with the observed depth and position of a gap may be strong evidence of a fault; but it is not conclusive since a fault may terminate against a hiatus, and pene-tration of the hiatus near the termination of the fault is possible (see Fig.11-7, well 28 below marker 16, and fault "A").

From the point of view of recognition, point 1 hinges around concepts of probability. Any borehole that penetrates a hiatus, whether straight, deviated or just crooked, wherever it penetrates it, will show a gap that will always occur within rather narrow stratigraphic limits (specified in point 2). This is not true of a fault. Stratigraphic constancy of fault gaps is only obtainable in boreholes if they penetrate the fault in a narrow strip along the strike of the fault (strictly, along the intersection of a stratigraphic unit and the fault surface); or by chance coincidence of the stratigraphic position of gaps due to different faults. With two or more non-parallel faults, stratigraphic constancy of their gaps can only be maintained at one level in boreholes that penetrate both or all of them.

Point 3 is self-evident, with the reservation made in Chapter 2 that production from a field can alter the fluid relationships. Points 4 and 5 are self-evident.

The associated problem of lateral continuity of a stratigraphic hiatus is easily misunderstood. Lateral continuity appears axiomatic; but *recognizable* lateral continuity is not axiomatic.

Consider a stratigraphic hiatus that has a value of 100 ± 10 m (or ft.) of sediment missing in the first five wells drilled to an anticline. It is most unlikely that this hiatus will be detected; and if the variations in the sequence are noted, they will probably be ascribed to normal variations in the rock unit or units. If the next well is drilled in an area where the value of the hiatus is 100 ± 20 m (or ft.) it will almost certainly be interpreted as a fault with a throw of 10–30 m (or ft.), depending on the standard of reference used. In the unlikely event of the geologist's being called upon to defend his interpretation, he would say that it was a fault because the neighbouring wells correlate satisfactorily with each other and are therefore complete sequences over this interval. He would be wrong in his reasoning because an anomaly in one well does not necessarily imply that the other wells have complete sequences. The ambiguity of the data arises because the general "anomaly" of 100 m (or ft.) is undetected − and may well be undetectable. Perfect correlation between wells does not negate the concept of diastems; nor does it of some hiatus of larger value.

If a well is now drilled off-structure, in an area where the hiatus has a value of 100−20 m (or ft.), the additonal rock sequence would perhaps suggest a general hiatus because all the previous wells now show anomalies to some degree at this level. Alternatively, it might be interpreted as indicating wedging of a rock unit up-structure.

Recognizable hiatus may therefore be of limited areal extent,

and recognizable lateral continuity is not diagnostic of stratigraphic hiatus.

The approach to the problem

When studying an area in which boreholes have penetrated
stratigraphic sequences of variable bed thickness, the first step is
to construct a *Standard Stratigraphic Sequence* (in areas of growth
faulting it may be necessary to construct a Standard Stratigraphic
Sequence for several or all the fault blocks). The Standard Stratigraphic sequence is a composite log that represents the most
complete sequence of the area rather than a representative sequence. It is usually unpractical to take each rock unit separately
from the borehole log in which it is most complete; but it is
usually necessary to use parts of several logs. We are concerned
more with rock units and elements of rock units, than thickness —
but the most complete sequence is usually the thickest. It may
become necessary to revise the Standard Stratigraphic Sequence
with the acquisition of new data, and the Standard Stratigraphic
Sequence should never be taken as definitive.

In the examples shown in Fig.11-3 and 11-5, the gaps are
marked in for each borehole, indicating the part of the Standard
Stratigraphic Sequence missing. Any tendency for minor or major
gaps to show a stratigraphic constancy immediately becomes apparent. These must be examined for geological significance, and
significance in this context is not quantitative because, as we have
seen, the minor variations may indicate the nature of the larger
variations.

Experience suggests that intuitive judgement on these matters is
unreliable. The preconception that an isolated gap in a borehole is
necessarily a fault gap is so prevalent that it requires a concious
effort of mind to accept that it may not be so. Fig.11-3 shows the
results of ten boreholes that have been drilled through a stratigraphic sequence. Two boreholes encountered a gap in closely
similar stratigraphic positions, but they are not adjacent boreholes.
Would it be reasonable to interpret them as fault gaps? A conventional geological argument might run as follows: since no gaps are
observed in eight of the ten boreholes, and since boreholes with

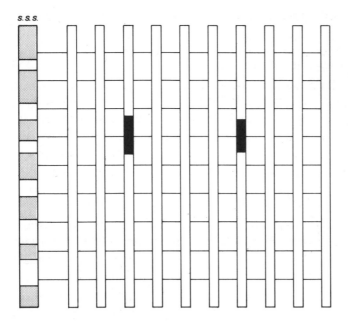

Fig.11-3. The stratigraphic position of gaps marked on Standard Stratigraphic Sequence (ten wells).

complete sequences come between those with the gaps, these gaps represent one or two faults — the dip and strike of this or these will be determined by the well-spacing — the coincidence is just a coincidence.

If the eleventh borehole also encounters a gap in a closely similar stratigraphic position to the other two, how does this alter the assessment? Intuitively we may be sure that the *chances* of the third coincidence are such that a fault hypothesis becomes less tenable. Qualitative argument is clearly inadequate, because "less tenable" is not necessarily the same as "untenable".

Statistical arguments

It must be emphasized at the outset that statistical arguments rarely, if ever, constitute satisfactory proof of a hypothesis. This is perhaps better understood by analogy. If a six-sided die is thrown six times (and only six times) and it comes up each time with the same number, one may suspect it is loaded. The hypothesis that the die is loaded may be wrong, for there is a probability of $(1/6)^6$ — or one in 46,656 — that a true die would give the same result. The alternative hypothesis, that the die is true, is unlikely to be correct but not impossible. Both hypotheses, in this case, could be tested by further throws. Thus if one is led to assert that the stratigraphic incidence of gaps is unlikely to be random, then the conclusion is simply that one is more likely to be right than wrong if the geological interpretation implies (or recognizes) some systematic cause for the association between the gaps and a particular stratigraphic level. High on the list of such causes will be stratigraphic hiatus, because that is their nature. It is conceivable, though, that the coincidence is due to physical restraints on drilling site selection, such as a coastline that is parallel to the faults. If a grid pattern is used for drilling sites on an elongated anticline, it is quite possible that one diagonal or both may lie parallel to faults.

It is also important at this point to understand clearly the nature of the arguments, and so reduce the risk of being seduced by the magic of numbers. The object is to support weak or ambiguous geological arguments with less ambiguous statistical arguments. The premises are usually more important than the arguments that follow from them.

Drilling is a sequential operation in which the results of one borehole contribute towards the siting of the next. The geological interpretation is also sequential, being modified by the results as they are obtained. Satisfactory prediction of the stratigraphic level at which a borehole will penetrate a fault can only be achieved in simple structures with many control points. Early knowledge can rarely be complete enough for satisfactory prediction. The more complicated the structure, the longer will satisfactory prediction be postponed. The basic premise in the statistical argument is, thus, that until satisfactory prediction of the stratigraphic position of the intersection of boreholes with faults can be made, the stratigraphic incidence of fault gaps will be random. The corollary is that gaps that are not randomly distributed stratigraphically are only fault gaps if it can be demonstrated that some systematic influence has affected the basic assumption of randomness.

Fig.11-4. Effect of borehole drift on stratigraphic position of fault-gap in borehole.

Few boreholes are drilled perfectly vertically; and in the interests of economy, deviations of 4° or 5° from the vertical may be allowed. A deviation of 2° is a deviation of about 35 m (or ft.) laterally for every 1,000 m (or ft.) vertically. Thus, even if the position of a fault is known accurately, its stratigraphic position in a borehole may very well vary by ± 100 m (or ft.) vertically at 3,000 m (or ft.) of depth (Fig.11-4). It is almost inconceivable that under these conditions gaps of small values could satisfy the requirement that correlative rocks cannot occur on both sides of the same gap if the gap is due to stratigraphic hiatus. Gaps of large value do not pose a large problem.

On the premise that the coincidence of fault, stratigraphic level and borehole is unpredictable and therefore random, the borehole may be divided into equal intervals of depth, and the probability of a fault intersecting one interval of one block in a borehole is equal to the probability of its intersecting any other interval in that block. Since these intervals are arbitrary, they may be drawn on the Standard Stratigraphic Sequence (with some loss of precision if the thicknesses of rock units vary considerably from borehole to borehole). The size or thickness of the interval depends to some extent on the quality of correlation possible between boreholes, for this determines the precision with which gaps can be determined. In general, the intervals should be as small as the accuracy of correlation permits.

A point of reference in the gap is required. The top is chosen because the stratigraphic position of the top of a stratigraphic hiatus is likely to be more constant; and the point of reference in fault-gaps is immaterial. The incidence of gap tops in intervals and levels is therefore considered (a *level* on the Standard Stratigraphic Sequence consists of the *intervals* of each borehole penetrating that level).

Two statistical models are called upon: the Poisson and the binomial distributions (consult any elementary book on statistics, such as Moroney, 1956).

In a borehole, one can count the number of times a part of the sequence is missing, but one cannot count the number of times it is not. With the premises stated above, the statistical model for this condition is the Poisson distribution. The Poisson *probability* distribution is:

$$= e^{-m} \left(\frac{m^0}{0!} + \frac{m^1}{1!} + \frac{m^2}{2!} + ... + \frac{m^x}{x!} + ... \right)$$

$$= e^{-m} \left(1 + m + \frac{m^2}{2!} + ... + \frac{m^x}{x!} + ... \right) \tag{11-1}$$

the successive terms of which exhibit the probabilities of 0, 1, 2, ..., x, ... gap tops in an interval when m is the average number of gap tops per interval. (The problem arising from the fact that gap tops cannot occur in intervals that are missing in a borehole is considered later.) For practical reasons we are not concerned with multiple gap tops in an interval, but only with the probability of 0 gap tops (e^{-m}) and that of *one or more* ($1 - e^{-m}$).

The occurrence of gap tops by levels (i.e., the same interval in all boreholes) is binomial because one can count the number of intervals with gap tops and the number without. Hence the probability function for the random distribution of gap tops by levels in n boreholes is binomial of the form:

$$[(1 - e^{-m}) + e^{-m}]^n \tag{11-2}$$

and the *frequency* function for the distribution of coincidences in *s* levels is:

$$s[(1 - e^{-m}) + e^{-m}]^n \qquad (11\text{-}3)$$

which should describe the frequency of stratigraphic coincidence, within levels, of the tops of fault gaps if the incidence of faults in boreholes is random. Perfect correspondence is not to be expected; but the significance of discrepancies between the theoretical result derived from the model and the observed result can be assessed with the chi-square test. The mean of the binomial frequency distribution (11-3) is $n(1 - e^{-m})$, and its variance $n(1 - e^{-m})e^{-m}$. By the nature of the problem, we are concerned with those levels that appear to have more gap tops than expected.

Example 1: In the problem posed earlier (p.240) and illustrated in Fig.11-3, the Standard Stratigraphic Sequence has been divided into ten levels. Only two gaps are observed in ten boreholes; the tops of both are in the same level, but they are not in adjacent boreholes. Two intervals in each borehole are missing. Well-spacing is such that they could be faults. Would it be reasonable to interpret them as faults?

There are $10 \times 10 = 100$ intervals. Two gap tops did fall in two intervals and occupy four intervals: no gap could have fallen in $4 - 2 = 2$ intervals that are missing. Therefore two gap tops could have fallen in any two of 98 intervals, giving an avarage of $2/98 = 0.0204$ gap tops per interval. (While spurious precision should be avoided, this should be weighed against the practical advantages of using the same number of figures as in the mathematical tables being used.) The probability of no gap tops in an *interval* is $e^{-0.0204} = 0.9798$; and that of one or more is $(1 - 0.9798) = 0.0202$.

The probability function for the coincidence of these gap tops in ten boreholes is $(0.0202 + 0.9798)^{10}$; and the frequency function over 10 levels is $10(0.0202 + 0.9798)^{10}$. The probabilities, and hence the expected frequencies, of 0, 1, 2 gap tops in one level can be calculated and compared with the observed frequencies (Table 11-I).

This result cannot be tested with the chi-square test as the frequencies are too small. However, if the stratigraphic incidence

TABLE 11-I

Comparison of observed frequencies of stratigraphic coincidence with those expected from the binomial model $10(0.0202 + 0.9798)^{10}$

Number of coincidences *	Probability	Expected frequency	Observed frequency
0	0.815	8.15	9
1	0.170	1.70	0
2	0.015	0.15	1
	1.000	10.00	10

* "Number of coincidences" refers to the number of coincident gap-tops in a level. The frequency refers to the number of levels (observed or expected) that contain the stated number of coincident gap-tops.

of gap tops is random, this result could be expected with a frequency of *about* 15%; hence one must conclude that the coincidence could have arisen by chance (about 1 in 7; not very different from nominating correctly the fall of a six-sided die on one throw) and that the gaps could reasonably be interpreted as due to faulting. Once again, it must be emphasized that a fault interpretation is not necessarily the correct one: the problem is geological, and if the geological interpretation with faults is reasonable, this is not denied by the statistical analysis.

However, if the 11th well reveals a gap top in the same level as the other two, the expected frequency of the three coincidences in a level becomes about 3% and there is no longer a good case for accepting the hypothesis that this is a chance coincidence. A cause must be sought, and if one cannot be found that is consistent with the fault hypothesis, the hypothesis will *probably* be wrong.

When the numbers of boreholes, gaps, and levels are small, a "binomial" argument may be used. The first gap top is bound to fall in one of the levels, and it is immaterial which one. The second gap top may therefore fall in any of 98 intervals, 9 of which are in the same level as the first gap top. Since there are two possible arrangements (either might be the first gap top encountered) and both are equally likely, the probability of both gap tops occurring in the same level is $2 \times 9/98 = 0.18$.

The theoretical arguments that lead one to prefer a Poisson

model to a binomial for the vertical distribution of faults in boreholes are unimportant from a practical point of view. When the probability of one of two possible events is very small, the binomial approximates to a Poisson. But perhaps more importantly, the Poisson probabilities are easier to calculate when the numbers of boreholes, levels, and gaps, are large.

Example 2: In an oil field with 107 wells, the Standard Stratigraphic Sequence has been divided into 66 levels. 107 wells penetrate the upper 29 levels, and 105 penetrate the next 37. There are 281 gaps. What is the probable limit of chance stratigraphic coincidence of fault gaps, and which (if any) are the levels that might contain a stratigraphic hiatus?

The data are set out in Fig.11-5. Inspection shows that certain levels appear to be rather prone to gap tops. There are $29 \times 107 + 37 \times 105 = 6,988$ intervals in an average of 106 wells. There are 281 gaps occupying all or part of 1,532 intervals. Gap tops did fall in 281 intervals, but could not fall in the $1,532 - 281 = 1,251$ intervals that are missing. Therefore, the 281 gap tops could have fallen in $6,988 - 1,251 = 5,737$ intervals, giving an average of $281/5737 = 0.04898$ gap tops per interval.

The probability of no gap tops in an *interval* is $e^{-0.04898} = 0.9522$. The probability of one or more gap tops in an interval is $1 - 0.9522 = 0.0478$. The *frequency* function for 281 gap tops in an average of 106 wells over 66 levels is:

$$66(0.0478 + 0.9522)^{106}$$

Table 11-II shows the probabilities, and expected and observed frequencies of 0, 1, 2, ..., coincidences with their contributions to chi-square. The chi-square test indicates that the hypothesis of random distribution of gap tops is untenable, the value of χ^2 being twice that for the 0.01 confidence level.

Fig.11-6A, comparing the observed with the expected frequencies, shows that the observed frequencies of 0 to 3 coincidences all exceed the expected, while those from 4 to 7 are all smaller than expected. Visual inspection suggests that the coincidences 0 to 7 and part of 8 could be random; while part of 8, and 9 to 11, could be systematic.

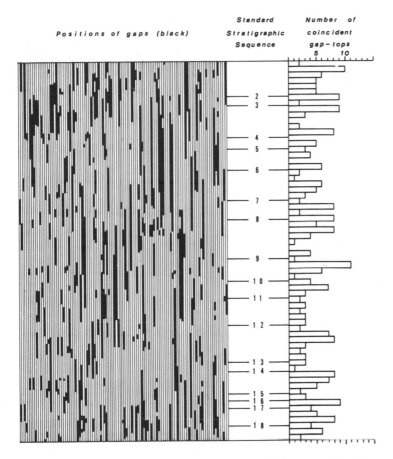

Fig.11-5. Data array of gaps against Standard Stratigraphic Sequence (107 wells). Markers as in Fig.11-1.

For many purposes, this conclusion is sufficient, for each level with more coincidences than expected must be examined for a systematic cause. Nevertheless, some of the gaps that go to make up those levels will probably be random fault gaps. These must be identified by geological argument that takes probability arguments into account.

The statistical argument can be pursued by extracting the apparently systematic gaps from the data. If one extracts the 11 levels with 96 gap tops (6×8, 3×9, 1×10, and 1×11) that are

TABLE 11-II

Comparison of observed frequencies of stratigraphic coincidence with those expected from the binomial model, $66(0.0478 + 0.9522)^{106}$

Number of coincidences *	Probability	Expected frequency	Observed frequency	χ^2
0	0.00556	0.4 ⎫	4 ⎫	
1	0.02959	2.0 ⎬ 7.5	5 ⎬ 21	24.3
2	0.07798	5.1 ⎭	12 ⎭	
3	0.13571	9.0	11	0.4
4	0.17543	11.6	6	2.7
5	0.17965	11.9	8	1.3
6	0.15181	10.0	5	2.5
7	0.10887	7.2	3	2.5
8	0.06763	4.5 ⎫	7 ⎫	
9	0.03697	2.4 ⎬ 8.9	3 ⎬ 12	1.1
10	0.01800	1.2	1	
11 and more	0.01280	0.8 ⎭	1 ⎭	
	1.00000	66.1	66	34.8

apparently systematic, the remaining 55 levels have a mean number of $185/55 = 3.4$ gap tops per level. Since the mean of the frequency distribution is equal to $106(1 - e^{-m})$, the probability of one or more gap tops in an interval, $(1 - e^{-m})$, may be taken as equal to $3.4/106 = 0.03$. Hence an approximation to the frequency function for 185 random gap tops in 106 wells over 55 levels is:

$$55(0.03 + 0.97)^{106}$$

Table 11-III and Fig.11-6B show these distributions. The expected distribution is seen to be a satisfactory model for the lower frequencies of coincidence, but it understates the higher. It is not realistic to test the comparison using χ^2 because of the manipulations in the data, but χ^2 contributions are a useful guide. Further refinement is possible, but from a practical point of view the limits of usefulness of the statistical approach have been reached. The conclusions are:

(1) 0 to 4 coincidences in a level are probably random, and the gaps contributing to these may reasonably be interpreted as faults.

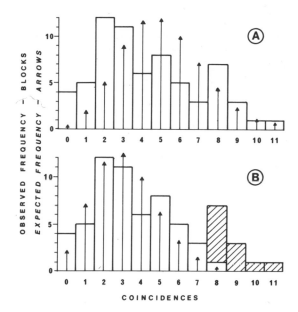

Fig.11-6. Histograms showing the observed and expected frequency of the stated number of gap-tops coincident with levels ("coincidences"). For example, the column marked '4' above 'coincidences' shows that there are 6 levels that contain exactly 4 gap-tops. A. The data of Fig.11-5, and Table 11-II. B. The same data adjusted by extraction of probable systematic levels – Table 11-III.

(2) 5 to 7 coincidences are probably also faults, but some of the levels *may* be systematic in whole or in part.

(3) One or two levels with 8 coincidences could be made up of fault gaps; but the remainder are most unlikely to be made up entirely of fault gaps.

(4) 9 or more coincidences are predominantly systematic.

(5) Some systematic gaps may have been "cut out" by faulting.

These conclusions constitute the premises on which the geological interpretation should be based. The data array (Fig.11-5) facilitates the location of the levels of interest. If it can be concluded that the systematic gaps are due to stratigraphic hiatus, each level with more gap tops than expected must be examined. Since stratigraphic hiatus may not be confined to one level, adjacent levels should also be examined.

TABLE 11-III

Comparison of observed frequencies of stratigraphic coincidence with those expected from the binomial model, $55(0.03 + 0.97)^{106}$

Number of coincidences *	Probability	Expected frequency	Observed frequency	χ^2
0	0.0396	2.2 ⎫ 9.4	4 ⎫ 9	0.0
1	0.1301	7.2 ⎭	5 ⎭	
2	0.2117	11.6	12	0.0
3	0.2275	12.5	11	0.2
4	0.1816	10.0	6	1.6
5	0.1148	6.3 ⎫	8 ⎫	
6	0.0599	3.3 ⎪ 11.6	5 ⎪ 17	2.5
7	0.0265	1.5 ⎪	3 ⎪	
8 and more	0.0083	0.5 ⎭	1 ⎭	
	1.0000	55.1	55	

* See note to Table 11-I.

Of particular interest are anomalous levels that occur where rock units are thinner than average, because there is a possible causal relationship between stratigraphic hiatus and bed thickness if both are due to reduced rates of sediment accumulation. Such associations are found around markers 2 and 3 (Fig.11-5) and between markers 14 and 18. The latter group is chosen for further discussion because it illustrates the interrelationship of probability arguments and geological arguments.

Fig.11-7 shows a section through four wells. The interpretation hinges around the interpretation of the gaps below marker 16 in wells 46 and 28 — particularly that in well 28. The tops (and bottoms) of these two gaps are in closely similar stratigraphic positions, and they fall in a level with 9 observed coincidences of gap tops (Fig.11-5). To interpret these as faults would be to ignore the role of chance. Accepting them as a stratigraphic hiatus leads to the conclusion that the hiatus is confined to the upthrown block of fault A, and that fault A terminates against it. The gap below marker 17 in well 78 contributes to a level with 8 observed coincidences of gap tops, and marker 18 occurs only in one well in this section. While this gap (below marker 17) could be interpreted as a fault, it is unlikely to be, and it is also stratigraphically

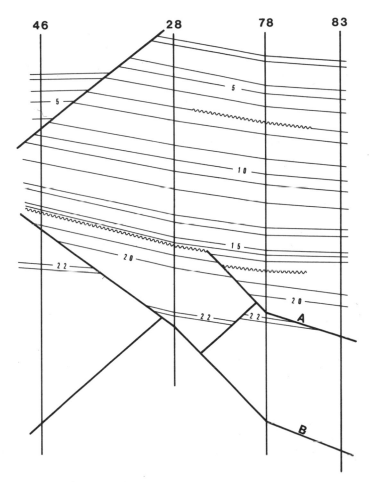

Fig.11-7. Cross-section through four wells included in data of Fig.11-5. Horizontal and vertical scales equal.

consistent with the hiatus below marker 16 (but representing a shorter time interval). Fault B may be similarly related to one or more hiatus elsewhere.

Hence the interpretation shown in Fig.11-7 is supported not only by individual probabilities, but also by the collective probabilities arising from the relationships between faults and postulated hiatus. It seems fair to say that the interpretation is geologically consistent with the nature of growth structures, but it would

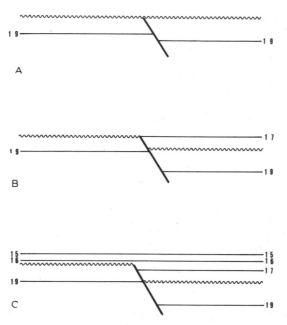

Fig.11-8. Postulated sequence of events leading to observed relationships in Fig.11-7. A. Period of non-accumulation after "growth" activity of fault. B. Renewed movement of downthrown block. C. Renewed movement of up-thrown block, no relative movement of fault.

be unlikely to result from qualitative arguments. The postulated sequence of events is shown in Fig.11-8.

While this is a hypothetical example based on a field example, it is not hypothetical geology. Working on surface exposures near Girvan in Scotland, Williams (1962) deduced a similar relationship between Ordovician sediments and contemporaneous growth faults (shown here in Fig.11-9).

Once an hypothesis involving stratigraphic hiatus has been postulated, the most discriminating method of testing it consists of *prognosis* before each new borehole is drilled. The value of prognosis lies in the disparity between the probability of success-ful prognosis from the two possible hypotheses — faulting and stratigraphic hiatus. The successful prognosis of the stratigraphic position of a fault gap in borehole depends not only on an

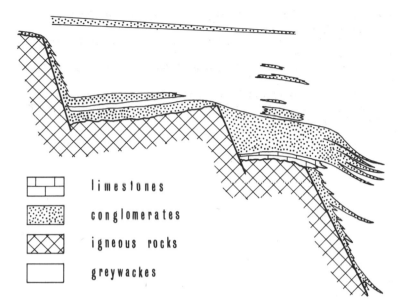

Fig.11-9. Growth faults inferred in Ordovician rocks of the Girvan district, Scotland. (After Williams, 1962, p.67, fig.5.)

accurate knowledge of the position of the fault and the structure of the rock units on either side of it, but also on accurate knowledge of the positions of the borehole in the subsurface (the drift from the vertical). On the other hand, successful prognosis of the stratigraphic position of a hiatus is largely independent of this knowledge.

Selected bibliography

Barrell, J., 1917. Rhythms and the measurement of geologic time. *Bull. Geol. Soc. Am.*, 28:745–904.

Clarke, G.M., 1969. *Statistics and Experimental Design*. Arnold, London, 161 pp.

Hodgman, C.D. (Editor), 1959. *Standard Mathematical Tables* (12th ed.). Chemical Rubber Publishing Co., Cleveland, Ohio, 525 pp.

Hoel, P.G., 1971. *Elementary Statistics* (3rd ed.). Wiley, New York, N.Y., 309 pp.

Lindley, D.V. and Miller, J.C.P., 1966. *Cambridge Elementary Statistical Tables*. Cambridge University Press, Cambridge, 36 pp.

Miller R.L. and Kahn, J.S., 1962. *Statistical Analysis in the Geological Sciences.* Wiley, New York, N.Y., 483 pp.

Moroney, M.J., 1956. *Facts from Figures* (3rd. ed.). Penguin Books Ltd., Harmondsworth, 472 pp.

Owen, D.B., 1962. *Handbook of Statistical Tables.* Addison-Wesley, Mass. 580 pp.

Williams, A., 1962. The Barr and Lower Ardmillan Series (Caradoc) of the Girvan district, southwest Ayrshire, with descriptions of the Brachiopoda. *Mem. Geol. Soc. Lond.,* 3:267 pp.

Chapter 12. **EPILOGUE**

Prognosis

The goal of petroleum geology, as of applied geology in general, is the construction of a deterministic model of the geology of potential and actual petroleum occurrences. This goal is not attainable because full knowledge of the geology of an area is unobtainable (except possibly in the limited area of extractive mining). There is always a tendency for extensive knowledge of an area to be achieved too late, so that a petroleum field is only completely known when it is drilled up. These reservations do not mean that the goal is not worth seeking, nor that incomplete knowledge has no value. On the contrary. It is the petroleum geologist's task to achieve a workable model at a very early stage in the study of an area or the development of an accumulation; and it is accepted that this model will need revision from time to time, as data are obtained. This model, however incomplete, is the basis on which further work is planned.

The seismic survey is planned on the basis of a regional survey, and from this likely targets for drilling are chosen. The exploratory borehole to a potential trap is based on the seismic model. This model is then refined by incorporating the data obtained from the borehole. The resulting model leads to the selection of further drilling sites; and the results of these lead to further refinements of the model. With increasing knowledge, the risk of failure decreases. Ultimately, it should be possible to predict with considerable accuracy the outcome of a borehole, both geologically and commercially; and the depths and thicknesses of reservoirs, their fluid contents and production characteristics, faults and hiatus, should be found to agree closely with those expected. Prognosis is the forecasting of the results that will be obtained in a future borehole. Prognosis and planning are complementary exercises.

The value of prognosis to the geologist is that it requires him to make a statement, as it were, the truth of which will be assessed. If the results indicate that his statement was accurate, his confidence in his postulated model is increased. On the other hand, if the results are significantly different from those expected, it indicates that the model is in need of revision. Failure to make a prognosis concerning a borehole denies the geologist this check on his thinking, because there is then no objective standard to which the result can be compared. It follows, therefore, that prognoses must be as precise as the model permits.

Prognoses have another value — that of indicating to the petroleum and drilling engineers the sequence of rocks to be penetrated, the likely fluid contents and pressures to be encountered, and the depths of potential petroleum reservoirs. Mud programmes, logging programmes, casing programmes — and even what types of bit to be used — must be agreed before a borehole is spudded; and these can only be specified against the prognosis for the well. Such programmes may need modification in the light of reality, and this must be expected from time to time.

The prognosis for a borehole in a producing area is based mainly on the data available in stratum contour and fault contour maps and sections, and in isopach maps. When the borehole to be drilled is to be an "in-filling" well in an area in which there are reasonable borehole data, the problems are few. More problems arise when planning an "out-step" well, to prove an extension to the accumulation, or to define its limits. One must extrapolate the data. The critical lines are those of the intersection of fluid inter-faces with the tops of reservoirs. A slight increase in dip outside the area drilled may result in a dry hole: a slight decrease, in success (Fig.12-1).

While each case must be argued on its own merits, two principles are clear. First, one must not unduly fear failure when outstepping, because it is essential to determine the limits of accumulations as early as possible. Secondly, one must make the *best* estimate of dip trends on the evidence available. Prognoses should not include subjective influences reflecting caution or

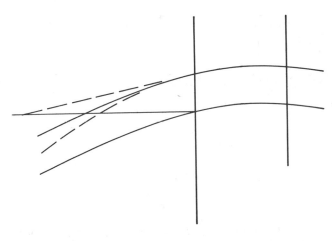

Fig. 12-1. An extrapolated dip has a range of uncertainty. Fluid content can only be extrapolated above the horizontal line.

otherwise, because these introduce an element of confusion. Based on the best available evidence, *sites* may be chosen with cautious or other thoughts in mind. When reasonable alternative interpretations lead to very different prognoses, consideration should be given to presenting both extremes.

A recurrent problem in petroleum geology concerns the "best" interpretation of available data. The degree of detail possible in an interpretation — whether it be correlation or structural detail — is a function of borehole density and the quality of the correlation between borcholes. For example, considerable detail is possible (and expected) in an interpretation based on many wells at 200-m spacing. This detail was not available when the first well was drilled. The corollary is that there is a level of detail that is unrealistic for the data available. The "best" interpretation of the data is that deducible from the data itself, enhanced a little by the geologist's imagination but not dominated by it. This level of credence is subjective: it is more readily recognized than defined. Where interpretative detail derives from the imagination rather than the data, this should be clearly indicated.

Well prognoses commonly emphasize expected rock unit and reservoir depths, neglecting faults. While it may be true that the faults are of no consequence operationally, they cannot be so

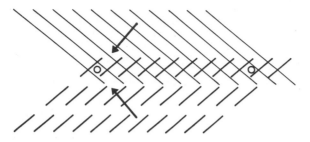

Fig. 12-2. Two data points on a single fault are insufficient to determine its trend.

regarded geologically. The depth and throw of each fault through which the borehole is expected to pass should be estimated and stated. This is particularly important when one seeks to distinguish between faults and stratigraphic hiatus.

Sparse data in few wells are commonly ambiguous, and several possible and plausible alternative hypotheses may be apparent. It is essential to eliminate unlikely hypotheses as early as possible. Two boreholes, each with a fault may be interpreted in several different ways: a single fault with two possible trends (Fig. 12-2), or two faults with a wide variety of possible trends. Regional geological considerations may lead one to prefer one hypothesis to another. While it will be necessary to consider the consequences of drilling in a particular site under all the hypotheses, there are distinct advantages to the geologist if he reasons towards a choice before drilling, so that his line of reasoning can be tested.

It is one of the great challenges of applied geology that geological inference is put to the test. It protects him from the indulgence of light-headed fantasy. He will not be expected to be right always — nor will he, of course, be expected to be wrong always. His results must be significantly better than those that would have been achieved by a random approach if he is to justify his job. The matter of rightness and wrongness must be considered by the geologist primarily in its geological context, rather than its economic context.

If a geological or geophysical survey indicates a large anticline in a part of a sedimentary basin in which both reservoir rocks and cap rocks are likely to be present, there is no alternative but to drill to it to find out if it has accumulated petroleum. If the exploratory hole discovers a considerable thickness of net pay, then the operation has been a success geologically and geophysically. Whether or not it will be a success commercially is another matter. The geologist's responsibility is to plan the appraisal of the accumulation as efficiently as possible in order to establish the limits of the accumulation and to provide the basis for the economic appraisal of it. If this work leads to the conclusion after, say four or five appraisal wells that the accumulation is uneconomic, then this too is a geological success. It would be a geological failure if the appraisal drilling led to the wrong conclusions. (Even economic disappointments must be viewed in a broad context. The Moonie field in Australia was discovered in 1961. It could not be properly appraised until a pipeline had been built; so the decision to go ahead was based on inadequate data. It cannot be said to have been a great success commercially. Yet there is no doubt that its discovery provided encouragement to continue the search for petroleum in Australia, as a result of which significant discoveries have been made.)

An important part of prognosis is to determine the depth to which a borehole should be drilled. This is an aspect that affects exploratory holes mostly, and exploratory depths are subject to overall economic limits. Again, each case must be argued on its merits; but two principles are clear. Petroleum is associated with the upper part of the permeable facies of transgressive sequences, and the lower part of the permeable facies of regressive sequences. Hence no area can be said to be unprospective until these parts of the sequences have been penetrated in areas of potential accumulation. Sooner or later, a transgressive sequence must be penetrated to economic basement: a regressive sequence, to thick clays (in which abnormal fluid pressures are to be expected).

Economic and political influences

The applied geologist must be aware of (even if not interested in) the economic and political influences on his work and on the actions taken as a result of his work. W.S. Gilbert wrote for one of his characters, "You are paid to make money." The applied geologist, crudely, is paid to make money; and to do this he must play a role in the immensely complex task of finding and producing petroleum at a cost competitive with that found and produced elsewhere.

The geological work on the petroleum industry cannot be divorced from the commercial aspects of the industry. A few geologists in a few companies will be paid to think without restraint: but for the vast majority, in common with their colleagues in other geological activities, their work will be carried out under various restraints.

The realities of the petroleum world include economic and political influences, and these may take several forms. A thoroughly competent geological investigation may lead to a clear recommendation to drill an exploratory borehole in a specific site. The geologist must clearly understand that failure on the part of the company to carry out his recommendation may be entirely due to factors other than the geological ones that go towards the decision. Even the largest petroleum companies have limited funds available for exploration (or any other aspect of their activities) and when the various proposals are graded in accordance with all the factors — geological, political, economic, availability of drilling rigs and manpower, supplies of crude and gas and their locality, markets, and so on — the specific proposal may not rate sufficiently highly for action at that time. Indeed, the need for crude supplies from a particular part of the world may mean that prospects that have less geological merit may take priority because any success in these will be more rewarding. In an area of surplus crude oil or gas, further supplies may have little value for the time being.

The recent surge of activity in the North Sea in northwest Europe was not solely the result of geological thinking. It was partly the result of advances in technology, making offshore exploration and production in those water depths and under the prevailing weather conditions viable; partly the industrial growth of northwest Europe with its consequent demands for fuel; partly the economic and political disadvantages of dependence on other areas for supplies; partly the success of onshore exploration in neighbouring countries (particulary the discovery of the Groningen gas field in The Netherlands in 1959). Good geological thinking has contributed greatly to the success of the effort.

Economic and political influences operate at various scales, and even within relatively small operations, geological merit is not the only criterion that leads to a decision to drill or not to drill. No company can operate entirely at its own discretion. All operate within legislation enacted by the government of the land, and such legislation stipulates the terms under which an area may be explored and any discoveries produced. A company or group of companies is given the sole right to explore an area for a period of time, and an obligation to commit certain sums of money on its exploration. At the end of this period, part of the area must usually be relinquished, and the explorers have the right to retain part for a further period of time. These stipulations are disigned to benefit the country by ensuring a certain level of competitive activity over a period of time. The geologist also has to work within this framework, and priorities may require him to work on those areas for which a decision on relinquishment is required by a specific date.

On a different scale, limited funds may require a company to spend more on production facilities and development drilling, and less on exploration — whatever the geological merit of various proposals may be. Or the economics of operating in an area may preclude the drilling of boreholes deeper than a certain depth. There are many restraints influencing both the nature of the geologist's work, and the time he can spend on any assignment.

It is clear that the petroleum geologist, in common with most other applied geologists, must develop the ability to work under pressure when the need arises, and to produce results within a specified period of time that he will frequently regard as insufficient for the propert execution of the assignment. These pressures take various forms, and there is no simple formula for working successfully under them.

It may be, for example, that he is given two weeks in which to site three appraisal wells to a prospect for which there is a single discovery well and a set of seismic maps. The reasons for the haste are probably good ones — such as the need for appraisal before some other activity (a pipeline or refinery contruction plan for example) is finalized, or the need to drill during a particular season of the year, or before a rig is required elsewhere. Such assignments must be properly planned for their successful execution. The geologist must decide how many days he may spend on collecting data, how many days on studying the data collected, how many days on drawing maps and sections (and how many of each to draw), and how many days on writing the recommendations. He must present his recommendations with supporting data by the deadline, and the recommendations must be definite, because indefinite recommendations are useless. He must accept that he could have done better had there been more time, and trust that his superiors will believe that also.

Working under pressure from time to time is not entirely to the geologist's disadvantage. True, he has to come to conclusions that are based on inadequate study; true, he may have little confidence in his conclusions: but he learns an intuitive assessment of geology that is valuable in his work provided it is tested by drilling. While continual pressure at work is to the liking of very few, all work must be under a little pressure if we are to be stimulated to the best results we are capable of. It is probably true that much valuable geological work would have remained undone without the incentive of a deadline. There comes a time when further work is not rewarded by significantly improved results, and the work must be finalized.

Reports

The presentation of results is an integral part of the work, for it is the medium by which they are brought to the attention of others. It is not to be regarded as a tedious sequel to the work, but rather as a phase of clarification. Indeed, the outline of the ultimate report should be borne in mind during the execution of the work, as a check-list of aspects to be covered. Most companies and organizations have a standard format for the organization of reports; it is the author who makes this effective. Skill in presentation is a valuable asset: some are naturally more skilled than others, and practice will improve both the more skilled and the less skilled. The principles of presentation are simply stated: Geological assignments have one or more objectives. These objectives, and the results achieved, must be clearly stated twice — once on the first page in the form of an abstract or "summary and conclusions", then in the body of the report with supporting data and arguments.

A report will be read by different people for different purposes — colleagues for the general information it contains, specialists for the more detailed information, managers for the background and basis for decisions. They will be busy people, and the messages of the report will be conveyed most effectively when they are conveyed efficiently.

Abstract

Anyone who has had to read many reports will know how irritating it is to have to search through a report for the information he needs. If the report is on exploratory well, for instance, the salient results should be stated in the "abstract" or "summary and conclusions" at the beginning of the report. These are: *whether or not petroleum was found,* the lithological sequences and ages of the sediments, the apparent position of the borehole relative to the geological model on which it was sited, its total depth and casing depths, significant drilling difficulties, and its cost.

Text

As regards the body of the report, there is no merit in length. (One is reminded of the letter-writer who concluded "Had I had more time, this letter would have been shorter".) It is here that skill in presentation is most required, and also judgement on what to include and what to leave out. The important thing is to keep the objects of the report clearly in mind, and to narrate and discuss the topics that are relevant to that object. Most studies accumulate data, such as detailed sample descriptions, that are certainly valuable but not in themselves relevant. These can usefully be relegated to appendices, where they are available to the specialist without obscuring the narrative.

More specifically, we see that certain topics are essential for the understanding of petroleum occurrences, and these must be given prominence in any geological report concerned with petroleum. One must be as specific as the data permit about the possible source rocks of the area, the cap rocks, the reservoir rocks, and the various possibilities of trapping. These are largely matters of lithologies, and the development and distribution of lithologies over the area studied *and beyond.* The relative ages of these lithologies are more important in these contexts than the absolute ages, and it may be quite unimportant whether a particular sequence is Pliocene or Miocene, for example, if this information does not contribute materially to the understanding of the petroleum potential.

In describing the development of the sedimentary sequences, emphasis must be placed on dominant transgressive and regressive sequences, on whether a transgressive sequence represents the initiation of the sedimentary basin, or whether it succeeded an earlier regressive sequence. These are fundamental aspects that affect the petroleum potential of an area, and suggest the type of trap to be expected. In addition, dominant regressive sequences (and associated features, such as mud volcanism and petroleum seepages) should suggest the probability of abnormal interstitial fluid pressures; this information should be included in the abstract of any report dealing with an area in which drilling may take place.

The presence of thick clay sequences, or evidence of clay diapirism (mud volcanoes or anticlines with clay cores) is a matter of importance not only to the geologist but also the geophysicist. Abnormally pressured clays have abnormally low sonic velocities, and the sonic velocity is, of course, a vital parameter in geophysical interpretation.

Petroleum seepages, particularly those associated with an area of regressive sedimentary sequences, are significant because they indicate at least that petroleum has been generated in the area. If they are not associated with regressive sequences, then some attempt must be made to understand them.

Structurally, the nature of folding and faulting is a central theme. It is not usually possible to demonstrate growth structures in the field, but awareness of them may sharpen the perception. Just as small scale folds and faults may indicate the nature of the larger scale features so may the presence of small growth structures suggest the presence of larger. The *age* of folding is significant because, as we have seen, the folding and faulting of reservoir rocks during the period of migration of the bulk of the interstitial fluids during compaction is important in the petroleum context. If the folding and faulting takes place after the migration of the bulk of the fluids of compaction, such structures are likely to be dry.

Hence thickness variations in rock units are as important qualitatively as their absolute thicknesses in the type sections. Breaks in the sequence are similarly important, as is their association with transgressive or regressive sequences. Even if these features cannot be mapped usefully, the existence of thickness variations and hiatus indicates the nature of the local development of the sedimentary basin.

The nature of lithological boundaries requires attention in the field and during the study of well logs. If just one intertonguing relationship between two lithologies can be demonstrated, a wealth of data is obtained. It indicates that the two lithologies were accumulating (at least in part) contemporaneously and that the facies migrated. The direction of migration is indicated, and so the local development of the physiographic basin with time assessed. It has been stated earlier that the units of alternating lithologies must generally be regarded as diachronous. An intertonguing relationship demonstrates this, and may lead to the identification of facies faunas. While such a relationship may be lost on the map on account of scale, its significance must be given proper weight in the report. Indeed, one of the main functions of a geological report is to draw attention to such features.

Conclusions and recommendations

The conclusions of a study (which may well be placed at the beginning of the report with the summary) set out both geological and operational conclusions drawn from the study, with the recommendations for further study or action. These must be both concise and as specific as possible. It is the geologist's duty to assess the merits of drilling or further drilling, for example, even if is it not his duty to make the decision. If the conclusions are that potential source rocks, reservoir rocks, and traps exist, then there must also be a specific remommendation to drill, or a specific recommendation for further work to establish where to drill.

Maps and cross-sections are the essence of geology and are the most succinct summaries of geological fact and opinion (care being exercised to distinguish between the two). These must be supplemented by maps and sections on larger scales, diagrams and sketches, to illustrate features of importance. For example, it may be impossible to indicate the lenticularity of sands in a rock unit on the main maps and sections, but the lenticularity may be significant for an understanding of the geology of the area.

Geological writing is a creative and illuminating process. The very act of putting one's observations and thoughts on paper reveals to *the writer* his understanding of the subject. Deficiencies become apparent. He is a fortunate person who can write a lucid report at the first attempt. After preparation of the first draft, as many of the deficiencies as possible should be studied further in order to clarify them. Those that cannot be resolved must not be ignored, but rather the nature of the problem and the possible sources of solutions should be stated. Finally, a colleague should be asked to read and criticize the draft candidly, for the mental absorption in writing often blinds one to self-criticism, and what is absolutely clear to the writer may not necessarily be clear to the reader.

In summary, then, reports must be concise, lucid and well illustrated. They must present the data relevant to the topic of the report, and discuss these data in that context. Special attention must be given to those features that control petroleum occurrences — source rocks, cap rocks, reservoir rocks; and their sequences, whether transgressive or regressive, and hence the likely nature of traps. The report should be summarized on one page at the beginning, so that busy colleagues can get the salient points at a glance.

POSTSCRIPT

Several important papers and one Memoir have been published since this book went to press.

Memoir 16 of the American Association of Petroleum Geologists is devoted to *stratigraphic traps* (King, 1972). This would have been of considerable use in the writing of this book. From a quick reading, I do not wish to alter the views I have expressed here. Many of the examples are explicitly or implicitly transgressive sequences. Also, many concern Cretaceous rocks — and the Cretaceous System has a world-wide transgressive tendency.

Likewise, R.J. Cordell's paper on the depths of origin of oil and primary migration (Cordell, 1972) is a more competent review than that provided in Chapter 6. The reader will note that an important difference concerns the retention of original pore fluids in clays at various depths (a matter discussed independently in Chapman, 1972).

C. Barker's note on a thermal contribution to abnormal interstitial fluid pressures (Barker, 1972) covers an aspect that I dismissed lightly, perhaps too lightly (p. 80).

Dickey et al. (1972) report that waters that are abnormally pressured in Louisiana have a lower concentration of dissolved solids than waters that are normally pressured at the same depth.

Perry and Hower (1972) provide some more data on late-stage dehydration of pelitic sediments.

References

Barker, C., 1972. Aquathermal pressuring — role of temperature in development of abnormal-pressure zones. *Bull. Am. Ass. Petrol. Geol.*, 56 (10): 2068–2071.

Chapman, R.E., 1972. Primary migration of petroleum from clay source rocks. *Bull. Am. Ass. Petrol. Geol.*, 56 (11): 2185–2191.

Cordell, R.J., 1972. Depths of oil origin and primary migration: a review and critique. *Bull. Am. Ass. Petrol. Geol.,* 56 (10): 2029—2067.

Dickey, P.A., Collins, A.G., and Fajardo M.I., 1972. Chemical composition of deep formation waters in southwestern Louisiana. *Bull. Am. Ass. Petrol. Geol.,* 56 (8): 1530—1533.

King, R.E. (Editor), 1972. Stratigraphic oil and gas fields — classification, exploration methods, and case histories. *Am. Ass. Petrol. Geol.,Mem.,* 16: 687 pp.

Perry, E.A. and Hower, J., 1972. Late-stage dehydration in deeply buried pelitic sediments. *Bull. Am. Ass. Petrol. Geol.,* 56 (10): 2013—2021.

March, 1973.

GLOSSARY

Appraisal — The drilling undertaken to determine the significance of a discovery is *appraisal* drilling — it appraises the discovery. Development drilling follows if the appraisal indicates that the discovery is commercial.

Assembly — The components of the drilling string below the drill pipe — bit, drill collars, reamers, stabilizers — are referred to collectively as the assembly. "To change the assembly" means to change the arrangement or to substitute reamers for stabilizers (for example).

Autodiastrophism — A term used here for diastrophism (q.v.) that results from internal causes, as distinct from that that is caused by forces external to the sedimentary basin. Diapirism is autodiastrophism: some growth structures are autodiastrophic, others not (being due to basement movements).

Basement — Geologically, the rocks that underlie, surround, and predate those of a sedimentary basin. When basement is of sedimentary rocks, these have usually suffered deformation prior to the development of the sedimentary basin, and may have been metamorphosed.

Economic basement refers to rocks that have no economic prospects. In the context of petroleum geology, the two are commonly synonymous. It is dangerous to regard volcanic or metamorphic rocks as economic basement for petroleum, for they may (and do) form important reservoirs.

Billion — An ambiguous term that should only be used in a local context. 10^9 in U.S.A.: 10^{12} in many European countries and Australasia. Write 150×10^9 m^3, for example.

Block — A volume of rock bounded by a significant fault (or several). A fault usually gives its name to the upthrown block in subsurface geology.

Blowout — An uncontrolled flow of fluid (gas, oil, or water) from a borehole that results when the pressure exerted by the mud is insufficient to contain the formation fluids *and* a human or mechanical failure prevents this excess pressure being contained at the surface by means of the blowout preventers (BOPs).

"Bottoms up", to circulate — To circulate mud through drill pipe or the drilling string in order to bring the mud at the bottom of the hole to the surface. This procedure is carried out whenever a change in the drilling performance suggests a significant change in the rocks and their contained fluids — e.g., after a drilling "break" (q.v.)

Bottom water — The water below the petroleum in a reservoir, occupying the same general area (Fig.G-1).

Fig.G-1. Bottom water.

Buttress sand — Sands that terminate against an *underlying* unconformity.

Capillary pressure — The difference in pressure across an interface between two fluids (e.g., water and oil). When oil and water, or gas and water, occupy the same pore space in a rock that is water-wet, the petroleum occupies the central position of minimum energy in the space. The pressure is higher on the concave side of the interface in oil than on the convex side in water, and the amount of this difference is related to the size of the pore space, and to the relative proportions of petroleum and water. The petroleum can only be moved from one pore space to the next by exerting a displacement pressure that exceeds the capillary pressure. This increases as the size of the constriction decreases (it is a function of the radius of curvature of the interface). In oil-wet rocks (rare), the water occupies the central position of minimum energy, bounded by a surface across which the pressure decreases. (See

Hubbert, 1953: *Bull. Am. Ass. Petrol. Geol.,* 37:1954—2026; Levorsen, 1967: *Geology of Petroleum,* for fuller explanations.)

Cap rock — (a) The rock that prevents petroleum from escaping from a trap. Fine-grained rocks (clays, marls, etc.) and evaporites are common cap rocks.

(b) The material near the top of the salt plug, stock, or dome that is not salt. Usually gypsum and anhydrite.

Carbon, fixed — A curious term that relates to the matter in coal that is not volatile. It is an empirical measurement of considerable value. Coal consists of ash, moisture, volatile matter and *"fixed carbon".* On heating, volatiles and moisture are driven off (there is no general standard procedure, each country has its own) and what is left is ash and fixed carbon. It is simpler and quicker than full analysis, and reflects the rank of coal. Expressed as a percentage, the higher the fixed carbon the higher the rank of the coal, for volatiles decrease with rank.

Carbon, total — *Total carbon, dry mineral matter free* relates to the total carbon, including that in the volatile constituents in a coal.

Circulate — In rotary drilling, the mud *circulates* from the suction tank through the pumps, the drilling string, up the annulus between the drilling string and the wall of the hole, or the casing, and so through the shale-shaker and settling tanks back to the suction tank.

Clastic ratio — A parameter used in some facies maps. It is the total thickness of *conglomerate + sand, sandstone + clay, shale* divided by the total thickness of *limestone + dolomite + evaporites.*

Clastic/shale ratio — A parameter used in some facies maps. It is the total thickness of *arenites* (sandstones and calcarenites) divided by the total thickness of *clay, shale.*

Completion — A well is *completed* on one or more petroleum reservoirs, after drilling and casing the hole, with a view to producing petroleum from it or them. If production is, or becomes, impossible or undesirable (due to high water cut, high gas/oil ratio, low yield or other reason) the well is *recompleted* on another reservoir or group of reservoirs.

Concurrent fault – Synonym for *growth fault* (q.v.) over which it probably has priority (Tiddeman, 1890, on p. 101 of this volume). It is rarely used.

Contemporaneous fault – Synonym for *growth fault* (q.v.). Commonly used in the literature.

Depositional fault – Synonym for *growth fault* (q.v.). Commonly used in the literature.

Diachronous – A rock unit is said to be diachronous when its age range varies from place to place. The surface of sediment that accumulated at the same time (isochronously) is not strictly parallel to the surface of the rock unit.

Synonym (undesirable): time-transgressive.

Antonyms: isochronous, synchronous.

Diastem – A break in a stratigraphic sequence that is more often inferred than observed. Bedding planes within a lithological unit may be diastems. See Fig.1-1. Defined by Barrell, 1917: *Bull. Geol. Soc. Am.*, 28:794.

Diastrophism – A general word that refers to the deformation of the earth's crust on small or large scale, including the formation of folds and faults, orogeny, etc.

Differential sticking – See *wall sticking.*

Dog-leg – A sharp or sudden change of direction in a borehole. Dog-legs often have geological significance (change of lithology, fault, steep dip) but may also be caused by the driller. Obviously undesirable.

Down time – Time lost during drilling due to repairs on drilling machinery, waiting on equipment or bad weather. Conditioning the hole, fishing, round-trips, and other operations that are integral to the drilling operation, are not strictly "down time".

Drilling break – A sudden increase in the rate of penetration. May be due to a change in the lithology of the rocks being drilled, but must be assumed to be due to an increase in the value of λ (the ratio of fluid pressure to depth in the practical context).

Dry — A borehole that finds no accumulation of petroleum is said to be *dry*. cf., *wet* (q.v.).

Economic basement — See *Basement.*

Edge water — Refers to the water below and lateral to a petroleum accumulation (Fig.G-2).

Fig.G-2. Edge water.

"Ethane plus" — Gases of the paraffin series of higher molecular weight than methane (CH_4), i.e., ethane (C_2H_6), propane (C_3H_8), butane (C_4H_{10}), and pentane (C_5H_{12}).

Facies (singular and plural) — The character of lithological and rock units may change from place to place. The general aspect of a rock is its *facies:* (1) in its lithological context (lithofacies), e.g., sandstone facies; (2) in its biological context (biofacies), e.g., graptolite facies; (3) in its environmental context, e.g., littoral facies. The concept has been extended to metamorphic facies.

A *facies fauna* is a fauna that is confined to a particular lithology, or one in which environmental influences are more marked than evolutionary.

Fish, fishing — When seeking to recover equipment accidentally left in a borehole, such as part of the drilling string, one is said to be *fishing*. The equipment accidentally lost in the hole is, of course, the *fish.*

Fluid potential — The mechanical potential energy of an element of fluid with respect to its physical environment. It is also (and equivalently) the amount of work required to move unit mass of fluid from the reference state and position (sea-level and atmospheric pressure) to the point specified. Defined by Hubbert, 1953: *Bull. Am. Ass. Petrol. Geol.*, 37:1954—2026

$$\Phi = gz + \frac{p}{\rho}$$

where g is the acceleration of gravity, z the elevation of the point above sea-level, p the gauge pressure at point z, and ρ the density of the fluid.

The potential of a fluid can be determined for any point occupied by that fluid or capable of being occupied by it (cf. potentiometric surface of an artesian aquifer).

Fluid potential gradient — When a fluid is at different potentials in two points in subsurface space, there is a fluid potential gradient between them, and fluid tends to flow from the point with higher potential towards that with lower potential.

$$\text{grad } \Phi = g \text{ grad } z + (1/\rho) \text{ grad } p$$

More generally, fluid potential gradients exist in fluid that is not at rest (not in hydrostatic equilibrium).

Formation — (1) General term in petroleum industry for "bed", "reservoir", or any rock unit or group of rock units, e.g., formation water, producing formation, formation density log.

(2) Strict geological usage: a mappable unit on the surface or in the subsurface that consists of one or more lithologies.

Gas-cap drive — See *Water drive.*

Gas cut mud (GCM) — The mud in circulation in rotary drilling is said to be **gas cut** when it contains bubbles of gas at the shale shaker. Release from solution may be involved, but gas can be incorporated in the mud from the volume of rock drilled. The bubbles expand as they approach the surface due to the decreasing confining pressure. The mean density of the mud column is thus reduced: this constitutes a risk of a *blowout* (q.v.). See also *Trip gas.*

Gas/oil ratio (GOR) — The ratio of a volume of gas to a volume of oil (not necessarily the same volume of each) at a specified temperature and pressure. The standard conditions of measurement vary from country to country, but are usually either 15°C and 760 mm of mercury or 60°F and 30 inches (760 mm) mercury. Common units are: m^3/m^3, cubic feet of gas per barrel of oil.

Gauge pressure — Absolute pressure less atmospheric pressure — that is, the reading of a pressure gauge at atmospheric pressure is zero.

Genetic rock unit(s) — Lithological unit(s) that are recognizable representatives of modern sedimentary environments that have been preserved in the stratigraphic record, e.g., point bar, barrier bar, channel fill, etc.

It is unwise to suppose that all rock units may be recognizable in terms of genetic rock units. More generally, it refers to rock units with a common origin.

Growth fault — A fault that separates correlative sequences of which the thicker is on the downthrown side (Fig.4-1). More generally it is used of faults that are inferred to have been moving during the accumulation of sediment on at least the downthrown block.

Synonyms: *concurrent, contemporaneous, depositional, gulf-coast type, progressive, recurrent, synsedimentary* ff.

Halokinesis, halokinetic — "Salt tectonics". The deformation of sediments by a salt dome is halokinetic deformation, and the process is halokinesis. Mainly European terminology.

Head, pressure head, etc. — The interstitial fluid pressure, p, at a depth z is equal to that exerted by a column of water of depth h above z. h is said to be the pressure *head*. It is the height to which water would rise in a manometer at depth z, measured vertically from point z (Fig.G-3):

$$h = p/\gamma_w$$

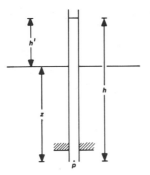

Fig.G-3. Pressure head.

where γ_w is the specific weight of the water. H' in Fig.G-3 is the total head.

Hiatus (plural, *hiatus* or *hiatuses*, not hiati) — A break in the sequence of accumulated sediments: a surface that represents the passage of time without the accumulation of sediment. See *Non-deposition.*

Homologue — Molecules of different substances that have the same general relationship between the atoms are said to be *homologous.* Ethane is a homologue of methane (see Fig.2-2).

I.D. — Internal diameter (of drill pipe, casing, etc.).

Isochore — When the thickness of a lithological unit, a rock unit, or a time unit, is taken from borehole data, *not corrected for dip or borehole deviation,* and used in a map on which lines of equal thickness are drawn, these lines are said to be *isochores.* They are *isopachs* uncorrected for dip or borehole deviation.

Jar — A tool by means of which an upward or a downward shock can be given to the drilling string beneath it or the fish. It is a means of freeing stuck pipe, and may be incorporated in the drilling string or in the fishing string.

Joint — A single length of pipe. A joint of drill pipe, and a joint of casing, are 30 ft. or 10 m long (nominal: that is, their actual length may be rather more or less than their nominal length). A drill collar is not a joint, viz., "two drill collars and 3 joints of drill pipe".

Juxtaposed — When two different lithological units are brought together across a fault, they are said to be juxtaposed.

Kelly bushing — Two half-sections that fit into the rotary table leaving a square or hexagonal opening through which the kelly passes. It is the means by which rotation is imparted to the kelly while leaving the latter free to be raised or lowered.

Kick — A borehole is said to "kick" if the pressure of the formation fluids comes to exceed that exerted by the mud column in the hole. A kick is the first stage of a blowout, but by no means all kicks lead to blowouts. Indeed, the safest way of drilling to abnormal pressures is to drill with the lightest practicable mud so that the borehole kicks as soon as abnormal pressures are reached.

Kozeny equation — Relates permeability and porosity in a porous and permeable solid. It may be written in various ways:

$$K = f^3/kS^2$$
$$K = f^3/kS_o^2(1-f)^2$$
$$K = f^3/kS_p^2$$

where K is the coefficient of permeability, f the porosity, k Kozeny's constant, S the surface area per unit volume of rock, S_o the surface area per unit volume of solids, and S_p the surface area per unit volume of pore space. The Kozeny equation must be used with care. It is most unlikely that it is applicable to a compacting clay, for instance, because it is most unlikely that Kozeny's constant is a constant when the geometry of the grains and pore spaces alters. See Wyllie and Spangler, 1952: *Bull. Am. Ass. Petrol. Geol.,* 36:359—403, for derivation, discussion, and references.

Liner — A string of casing that is not continuous to the surface. It is *hung* in a casing that has been cemented; and it is cemented through drill pipe that is later diconnected. It is an alternative to conventional casing as a production string.

Lithostatic — Used synonymously with *geostatic,* the total pressure exerted by the overburden, solid and liquid. Undesirable.

Marker — Any recognizable and characteristic (but usually thin) part of a stratigraphic sequence that can be followed over an area or from borehole to borehole. In subsurface geology, it is commonly a point on the electrical log that is recognizable on the logs of different boreholes by correlation.

Non-deposition — Commonly refers to a hiatus. It is a phrase that has no merit. Non-deposition may mean the same as non-accumulation; but non-accumulation is factual and much to be preferred. An area of non-accumulation may well have been an area of deposition.

O.D. — Outside diameter (of a bit, casing, etc.)

Offlap — Used in the opposite sense to onlap (q.v.). It is doubtful whether this is a useful word (or concept). It is not strictly synonymous with regression or regressive. *Offlap* should not be used unless successively younger strata are observed to be offset seaward.

Onlap — The accumulation of successively younger strata, each overlapping the other, in a transgressive sequence. It is not synonymous with transgression or transgressive: it refers to the distribution of rock units relative to each other, and is thus a consequence of a transgression.

Outstep — A borehole drilled during the development phase (see *Appraisal*) outside the area already drilled, but still to the same structure or trap, is an outstep well.

Paralic — The general environment of the marine margin of a physiographic basin is *paralic*. It includes the littoral, lagoonal and shallow marine environments.

Permeability — A porous rock through which fluid can be passed is said to be *permeable,* and the rock has the property *permeability.* A rock through which fluid can easily be passed is said to have high or good permeability: conversely, low or poor permeability. In general, rocks with high permeability have high porosity, but the relationship is not precise (see *Kozeny equation*). Permeability can be measured. There are two concepts: permeability of a rock regarded as a parameter of that rock independent of the fluid that passes through it (*intrinsic* permeability), and the permeability of a rock to a specific fluid of specified density and viscosity (*hydraulic conductivity*).

Darcy concluded from his classical experiments that the rate of flow (Q) through a porous medium is inversely proportional to the length of the flow path, proportional to the loss of head along the flow path (dp/dl), and proportional to a coefficient (K) that reflects the nature of the porous material and the fluid passing through it. Darcy's law may be written:

$$Q = KA \frac{dp}{dl}$$

where A is the cross-sectional area. The coefficient K is not a constant, for it varies when different fluids are passed through the same sample of rock. K, the hydraulic conductivity, is related to k, the intrinsic permeability, by:

$$K = k \frac{\rho}{\mu}$$

where ρ and μ are the density and dynamic viscosity of the fluid. The measurement of permeability involves determining the value of K or k for the rock. In petroleum geology and petroleum engineering, the unit of permeability is the Darcy (with dimension L^2). The measurement is made by passing a standard fluid from a sample of standard dimensions under standard conditions. The result may be regarded as a measure of intrinsic permeability (k), and is commonly expressed in millidarcies (1 mD = 10^{-3} D). Permeabilities of less than 1 mD are poor: 100 mD and more, good. Permeabilities greater than 1,000 mD are excellent — but rare. But what is good permeability for gas may be poor for oil.

Effective permeability. When two separate fluid phases, such as oil and water, occupy a pore space a film of water is retained over the grain surfaces and this interferes with the movement of both oil and water. We may then speak of the effective permeability of a rock to oil (or to gas, or water).

Relative permeability is the ratio of effective permeability of a material to a fluid and the permeability of that material with that fluid as a single phase.

For more detailed discussions, see Levorsen, 1967: *Geology of Petroleum,* Freeman, San Francisco, p.104 *et seq.;* Hubbert, 1940: *J. Geol.,* 48:785–944 (particularly pp.785–819 and p.915 *et seq.*); De Wiest, 1965: *Geohydrology,* Wiley, New York, N.Y., p.161 *et seq.*

Permeability barrier — A reduction of permeability along a migration path that tends to inhibit further migration. It may be a facies change or a fault. The force of capillarity is more significant than permeability in a barrier to petroleum migration.

Piezometric surface — See *Potentiometric surface.*

Pore ratio — See *Void ratio.*

Porosity (*f*) — The ratio of pore volume to gross volume of rock, that is, the volume of the pore spaces divided by the volume of the pore spaces and the volume of solids. It may also be expressed as a percentage.

Potentiometric surface — If the total head (see *Head*), relative to a datum surface, is computed for various points in a body of fluid, a notional surface is obtained. This is the potentiometric surface of that body of fluid. It can be contoured, and the contours are isopotential lines. Within that body of fluid, fluid tends to flow in the direction that is down the potentiometric surface normal to the isopotential lines.

Progradation, prograde — The migration of facies seaward due to a surplus of sediment supply over the energy available for its wider dispersal.

Synonymous with regression.

Progressive fault — Synonym for *Growth fault* (q.v.).

Recompletion — See *Completion.*

Recurrent fault — *Synonym for Growth fault* (q.v.).

Regression — Strictly, a fall of sea-level relative to the land, with a consequent extension of land area at the expense of the sea.

Sedimentary sequences that contain shallow-water sediments on deep-water sediments, or continental on marine, are called regressive. Many regressive sequences, however, are more readily understood in terms of an excess of sediment supply over the energy available for its wider distribution, so that the land is extended at the expense of the sea by progradation (q.v.). Rather than coin a new expression that would be in conflict with the established expression "regressive sequence", regressions may be usefully qualified as "erosional" when used in its strict sense, and "depositional" when they result from progradation.

Round trip – Rotary drilling. Pulling the bit and running in a new one.

Sand/shale ratio – A parameter used in some facies maps. It is the total thickness of *sand, sandstone* and *conglomerate* divided by the total thickness of *clay, shale.*

Secondary recovery – A petroleum reservoir is produced either by utilizing the energy in the reservoir itself (a flowing well) or by pumping. Not all the petroleum in the reservoir can be produced in this way (primary recovery). Secondary recovery refers to attempts to produce the petroleum not produced by primary recovery.

Sidetrack – If part of a borehole is lost while drilling (for example, on account of a fish that could not be recovered), the hole is plugged back with cement and *sidetracked* to drill past the hole lost, alongside it.

Slug – A concentration of one fluid in another in a pipe or borehole, such as water slugs in an oil pipeline.

Sonde – The down-hole logging device that contains the moving electrodes for the electrical log, the source and detector(s) for the radioactivity log, and so on, each sonde being for a specific purpose. The sonde is attached to a cable within which pass the electrical cables that transmit signals to the surface equipment.

Stand – Rotary drilling. When pulling out of the hole, the drill pipe is stacked or stood in the derrick or mast in *stands* of three joints. A *short stand* consists of two joints: a long stand, of four.

Strain — The deformation of a material under stress.

Stress — A force per unit area. It may be compressive, tending to shorten the dimension of the material under stress in the direction of the stress; or tensional.

A *principal stress* is a stress acting perpendicularly to a surface along which there is no shear stress. The principal stresses in a rock

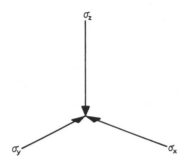

Fig.G-4. Stress.

in situ are considered to be as in Fig.G-4, σ_z being vertical by convention, σ_x and σ_y horizontal. It is possible that inclined stress fields exists in the subsurface, e.g., around a growing diapir.

When the three principal stresses are unequal, they are called maximum, intermediate, and minimum stresses; and are designated σ_1, σ_2, σ_3, respectively. The principal stresses may be resolved into components, such as that normal to a fault plane (normal stress, σ_n) and a shear stress, τ, along the fault plane.

Subcrop — The area of a rock unit or lithological unit that is in contact with an overlying unconformity is the *subcrop* of that unit. A subcrop map may be regarded as a palaeogeological map at the time of the unconformity (strictly, the commencement of post-unconformity sediment accumulation).

Synsedimentary — Occurring contemporaneously with sedimentation or sediment accumulation, e.g., *synsedimentary* fault, a synonym for *Growth fault* (q.v.).

Syntaphral — "Towards the trough". Used in Australia (mainly) for gravity sliding of rocks or sediments down a slope.

T.D. (Total depth) — The total depth of a borehole measured along the borehole from the derrick floor or rotary table. May be qualified by addition of s.s. (sub-sea level) or s.d. (sub-datum). This figure may be very much larger than the *True vertical depth* (T.V.D.) in a deviated borehole. T.V.D. need not be qualified, for it is normally below sea-level or other datum.

Transgression — Strictly, a rise of sea-level relative to the land, with a consequent reduction of land area. Sedimentary sequences that contain deep-water sediments on shallow-water sediments, or marine on continental, are called transgressive. Transgressions may also result from erosion of the land without changes in relative sea-level (cf. *Regression*).

Trillion — 10^{12} in the U.S.A.: 10^{18} in many other countries. Like *billion* (q.v.), the word should only be used when there is no danger of misunderstanding.

Trip Gas — When resuming circulation (breaking circulation, in the jargon) after a round trip, the mud that was near the bottom of the hole is sometimes found to be gas-cut (q.v.) when it reaches the shale shaker. This is trip gas. It is distinguished from true gas-cutting of the mud by its short duration, and its relationship to a round trip.

Tubing — Small diameter pipe run inside the casing of a well for the production of petroleum. The oil or gas flows inside the tubing.

T.V.D. (True vertical depth) — See T.D.

Twist off — Rotary drilling. Failure of the drilling string is of two sorts: excessive torque or excessive tension. The former is called a *twist-off*. When the latter happens, the drill string is said to *part*. Parting of the drill pipe (dp) and twist-offs (beware of pedantry!) entail a fishing job (q.v.).

Void ratio — The ratio of pore volume to solid volume in a sedimentary rock. The symbol is usually e. Thus:

$$e = \frac{f}{1-f}$$

It is useful in compaction studies, and has the merit that it is a ratio of a variable to a constant (in most practical geological contexts).

Wall sticking — Rotary drilling. If the fluid potential of the mud in the borehole is much greater than that of the fluids in the permeable formations that have been penetrated, the mud cake is

Fig.G-5. Wall sticking.

the site of a high fluid potential gradient. If now the drill pipe impinges on the mudcake, the pressure differential may be sufficient to hold it to the wall of the hole (Fig.G-5). It is corrected by washing the well to water or lightening the mud — thus reducing the fluid potential gradient. The risk of wall sticking is incurred when drilling through depleted petroleum reservoirs, or when drilling into abnormally pressured formations. Synonym: differential sticking.

Water drive, gas-cap drive — When the volume of oil produced from a reservoir is replaced wholly or partly by upward displacement of the oil/water contact, that reservoir is said to have *water drive*. When the water drive is strong, loss of pressure in the reservoir is relatively small; when weak, it may be relatively great, and lead to a secondary gas cap.

As reservoir pressure declines, the gas-cap (primary or secondary) expands, and displaces the gas/oil contact downwards. This is *gas-cap drive*.

Well — Strictly, a borehole that produces water, oil, or gas. In petroleum terminology, it is commonly used loosely for any borehole, whether or not it produces petroleum, e.g., outstep well.

Wet — When a borehole penetrates a formation that is a petroleum reservoir in other wells, the reservoir is said to be *wet* if it conatins water only. A dry hole may contain sands, for example, that are wet.

Workover — A well is *worked over* from time to time, to renew or clean the tubing, clean casing, reperforate — or any operation that is to maintain production from the same reservoir. Cf. recompletion (see *Completion*) which involves a change of producing interval.

REFERENCES INDEX

Numbers in italics denote Selected Bibliography listing

Alberding, H., *see* Renz et al.
Allen, J.F., *see* Grayston et al.
Anderegg, H., *see* Miller, J.B., et al.
Anisgard, H.W., *see* Miller, J.B. et al.
Archie, G.E., 197, *214*
Arrhenius, Sv., *118*
Athy, L.F., 54, *80*, 111, 112, *118*, 127, 130, 131, 132, *142, 143*, 154, *173*
Aubouin, J., *18*

Barrell, J., 3, 5, 6, 7, *18*, 233, 234, *253, 272*
Barss, D.L., Copland, A.B. and Ritchie, W.D., 13, *18, 173*
Barsukov, O.A., Blinova, N.M., Vybornykh, S.F., Gulin, Yu.A., Dakhnov, V.N., Larionov, V.V. and Kholin, A.I., *215*
Barton, D.C., 109, *118*
Bazer, D.A., *see* Griffin, D.G. and Bazer, D.A.
Beales, F.W., *see* Jackson, S.A. and Beales, F.W.
Beck, K.C., *see* Weaver, C.E. and Beck, K.C.
Beck, R.H., 104, *118*
Belyea, H.R., *see* Committee on Slave Point and Beaver-hill Lake Formations, and Belyea, H.R.
Billings, M.P., 84, *100*
Biot, M.A. and Odé, H., 110, *118*, 163, *173*
Blinova, N.M., *see* Barsukov et al.
Boatman, W.A., 65, *80, 215*
Bornhauser, M., *118*
Brantly, J.E., *188*

Braunstein, J. and O'Brien, G.D., 104, *118*
Bredehoeft, J.D. and Hanshaw, B.B., *80*, 155, *173*
Bredehoeft, J.D., *see* Hanshaw, B.B. and Bredehoeft, J.D.
Bridgeman, M., 139, 143
Brooks, B.T., *143*
Brooks, J.D., 126, *143*
Brooks, J.D. and Smith, J.W., 126, *143*
Buckley, S.E., Hocott, C.R. and Taggart, M.S., *47*, 135, *143*
Bullen, K.E., *47*
Burst, J.F., *80*, 141, *143*
Busby, R.C., *see* Curtis et al.

Califet-Debyser, Y., *see* Tissot et al.
Carey, S.W., 113, 114, 115, *118*
Carver, R.E., *100*
Castillo-Tejero, C., *see* Viniegra O., F. and Castillo-Tejero, C.
Cebull, S.E., *100*
Chapman, R.E., 62, 68, 70, *80*, 123, 131, 132, 133, 134, 136, *143, 173*
Clarke, G.M., *253*
Cloos, E., *100*
Cole, F.W., *see* Moore, P.L. and Cole, F.W.
Commitee on Slave Point and Beaver-hill Lake Formations, and Belyea, Helen R., 166, *173*
Conybeare, C.E.B., *143*
Copland, A.B., *see* Barss et al.
Craft, B.C., Holden, W.R. and Graves, E.D., *188*

SUBJECT INDEX